A Brotherhood Of Outlaws

Other Books by Bob Bitchin

Non-Fiction
Biker
Letters from the *Lost Soul*
The Sailing Life

Fiction
(The Treb Lincoln Series)
Brotherhood of Outlaws
Emerald Bay
King Harbor

A Brotherhood of Outlaws

Bob Bitchin

A Brotherhood of Outlaws

First published 1979 by Bentree House Publishing

Subsequent printings 1982, 1987, 2007 by
FTW Publishing, Inc.
Box 668
Redondo Beach, CA 90277
www.seafaring.com

This book is a work of fiction. Names, characters, places and incidents are either the product of the author's imagination, or are used fictitiously. Any resemblance to actual events, locals or persons, living or dead, are entirely coincidental.

Printed and manufactured in
the United States of America.
First edition. June 2007
Cover artwork by Bob Bitchin

ISBN: 978-0-9662182-0-6

Typesetting on a Macintosh by B. Baird, Beach People's Easyreader Publishing.

$14.95

This book is dedicated to the memory of the Dutchman

Introduction
By Bob Bitchin - 2007

In some ways it hardly seems like 30 years have passed since I wrote "Brotherhood." In others, it seems like a different lifetime. Sometimes I think a much easier lifetime.

This text is unchanged, so you might notice some slang you haven't heard in awhile, but I guess that makes it all the more real.

In the day's of the Biker there was a camaraderie and a freedom that the biker of today cannot grasp. They can't grasp it, because it no longer exists. You can never go back to those days any more than you can go back "home." Home wasn't a place, it was a time, and so were the days of the Biker.

In the day of the Biker you could go to Sturgis and sit on the lawn in front of the Armory and welcome the 1,500 bikers that would show up from all over. You knew them all, and all knew you. This was back when the Run to the Sun, now called "Daytona" first started, and 800-900 bikers would get together and ride together to watch the races in Daytona.

Today there are literally millions of people at these events, but a greybeard will feel more alone there than sitting on his rigid frame chopper crossing Nebraska.

Those days are gone, but they are not forgotten. This book was written in the days of the Biker, and today it is more relevant than ever.

R.T.L. - L.T.R. and F.T.W.!

Bob Bitchin

Chapter 1

Leroy Makelray of KABD news felt his body instinctively flinch in fear as 30,000 motorcycles rumbled toward him. He stood on an overpass to do the network feed while the cameras would tape the pack passing below them like an endless, roaring snake.

Traffic on the Golden State freeway sped on mindless. Sometimes being in the news business gave a real insight into the stupidity of man. Leroy wasn't sure that he like that. He could remember when he thought man was an intelligent animal, endowed as no other with free choice. But that was long ago. He'd lost a little of the pride he used to have in his species. Homo Sapiens. Wise man. He now realized how futile it really was to try and fight the real power: Money.

Like the stupid-ass bikers that would soon pass below. They had worked for almost a year solid trying to put together this protest, trying to get the helmet law repealed nationwide. Leroy knew that they were right, that law was about as unconstitutional as slavery, but there was more money on the side of the helmet manufacturers and the federal government than on the side of the bikers. So their cause was lost from the start.

The mandatory helmet law for motorcyclists was a brainstorm of the safety establishment in the federal government. On the surface the reasoning was simple: Bikers are too dumb to know what is good for them, therefore the police must force them to wear hard hats whether they like it or not. In truth, the safety bureau didn't give a damn about the bikers' heads. They were going to ban motorcycles anyway. What they needed was a legal precedent to force mandatory self-protection on car drivers and passengers. That's where the big money was. Nobody would pay much attention to a biker's rights and the motorcyclists themselves were too dumb and disorganized to do anything about it.

What worried him was what might happen when the bikers learned how futile their fight was. This was the first time that bikers had ever joined together for a political cause and it scared him a little. These people are not our normal citizens. They are just apt to really get mad, and if they do there was no telling what might happen.

Earlier he had asked what they would do if they lost the helmet law battle. Their leader was a large and scary individual by the name of Treb Lincoln. Lincoln stepped off his bike, towering above the newsman and camera, looked hard at Leroy and shrugged.

"Hell man, I'm just a dumb biker. If they don't drop the lid law I don't guess I can control by brothers here. They're likely to get a mean attitude."

Leroy knew that it was all carefully staged. For the first time the bikers had a cause and a real leader. Lincoln may have said he was just a "dumb biker," but there was something different about him that translated on tape. He was smarter than the rest of the bikers and they showed a fanatical loyalty to him. He had settled all the local gang wars and disputes and brought all of them together for the first time.

Cameraman and sound crew checked their equipment for the last time. Leroy wanted this shot to be just right. They would pick it up at the network in New York. It would be seen by the biggies. This could help his career, although it was a mystery why the network was interested in this bizarre biker item. The glint of chrome cut through the smog and haze like needles in his eyes.

It was frightening. All that noise and power could be felt as well as seen and heard. It was like a barbarian invasion, loud and menacing. Leroy swallowed.

When the bikes were in range he gave the sign for the sound to start, and then the camera. He wanted this to be very dramatic. He turned his back to the camera and watched Lincoln lead the bikes down the freeway. Just before he turned to speak, his eyes met Lincoln's and Makelray was startled at the energy that shot through him.

Slowly he turned to face the camera and began to speak.

Chapter 2

I glanced up from my speedometer and saw the broadcaster eyeballing down on me. Hell, I hope the pack is centered. I would hate to go to all this horsecrap and lose out on any of the exposure.

My fatbob Harley was running as good as it had ever run and the feel of the vibrating power came right through the handlebars. All I could think about was the snake behind me. I looked into my rearview mirror and once again my heart beat a little harder. Jesus H. Christ, there is no better feeling in the world than leading 30,000 bikes down the road. Unless it might be leading 40,000 bikes down the road.

Just before we passed under the bridge I looked back up at the broadcaster. I had seen him before, at the park. He was kind of a little guy, but he seemed to know the score. I like him. Most of the newsmen that were sent to cover this protest were cocky new, because, after all, it was just a bunch of bikers sniveling about their rights being stepped on. Makelray was different. Like he knew I had plans for this group. I don't know how, but he knew.

Passing under the bridge made us sound even louder. The thunder roared and it was beautiful. I glanced next to me at Rom and he had this big shit-eating grin on his face. I guess the sound was getting to him too.

Rom and I had been through a lot in the last two years together, and this was going to be the payoff. I reached into my cutoff jacket and felt for my security. It was my 357 Magnum. The heft alone made me feel good.

We turned off the Golden State and onto the Pasadena freeway, toward the civic center. Hell I hope those cops got the blockades up and the traffic re-routed. If they don't, I would just as soon take this pack through downtown Los Angeles. I was sick and tired of the bureaucracy bullshit that had been going on for the last few days and right now I really didn't give a rat's ass if they were ready or not. We got a point to make and brother are we going to make it.

We turned off the Pasadena and onto the Hollywood freeway. Just one more mile to go. As we dropped into the hollow under some bridges the echoing sounds of the pack came back to me and I was ready for anything. I could ride like this forever.

Our off ramp loomed ahead and I slowed the pack from 45 to 30 miles and hour. No use dumping some sidewalk commando and listening to the government turkeys harp on unsafe riding or other such horsecock. This day was set aside for bikers and damnit, that's whose day it is. Period.

As we approached the civic center I could see all the police there. A quick glance up showed a couple of helicopters in the silver sky. I could see this was going to be a well-chaperoned event.

I pulled by Hawg out of the pack and motioned Rom to lead them to where the police had set aside parking. I aimed by scoot toward the curb and hit the throttle. The front end came up off the ground about a foot and jumped right over the curb. I saw a couple of cops unlatch their holsters as I headed for the stand where the loudspeakers were set up. I knew that no cop was going to shoot me with all the bikers pulling in. As I hit the grass I turned on the throttle a little harder and felt the back wheel swerve as the brand new Goodyear Eagle cut its initials into the nice green lawn of city hall.

I could almost hear the groundskeeper swearing, but what the hell, he's getting paid.

When I was next to the pulpit I dropped my kickstand and turned off my engine. All I could hear was the sound of thousands of bikes pulling in.

I pulled a stick of gum out of my pocket and stripped it, throwing the wrapper on the ground. I could see the folks standing around were a little unnerved so I decided to try and take advantage of it.

I found a long time ago that when you stand six-feet-four and weigh close to 300 pounds there aren't a whole lot of folks who will mess with you.

For the next few minutes Rom and I walked through the bikes as they parked, talking with the presidents of the different clubs. We had established a chain of command and we didn't want to violate it. The clubs all retained their own identity and officers, all we did was try to aim them in one direction. I had kinda picked up this idea from the Romans. They didn't conquer, they just sort of absorbed. They would bend. So did I.

When you're dealing with clubs like the Hell's Angels, Mongols, Hessians and Vagos you can't afford to make mistakes. So far we had been pretty lucky. We had settled their fights and differences, re-aligned the territories to where most of them were happy and gotten most of the outlaw bikers to go along with a truce. That in itself is a chore.

The hard part was getting them to work together. Each club has a terrific pride in its own reputation; they hate to share any glory with any other club. It had been pretty damn ticklish.

The hardest part was to get the police to lay off during this protest. Hell, the police have books on each of the clubs, with the members' rap sheets and what they're wanted for. It took a lot of talking to get them to promise to leave all the bikers alone during this protest. I was still a little leery of their promises, but we had to believe in something.

It took over an hour for all the bikes to pour into the parking areas. The place was wall-to-wall bikers. As I stood on the steps looking over them I knew we would win. There was no way we could be ignored now.

I could see television cameras all over and the

different newsmen were picking out the dumbest looking bikers to interview so they would look stupid on TV. They didn't know it, but that was exactly what I wanted. Nothing will lull an adversary into a state of overconfidence easier than letting him think you are a bunch of dummies.

I tested the microphone a little bit and when I knew it was working I started to quiet them all down. This was what we had been waiting for.

Chapter 3

Mike Brandi wandered among the bikes like he belonged there. Actually he knew more about outlaw bikers that most of them did. The big difference was that he was assigned by the omega Squad to be a biker, while the rest of them did it by choice. He hated playing the biker role. It was worse than the two years he spent as a Klansman back in the sixties. Sometimes he thought he should get into another line of work, like his brother who was a plumber. But then, Omega paid better.

As Mike wandered toward the speaker's podium one of the members of the Widowmakers, his cover club, approached him. It was Rabbit. Of all the undercover cops in the club, Mike liked Rabbit the least.

"Hey, bro, ya gotta smoke?"

Rabbit wrapped his large body over Mike and breathed directly into his face. Mike knew he couldn't have brushed his teeth in a week and the acrid smell was almost overwhelming.

"Aw, come on Dogleg, ya must have one," he slobbered.

Dogleg was Mike's club name. They called him that because of the bend in his leg from when he went down on his scooter. At least that's what they pretended to outsiders. Actually it was a hunting injury that happened when he was in the academy many years ago, but it was a good story.

He reached into his ragged, greasy cutoff and handed Rabbit a marijuana cigarette.

"Here ya are brother, but ya owe me one," and he slapped a wide open kiss on Rabbit's mouth. Widowmakers carefully tended their reputation as the most violent, outrageous and unpredictable club of all.

Once again he started wandering through the bikes and heading toward the pulpit. His head was a little troubled. They had orders to disrupt this protest and make it look like the bikers caused the trouble. Normally that wouldn't be a whole lot of trouble, but since the wars had all been settled, it was going to harder. If they caused a hassle with one of the other clubs, the rules were iron clad. Any trouble at this rally had to come from the police. If a biker broke the truce, his club, with all the other clubs watching, was expected to enforce the brotherhood.

Yup, this was going to be a problem.

He took a position about thirty feet out from

the pulpit in the center of the crowd to await an opportunity. The news crews were idle and the target, the organizer of this whole thing, Treb Lincoln, was busy setting things up.

Mike thought about the first time he saw Treb. He almost liked him. The guy came walking into the Widowmakers' clubhouse all by himself. He told one of the new agents he wanted to see Animal, who was the president.

Now the agent, disguised as a prospective member, knew that no strangers were allowed in the clubhouse and told Lincoln to get out. Looking back, Mike gave the prospect a lot of credit for balls. That Lincoln was over six feet tall and looked like he lifted weights for a living. The prospect went to push him toward the door and before his hand landed Treb had picked him up and thrown him against three other agent-members at the bar. Mike jumped into it then, but the four Widowmakers couldn't even start to handle this big bastard.

Just when it looked like they were all going to get the shit kicked out of them, Treb started laughing. Not just a little laugh, but an all out belly laugh. Nervously relieved, all four of the Widowmakers joined in and when the prospect came up with a gun, to get the stranger out of there, he found everybody in a state of hysteria.

After a night of hard partying it was decided this new guy should be investigated.

The Omega file on Lincoln revealed two felonies, drugs and firearms, but he'd done his time. No warrants. He had grown up in Hollywood, kicked out of several schools for trouble making, although he had a high I.Q. He had been booted out of the Peace

Corps as undesirable after an accident involving a sacred cow in India while riding a motorcycle he was not authorized to have. He was believed to be armed and probably dangerous.

Mike's thoughts came back to the situation when he was jostled by One Arm and Cleancut. They were a couple of outlaws from the Philistines and he found he was standing between the two of them.

They were both so fucked up on reds they could hardly stand and Cleancut was leaning on him. It was with a typical biker sense of humor that Cleancut had been named. He was the dirtiest of the members in the club. His colors were so dirty that they looked like black leather, when actually they were just Levis that had never been washed and were covered with Harley oil. He smelled rank. The loudspeakers started squeaking and squawking and Mike knew he had better do something fast. His boss had given him a secret, strategic snuff assignment and orders how to carry it out.

Charlie Bainbridge, the chief of the Omega Squad, had all but promised him a transfer with a promotion if he could bring off this assassination without a hitch. Charlie was out of favor with his superiors for screwing up a bust when he was working narcotics. Being placed in charge of the Omega Squad was the Bureau's equivalent of Siberia. This biker situation was his chief's last chance to salvage his career. If he failed Mike knew that Charlie Bainbridge would take him down with him.

Mike leaned over to Cleancut and whispered in his hear. Cleancut's expression changed a little. He stood there like he hadn't heard right. Mike leaned closer and repeated.

"Hey, Cleancut, do you see that guy Treb? Well, he's a cop." He let it sink in.

Cleancut thought for a minute.

"Are you sure, bro?" He looked puzzled. "He's been to the clubhouse."

"Yeah, I head him talking to some other pigs. They plan to shoot a few people and blame it on us bikers. It's a trap to make us look bad."

That was about as much intrigue as poor Cleancut's head could handle. Mike let that sink in as he made his way to the rostrum.

Chapter 4

At the speaker's rostrum Rom watched the crowd. He felt good being there with Treb. After all they had been through it looked like it might soon pay off.

Dogleg from the Widowmakers walked up to him and offered him a smoke. They had partied together before and he seemed to be a pretty good guy. As he lit the cigarette Dogleg leaned close to his ear.

"Hey, I don't want to worry Treb, but I think Cleancut is a plant." He hesitated. "I saw him talking to an undercover pig a few minutes ago and he's got a gun. I think he's supposed to break this thing up and make it look bad for the bikers."

Rom looked at him for a moment and then searched the crowd for Cleancut. He saw him about 30 feet out and he was staring at Treb like his life depended on it.

"Are you sure?" he asked.

"I think so, bro. I sure would hate to see anything happen to Treb now. I'll go back there and keep an eye on him. If you see me signal like this," he brushed his fingers through his hair, "get ready for action."

With that he stepped off the podium into the crowd again.

Rom started to worry now. He always feared that the police would do something to make this protest look bad, but he didn't know what. Would they go as far as killing someone?

He didn't know.

He looked over at Treb, who seemed preoccupied with testing the equipment. It was going to be up to him to watch Cleancut and take him out if necessary. Treb had saved Rom's life at a rumble in New York two years a go and they had been inseparable since then. He would do anything for Treb, including give up his life. Their friendship went deeper than most. Rom really loved him.

Chapter 5

Well, I guess there's not much more I can do to put it off. It's time for the big speech.

Damn but I hate speech making. It's times like this I wish someone else would do these things.

Oh well, it's too late now. All I have to do is get these damn bikers to shut up a little and we can get started.

I held the button down on the mike and I heard the small high pitched squeak that let me know it was on.

"Alright, everybody shut up."

When you talk like that people usually listen and it looked like this time was no exception because they all started to get quieter.

"Hey, c'mon, we're all here for the same purpose, to be heard, so shut the fuck up so we can be heard."

I knew that the word fuck would quiet them down fast. Bikers seem to like shock value and that is their favorite word. Now all I have to do is remember what the hell I wanted to say.

I paused for a couple of seconds that seemed like an eternity and looked over the crowd.

As far as I could see in front of me were bikers. Most of the hard core clubs in the state were here. Out on the outskirts of the crowd I could see the cops. Hundreds of them. The helicopters were still overhead, too.

It was then I noticed the groups of snipers on the roofs of the federal building across the street and the county hall of records. I could even see the rifles in their hands. Man, I hope like hell they can control themselves.

I looked out into the crowd for a friendly face to talk at, which is what I always do when I speak to a crowd, and stopped at one of the Philistines, Cleancut. He is kind of a big, dumb sucker. But he's a nice guy, if a little crusty around the edges. I looked him in the eye and started talking.

The word is out that the state of California is planning to force all bikers to wear mandatory helmets. These laws are being enacted by bureaucrats that have never been on a bike in their life and known nothing about motorcycle safety."

I paused while the bikers roared their approval.

"The only reason you are trying to pass helmet laws is because bikers are a helpless minority, and you feel you can walk all over us. Well, damnit, we won't let you."

Again the crowds cheered. But not Cleancut. He kept staring at me. I glanced over at Rom and he seemed to be staring right at him.

"The last time you tied to pass a self-protection law it was mandatory seat belts for car drivers, but the auto drivers wouldn't allow it. Why now do you think we will allow lid laws?"

The cheers rose again. But Cleancut just stared, and I noticed Dogleg was with him. He looked real nervous.

"It has never been proven that helmets are safe, in fact they have been proven ineffective over 13 miles an hour. We feel it is time to let those who ride decide."

Dogleg whispered something to Cleancut. Cleancut reached into his cutoff. His eyes were filled with hate. Dogleg stepped aside, combing his hair with his fingers.

"Just because we are bikers doesn't mean we will stand by and take whatever you want to dish out!"

I saw Rom out of the corner of my eye reach into his cutoff where he wears his gun. It was like in slow motion. Cleancut's gun was now out and aimed at me! Why?

I started to reach for my 357 and saw Rom spin as he fired off a round at Cleancut. Just then I saw Dogleg pull his pistol and aim it right at me. I dodged to the left, down behind the pulpit, and fired one shot. It went in right below his left eye.

Then all hell broke loose. I heard shots from the roof tops and saw pieces of wood flying off the pulpit. People everywhere were screaming and running.

I crawled as fast as I could over to Rom. He was

hit but still breathing. It went in just below his chin, in the fleshy part of his neck, and came out the rear. The hole going out was bleeding pretty bad.

I looked up to see the newsman, Leroy Makelray looking down at Rom. He was in shock. I pulled him down and asked him how far away his truck was.

People were still running everywhere and the sound of Harley starting filled the air as bikers tried to get out of there before the police blockaded everything.

Makelray pointed to our right and I saw the truck about 25 feet away.

Pulling Rom by the jacket and pushing Makelray in front of me, I made it to the truck. The snipers on the roof were still firing. I heard screams for mercy and shouts of "I give up," but it was no use. The police were having a field day.

Once inside the truck I jabbed the gun in the newsman's ribcage and told him to hook it, fast.

I heard falling bikes as he ran over them trying to get out. People were dodging bullets everywhere.

When the truck was back on the street I told them to head for a hospital and I held Rom in my lap. He didn't look good.

A police car blocked one end of the street. Before we pulled up next to it, Leroy threw a blanket over us and told the police he had to get in with the story. When the cop hesitated, Leroy asked for his name so it could be mentioned in the broadcast. He gave it to him and we took off. Police aren't pigs, they're hams.

I thanked Makelray for helping us and pocketed the 357 and tried to stop the bleeding in Rom's neck.

During the whole trip Makelray kept telling me I should give myself up to the police because he could see what had happened, that it was self defense. They had taped the scene from my point of view, he said. He said it was the hottest evidence since the Nixon tapes.

I knew he was thinking about his career, but he didn't know that I had done a little time and the pigs would never believe a two-time loser, especially a biker. It was just no use. I had to split, but first we had to get Rom to a hospital.

The news van pulled into Cedars of Lebanon Hospital. They took Rom to the emergency room. After a long couple of minutes the doctor came out. He said that he might make it.

Then I got pissed.

"What the hell do you mean, 'might'?" I was almost crying.

"If he doesn't make it you won't get out of here, and that's a promise!"

I guess my mind kind of slipped. All I know is water kept running out of my eyes and I wanted to kill somebody. Everything had gone wrong and now my best friend was dying, and this asshole doctor ways he might make it.

All of a sudden there were five or six orderlies all around me. They had me where I couldn't move. One of them stuck a needle in my arm and about the last thing I remember was the face of Leroy Makelray looking down at me saying everything was going to be all right. Then it went black.

Chapter 6

Leroy watched helplessly as the orderlies jumped Treb and drugged him. He wanted to help him, but he couldn't figure out why. There was just something about Treb that they used to call charisma. In 13 years of broadcasting he had sometimes gotten involved in the stories he had covered and he felt it happening again.

Now he had to get him out of the hospital before the cops came. He wanted Treb to give himself up. To be captured while he was unconscious was not right at all.

He convinced the cameraman and soundman to help him, and as soon as Treb was left alone on a cart in the hallway they pushed him out the back door and loaded him into the van.

Before the doctors knew what was happening they were gone.

Now al he had to do was figure out where to take him and then get to the studio with his story, which now was a big one. It was no longer a slow news day story of a bikers' protest, but the story of a massacre, and all the networks would be in a race to put it on the air.

Then it hit him. He would take Treb to his house and when he came to Leroy would follow up with the real inside story from the source. He would have a clear beat on the rest of the media.

They dropped Treb, not too ceremoniously, on the bed, left one of the crew to watch over him, and played red light roulette all the way to the studio.

They made it to the studio in record time, but they weren't the first on the air with the story. Three local stations had beat them to it.

But Leroy's story was the best.

Only he knew that the assistant organizer, Rom, was in the hospital being operated on for a bullet wound at that very moment.

And only he knew that Treb Lincoln was alive and sleeping in his apartment.

Of course he didn't report that last little item.

That night the films of the gunfight on the steps of city hall were shown all over the country, including in the executive screening rooms in New York. By morning it was the talk of the nation.

But the story wasn't exactly like the police wanted it to be. It seems the identity of "Dogleg" was revealed when he was found dead in the plaza. It came out that he was an undercover policeman.

When certain film clips were shown it also became clear that he was taking aim and shooting.

Unfortunately, it also showed that Treb had shot him. That made him a wanted man. When you shoot a cop, even a bad one, you are in big trouble.

Chapter 7

By the time Treb came to, Leroy was back from the studio and making coffee. The execs from New York kept calling on the phone. They wanted more coverage for the network's evening news.

Treb agreed to help him with information in return for certain favors.

One of those favors was the loan of some money. Not just a little, but a whole lot. He had to get another bike. He knew that his was impounded by the police. He signed his pink slip over to Leroy and took the $3000 Leroy had in his bank account.

He called some friends of his that he knew he could count on in the Angels and they agreed to pick up some of his stuff and get it to him.

Now he had to get into hiding for a long time,

and there is no better place on earth to hide than in the outlaw biker culture in the United States.

Not many people know of the intricate system that exists for an outlaw biker on the run. There are systems for identification, code words and phone numbers, all of which will get a true outlaw biker a whole new identity and way of life.

No matter what a biker has done, as long as he hasn't cheated a brother or broken any of the bikers' rules, he is accepted. Especially if he is running from the police.

The amnesty even goes beyond the bounds of local and club wars.

If a member of one club is running from the police, he may very well stay with a warring club in another city. It is a way of life.

Leroy sat stunned listening to Treb make phone calls to the Angels in New York, the Huns in Quebec, the Sundowners in Utah, the Sons of Silence in Denver and the Banditos in Texas. He'd had no idea how well developed the lines of communications were between outlaw clubs. Before long Treb had a list of over twenty places where he would be welcomed with a new identity and a woman, a bike, and even a job if he wanted it.

Leroy had always thought bikers were poor and had nothing, when in reality they have more friends in need than most ordinary citizens have.

Treb wanted to tell Leroy where he was going, but decided not to, in case the police got to him. Leroy said he would watch after Rom and they said goodbye.

Chapter 8

Damn but it feels good to be back on a scoot again. I sure did hate to borrow so much from Leroy, but the price of hiding is going up.

Hell the bike alone cost me over $700. I really didn't like to buy that hot engine though. I knew the guy who owned it. He was with us at the protest. But when you're on the run you take what you can get.

The bike is running good though. The new cases bolted on with no hassle and those new pistons and jugs were a Godsend. Hope the shop doesn't miss them.

Now all I have to do is get to Salt Lake City and it will be party time for awhile.

I figure I'll head out I-15 past Vegas and then through the Virgin River Gorge and into Utah. That's a neat ride and I know there aren't a whole bunch of cops along there.

As I passed through Barstow I got the feeling I always get when I travel. That feeling of being totally free. When I passed into Nevada I was really back where I belong, on a bike on the open road.

The road kind of melts under you after you are putting for awhile. The white line becomes a ribbon leading you to your next adventure. Passing through Vegas I even turned off the interstate and went for a putt down the strip to check out all the big hotels and foxy young ladies.

I don't know why, but Las Vegas always attracts the most beautiful women in the world, and the longer they stay there the more they like bikers. The town is heaven for a hardcore biker.

As I cut across the city of lights I thought about how it was a few years back, when I was working a little ways outside of town at one of the hundreds of mines that dot the outskirts of Vegas. Most people don't even know there are some folks who actually work for a living in this town. I used to come in after working from sunup, shower, change into some clean threads and be out on the town all night long. Of course, that was before I was into bikes. Bikes changed my whole way of life and it was for the better. No doubt about it.

I think it was something my father said to me, way back when I was a punk kid. I had just gotten transferred into a class for specially gifted children. When I told him, after he got home from work late that night, he didn't get as excited as I had hoped. He kind of looked sad.

After a little while talking, he told me that he would rather see me be the smartest kid in the normal class than just one of the students in a bunch of smart kids.

Actually the way he put it was, “It’s better to be a big fish in a small pond than a small fish in a big pond.”

It took me a long time to figure out what he was right, but when I finally did, I started to use it in my life.

You know, it’s kinda funny. The older you get the smarter your folks seem to be.

A red light loomed in front of me and when I came to a stop I looked around a little bit. Across the street and to the left was one of the little bars that I used to hang out at when I lived there. It was only seven or eight years ago, but it seemed like a lifetime.

I sat there feeling the deep throb of my 74 inch engine keep the beat that made Harleys a way of life, and decided maybe it would be nice to stop for a cold one and check out the place for old time sake.

The name of the place was still the same, Diamond Dogs, but everything else was different. It used to look real new and clean, with the big shiny sign and the fresh stucco painted with a sparkle that looked like diamonds. I could tell it hadn’t been touched since the last time I was there and the sign looked a lot smaller now that all the other places had giant neon signs everywhere. The place just looked plain faded.

Jesus but it was dark in there. It took a couple of seconds for my eyes to get adjusted. I just stood there in the door, not even taking off my cutoff or my leather jacket. I don't like to get too comfortable until I know what I'm walking into.

Chapter 9

Dick Bondano didn't usually come to bars like this by himself, but today he just had to. He had been doing his job down at the airport as he had for the last eight months, when some package turned up missing. He knew he didn't take it, but they still blamed him. He was pissed, but there wasn't a whole lot he could do about it. He sat there over his third beer when all of a sudden the light coming through the door was blocked off by the biggest son-of-a-bitch he had ever seen. He was wearing the standard uniform of an outlaw biker, but he looked bigger than any two people. It could have been the sunlight that came around him that gave him an aura of something almost supernatural, or was it the beer? Dick didn't know what exactly, but there was something there for sure.

The guy just stood there like he was trying to impress everyone in the bar with his size. After a couple of seconds Dick realized he was probably just getting his eyes adjusted, but it still looked like something out of an old Kung Fu movie, which was his favorite kind.

Ever since he was a kid in Hawaii he was guided by the marital arts. His uncle was a Grand Master in Filipino Kali, and he followed closely in his footsteps. Ever since he could remember he had been trained, so now at the age of 25 he was a master in every art of combat.

He found the more he learned about the martial arts, the less he needed it. He found a mental relaxation far beyond the mere knowledge that he could take care of himself. It was almost spiritual.

As he sat there nursing his drink he decided when he finished it he would go over to the gym. He always felt a lot better after a good workout, and there were some guys from the Philippines there who really gave him a good workout whenever he wanted to practice.

The big guy in the doorway walked over to the bar stool a couple of seats away. He took off his jacket and Dick could see that the guy obviously worked out or something. He could tell by the little sings, like larger than normal triceps, that you only get from special exercises.

One thing was for sure, This guy had seen the inside of a gym before.

When he turned back to his drink he could hear a couple of guys at the end of the bar talking. They had been there for a while and their empty beer glasses told him they were probably pretty well underway to a good drunk. They looked like a couple of truck drivers by the way they were dressed, from their cowboy boots to the top of their imitation Stetson hats. The dead giveaway was the one tanned arm, where it hung out the window of the cab.

Yup, no doubt about it, they were truck drivers.

He could overhear their conversation a little better now because they were starting to get loud.

"I don't give a shit if he's big, he ain't' nothing but a God damn fuckin' biker and they ain't shit. All they do is get oil all over the road and take up all the good looking chickies!" With that he hoisted his glass and emptied it.

"Hey, barkeep, a couple more down here!" He shouted as he slammed it to the bar.

Dick turned to see how the biker was taking all of this. He just sat there, looking a little uncomfortable, but not in the least scared.

For some reason Dick like this big hulk. It was something in his eyes. He could see he wasn't looking for trouble, but he wasn't about to run, either.

A couple of minutes later the truckers were really getting loud. They shouted at the biker across the bar.

"Hey, Tiny, did you leave your bicycle outside? Wouldn't your mommy let you drive a real car?"

The dude just sat there for a second. Then he got up off the stool and picked up his jacket. He was going to split. Dick knew what was going through his head. He didn't want to get into it. Not because he was afraid, but because he didn't want the hassle.

As the biker walked for the door a beer mug sailed through the air and clipped him on the side of the head. He staggered a little bit, caught himself on a slot machine, and slowly turned around.

His eyes were as calm as could be.

"Which one of you assholes threw that?" He asked as calmly as possible.

They both stopped laughing and looked at him. The bigger one stood up. He must have been a good three inches taller than the biker. All Dick could think was, where the hell do they gown guys as big as this? Hell, he was at least six and half feet tall. His buddy was well over six feet, too.

The bigger one stopped smiling.

"I did, you chicken shit punk, why?"

"Well, how about you and I going out back so we don't mess up this man's place?"

With that he started walking toward the back exit. When he was halfway there, and about two feet away from the big trucker, he turned, and with his buck knife folded closed in his fist, and planted one square in the middle of the guy's face.

The trucker was so surprised he didn't have a chance to move. He just fell backward against the bar and sank to the floor. The trucker's friend slobbered something about not being fair, and took a couple of steps toward the biker. Dick was sitting right there and came up with a quick foot into his balls. The man fell to the floor, moaning.

The biker looked at Dick and he looked back at him. Not a word was said.

They both started to laugh. They took each other's hand in the biker's handshake and turned to the door.

Dick threw the bartender a couple of bucks for his tab.

When they got outside Dick checked out the scooter. It was a shovelhead top end on a pan lower. The frame was as rigid as a rock, with a Dick Allen springer about 25 inches over stock on the front. It was all black and there was no doubt about it being a real biker's machine.

He should know. He had one almost like it parked in back.

Chapter 10

How the hell do I get into things like this? Christ almighty damn, all I wanted to do was have a simple drink and the local truckers decide to use me for a punching bag.

Actually it was kinda fun though. The big one was easy. I knew he would be. Being big all my life I know the problems. First of all, most big guys are really chicken shit, but they put on like they are not so they don't look funny. They have relied on their size all their life and when they meet someone almost as big, they don't know what to do. I knew all I had to do was surprise him and I had it made.

His partner was another story. I didn't know if there was just one more or a whole bunch. The other guy in the bar, what's his name, Dick? Yeah, Dick was a pretty neat guy to meet. I guess it goes to show bikers are the only real people you can count on. Here I am alone, a stranger, and all I have to do is find a biker and I'm home free.

I looked over at my new found friend riding next to me. There was no doubt in my mind I had found a friend, and he was a true biker too. The one way to tell is by the scoot a man rides. If he rides a stretched hardtail with suicide clutch and the likes, the chances are he's cool. The guy didn't talk a whole lot though. He just asked if I need a place to crash, and when I said yeah he just motioned to follow him.

Not a whole lot of talk. I kinda like that. We turned right off of Paradise and headed out to Boulder Highway. From there we aimed south until we hit the little town of Pittman, about five miles out of Vegas. There we turned into a small tract, and turned into the driveway of a brown stucco house. It was pretty run down.

Dick unlocked the padlocks on the door and opened the garage. There were some exhaust pipes hanging from the rafters, a small tool box in one corner and some sleeping bags and camping gear. That was it. I pulled my bike in next to his and shut her down.

"It ain't much, but it's home," he mumbled, and went in the doorway at the back of the garage.

I took off my jacket, put my cutoff back on, and followed him.

The place was a typical bachelor house. A mess. There were beer bottles everywhere, dirty dishes in the sink, and a scruffy looking cat wandering around rubbing up and down his leg, meowing to be fed.

He wandered into the kitchen, which looked like a disaster had decorated it, pulled a can of cat food off the top shelf and opened it with his knife.

Man, those buck knives are used for everything.

He opened the refrigerator and handed me a beer. As I glanced past his shoulder I could see that there wasn't anything else in there, just three cans of beer and two empty six pack cartons.

We walked into the living room and sat down on the couch. Well, I think it was a couch. It was either that or a bunch of cushions covered with a sleeping bag, I couldn't tell for sure.

I found a long time ago that bikers may not have the neatest looking houses, but they always have the most comfortable. This was no exception.

Dick leaned over and turned on a Montgomery Ward cheap stereo and we settled back.

"Do you get into shit like that often?" he asked, kinda off the wall.

"Well, I don't try to, but it seems to follow me."

"Yeah, I know what you mean. I get into it too. I just got canned for no reason at all. They knew I was a biker and something was missing. That was all they needed. Assholes."

He said the last word more as a fact than a personal judgment.

After a couple of silent seconds he turned his face and looked right in my eye. I knew what his next question would be, and the answer.

"Where you headed?"

"No place particular, I'm just scooting around."

He thought for a second.

"Mind some company?"

I was right.

"Why not? Sure."

And that was it. In the last few years of being a biker I found that the strongest and best friendships are made in a split second, and I knew there was something about this guy that made him a little different. He had class.

He opened a cigar box and pulled out a small canister like the ones that hold 35 millimeter film. He dumped a small brownish pile of weed on the table.

"Thai stick," was all he said.

In a couple of minutes we were well on our way to oblivion as the opium-cured marijuana conquered our heads and sent us into lands only known by the enlightened. It was good herb, for sure.

Way into the wee hours of the morning we sat in a state of partial unconsciousness telling each other of our lives and of our loves. He was interesting as hell, especially on the subject of martial arts. I had a lot more respect for him by the time we hit the sack.

I don't think I could have picked a better man to ride with. He wasn't a heavy doper, he seemed honest, and best of all I think he could take care of himself.

Chapter 11

The morning was as crisp as a new hundred dollar bill. The temperature was down into the 30's and they could see the snow on top of Mount Charleston over 40 miles away. It was going to be a cold ride, but Dick was so glad to get out of this town that he didn't really care.

He called up a couple of his riding buddies and told them that he was splitting and they were welcome to anything he left behind.

Out in the garage he could hear his trusty scoot idling strong and loud. All he needed was a sleeping bag, his clothes and a helmet. The stupid helmet law dictated the last item.

He hadn't been this excited in years. Now he was almost glad he had been fired. Hell, he hadn't even cashed his paycheck yet, and he still had the rent payment in the bank. He was to have paid it today.

After a quick stop at the bank to close his checking account they aimed north on 1-15. He had almost $700 in his pocket and a good running scoot. He was in heaven.

His new found friend seemed to be someone he had been looking for for a long time. He wasn't the typical "dumb" biker like he had met so many times. He had a certain something about him that made you want to go with him. To follow him. Dick had heard about born leaders, but this was the first one he had ever met. It had nothing to do with his size, which was formidable, but more with his eyes. When he spoke you knew that he knew what he was talking about. It was like a destiny. His heavy eastern training let him accept that without question.

It felt so damn good to be out on the open highway that he wondered why he hadn't split before. He glanced over at Treb and their eyes met for a second. It was like communication without words. They were a team, no doubt about it. The two strong Harley engines were beating like one. The sound made a rhythm that played in your head like a sweet dream. It lulled you so you didn't even notice the miles passing.

Off to the left there were mountains that looked almost purple. On the right was the open American desert. It was times like these that Dick felt glad to be alive. A good bike, a good brother, and nothing to do but ride.

Soon the freeway turned into a two-lane highway and there was finally a break in the monotony. The road had a few small curves and grades in it. That broke up the sameness a bit.

They stopped at a two-pump gas station off the highway and soon they were heading north east on the new stretch of interstate that leads into Utah.

They hadn't been wearing their helmets, enjoying the freedom, when a cop car passed them going the other way. Treb signaled Dick to take the lid off his handlebars and put it on his head quick.

It was too late. The cop was turning around.

All of a sudden Treb looked like he was scared to death. Instead of slowing to let the cop pull them over, he jammed on the throttle.

What the hell was going on? A lid ticket was just a small thing and they would be on their way again. Why hassle by running?

Dick decided that he was with Treb, no matter what, and he cranked on his throttle too. It was about eight miles to the Arizona border and he got ready for the run.

It was times like this that he wished he had a speedometer. He knew they were doing at least 100 and getting faster all the time.

Unfortunately the cop was doing about a hundred and twenty. Dick glanced over his shoulder and could see the black and white gaining. Treb looked over his shoulder too, and crouched down to cut the wind resistance. It helped. He picked up a couple miles an hour. Dick did the same.

The cop was just a few hundred feet behind. Treb could see the state boundary just ahead. He twisted the throttle so hard he thought it would break.

They made it over the state line. They sat up and started to slow down.

But the cop kept coming. He crossed the line.

He pulled next to Dick and stuck a gun out the window.

"OK asshole, pull over," boomed the loudspeaker.

You win some, you lose some, thought Treb, and he stopped on the side of the road.

The cop came out of the car crouched behind his door with his gun in hand. He motioned them off their bikes and told them to get over to the car with their hands behind their heads.

They did. Arguing with a cop who is holding a gun when you are a biker is like playing Russian roulette with all chambers loaded. It ain't too bright.

The cop waited until the bikers had their hands on the car with their feet spread and he walked over to Treb. He searched him with one hand while he kept the gun on him with the other. When he hit the 357 in his vest he stopped and slowly pulled it out of the pocket. He handcuffed one of Treb's hands to the door latch and made his way over to Dick.

Dick was no dummy. He knew that they were going to be doing at least a couple of days for the speeding alone, if nothing else, and the fact Treb was packing multiplied his thoughts. There was also the fact that Treb chose to run instead of taking a simple lid law ticket. There was something here that didn't compute.

The cop held his gun on Dick as he ran his free hand up his left leg. Just as he reached the thigh Dick came up hard and fast with his left foot and spun to knock the gun out of his hand. As fast as lightning his open palm smashed into the surprised cop's face and he was down on the ground unconscious. Dick reached into his pocket and got the keys. Quickly he unlocked Treb's cuffs.

Treb took the cuffs and put them on the cop, with his hands behind his back. Then he lifted him like a toy and put him in the back seat of the squad car. The car had a screen between the back and front seat and no handles on the doors. He remembered the times he had been in one.

Then he took out his buck knife and cut the microphone from the radio. "Damn but those buck knives come in handy," he thought.

The keys were tossed as far as he could throw them out into the desert.

It all was done so fast that they were on their way before the first car passed.

The nearest phone was over 50 miles behind them and the next one ahead of them was in Utah.

But Dick had one hell of a big question for Treb at the next gas stop.

Chapter 12

All I could think of as we putted away from where we left that cop was how thankful I was to have Dick along, but I also knew I was going to have to trust him a hell of a lot if I tell him what happened back in L.A.

The more I rode and the more I thought about it, the more I realized it was no problem. Hell, he had just taken on a cop without asking a question. What more proof of friendship did I need?

But the first thing we had to do was get off the highway for awhile to let things cool off. We were safe until the cop came to.

Since we were just cutting across the corner of Arizona we would be in Utah in a few minutes, so I tried to think of any friends we might have there.

The biggest club in Utah is the Sundowners, but I didn't know if they had a chapter in St. George, which was the first city we hit.

We pulled off the highway right after we passed through the Virgin River Gorge, which is a neat little canyon dividing Arizona and Utah, and took a small farm road the back way into St. George. I knew that if the law had been aroused they would be looking for us to get off the highway there. Damn small gas tanks on motorcycles anyway! Makes it kinda hard to disappear, especially where gas is so scarce.

We pulled over in front of a rundown farmhouse and sat down to discuss our situation.

I told Dick all about Los Angeles and Rom and the newsman. He didn't interrupt once. He just sat there and listened. When I was through he looked at me for a second, smiled, and that was it.

"Okay bro, what do we do now?"

Damn, he was one of the good ones, for sure.

I thought for a couple of minutes. I knew they would be looking, but not as if we had robbed a bank or something. After all, the only thing we did was rough up a cop a little and maybe embarrass him. They wouldn't turn out the National Guard or anything like that.

But then I had another thought. Since we escaped across a state line they might get federal about it for interstate flight to avoid prosecution.

Oh, hell. I was getting too damn paranoid. A couple of small time bikers weren't worth it.

Unless they knew who I was. Interstate flight to avoid murder charges, of a cop, was a whole other story.

All of a sudden it hit me. What the hell was I doing here? I was wanted by the FBI for murdering a cop, now for beating up another one on a highway, and for crossing a state line, and all I was trying to do was get the bikers together to beat the stupid helmet law.

Jesus, but I do have a way of getting into it, don't I?

Oh well, back to the problem at hand. The first thing we have to do is figure how to get out of the public view for awhile.

The answer was sitting right behind the farmhouse. It was an old van, probably about a 1940 model. It was half buried under a bunch of hay and garbage.

We knocked at the back door and asked the farmer about it.

He said that it ran when he parked it, but that was about three years ago.

Oh Lord, why me? Why all the time me?

We bargained with the miser for awhile and soon we had a deal. He would sell us the truck for $300 and he would throw in the battery off the tractor for another $50.

Hell, fifty dollars for a battery like that was robbery, but not as bad as $300 for the truck. He must have had an idea we were in a spot, though. And he was right.

For the next two hours we worked on the van. We drained the oil and added new, which the farmer "let us have" for a measly $10. After that we changed batteries, pumped up the tires with a hand pump, and found one that wouldn't hold air.

Another $40 bought us the spare tire off his car.

What a crook.

As the sun was setting we pulled out of the farmyard with our bikes tucked snugly in the back of the van. It didn't run too good, but it did run and that's what counted.

We took off our leathers and put on a couple of old hats we found in the barn. We didn't feel at all guilty about taking them since we had ended up paying over $400 for a truck that wasn't worth a hundred.

With our hair tucked up inside the straw hats and our beards combed out we looked like a couple of good old boys from the farm. Of course you had to stretch your imagination to see a Hawaiian farmer, but what the hell, he almost looked Mexican, so it was all right. We pulled into St. George and gassed up the Blue Beast, which is what we named our new mode of transportation. I hoped we wouldn't be stuck with it for a long time.

At the gas station I made a few inquiries into any local bike clubs and found out there weren't any chapters of clubs, but there were a couple of "those kind of bikers" just a little way out of town.

After gassing up and stopping for some hamburgers and heartburn, we followed the directions out to the ranch where the bikers were supposed to be.

It had turned dark by now and it was pretty hard to see. We followed a small paved road alongside the interstate for awhile and then turned onto a dirt road. A couple miles along we saw a wagon wheel with a mail box on top and knew we were going the right way.

After a couple of false turns we found the place

we were looking for.

Or so we thought.

When we walked up to the door a goofy looking dude opened it up without even asking who we were. Obviously not a hard core type.

We told them we heard there were some bikers out here, and we were looking for a place to crash. Their eyes lit up and he opened the door to let us in.

There were three guys, ranging from 18 to 20 years old, all with too many pimples to fit on their faces, and three young sweeties, the oldest of whom couldn't have been over 18. I fell instantly in heat.

I glanced over at Dick and he looked back at me. His eye's were saying maybe this wasn't going to be too bad after all.

The guys kept asking us what we rode, so we told them to go out to the truck and check them out. They ran out so excited I thought they would wet their pants.

Dick and I checked out the young suckies. Not too shabby for farm girls.

They went into the kitchen to get us a beer and we could hear them giggling all the way out in the front room. This was going to be fun. It was obvious the chicks liked bikers, and these guys were the closest things to bikers that they had around here. We were big time. All we had to do was figure out how to get them away from the dudes without ruffling any feathers and this might be a damn good pit stop for us. The girls came back in just about the same time the guys did. They handed us our beers and the guys started asking questions about the bikes. We acted as if they were real bikers and talked real serious to them. We even asked what they rode.

A real touch of pride entered their voices as they told of their bikes. Yeah, they had "choppers" like ours. Of course they weren't Harleys, but they were Hondas, which was almost as good, wasn't it?

It almost made me puke, but I said yes.

We wandered out to the garage to see their bikes.

It was almost funny. There were two 350cc Hondas with front ends that had to be 15" over stock. The rake was stock, so the gas tank pointed almost straight up. If it weren't for the sissy bar, that was almost four feet tall on one of them, they would have fallen off from the sheer angle.

The other bike was a 750 Honda that didn't look too bad. The guy who built it had a little know how and he kept it looking like a motorcycle.

As they led us back into the house a plan started to form in my dirty little mind. It had been awhile since I had any good puss, and I wanted some of this. Young ones were always my favorite.

All we had to do was convince the guys to let us use their women for awhile.

Hell, with their combined intelligence a little lower than the cows that roamed the fields, I figured that would be easy.

Chapter 13

Cindy, Ann and Debbie sat on the couch giggling and whispering while the boys showed the two bikers their bikes. They were so excited they could hardly sit still. They had always wanted to get next to real bikers, and now they had their chance. They didn't care how, but they were going to do it.

When the two bikers came back in, Cindy started to get moist between the legs. She wanted the dark looking guy so bad she could taste it. She hadn't made love to a real man before, and this lean and mean biker was what she wanted.

The guy she was here visiting, Tom was okay for these parts. After all, he did ride a bike, even if it was a Honda, but this guy Dick was something else. When he sat down on the floor and crossed his legs by the fire she could outline the bulge in his pants.

Debbie had been to the big city before. Salt Lake City. Hell, she had even been to bed in a motel room with a grown man. He was almost 21 when it happened and she was 16. She felt that she really knew what was going on. As the guys crowded back into the room, she rubbed up against Treb, the big one, and she felt his hard arms under his Levi jacket. She was going to leave town with him, and nothing would stop her.

Dick took out a little smoking material, the Thai stick they had smoked the night before, and started to roll a couple of fat numbers. Treb looked at him and smiled. He knew that one small number among all of them would have done the trick, but two big ones would have them catatonic. He laughed inwardly. "Hell, this guy's as devious as I am."

They talked of bikes and protests and runs and things as the powerful herb passed from hand to hand. Each time it came around to Dick or Treb they would pretend to suck on it hard, but really just take a small toke. That was all they needed.

The other guys wanted to show they were "real bikers" so they toked hard and long. In a few minutes they were almost comatose.

Then Treb started to talk about what real bikers are like. He told of the nights in clubhouses all over the country when it would be turnout time, and the brothers would trade old ladies. The guys mumbled that was the way it should be. Dick smiled broadly at Treb. It was working. By now one of the sweeties had moved next to Dick and he had his hand resting on her sweet little leg. He moved it up and down until his fingers were drumming on her little mound. She almost cried, she was so ready. The guy she was with just smiled, to show he was a real biker.

Debbie walked over to Treb and stood there looking down at him. He was lying on the floor propped on one elbow looking into the fire. She stood in front of him and took his free hand. She knelt down and opened her blouse. Two of the finest young peach titties he had ever seen fell free. She took his hand and placed it over one.

Treb looked around at John, the one who owned the 750 Honda and who was with Debbie, and shrugged his shoulders. He could see John was upset, but he wanted to be a real biker, so he just smiled and bobbed his head in approval.

Treb kinda liked the guy, even if he did ride a Honda, and he vowed he would give him back his chick in the morning.

Actually it was working out pretty well, because the youngest girl there, Ann, had a crush on John for a long time, but was afraid to make a move. Now she had enough Thai in her to be bold, and she walked over and sat on his lap, placing her soft lips on his and kissing him like she had never kissed anybody else.

Tom and his friend Bill looked at each other through hazed and foggy eyes. They figured they were not needed so they just lay down and passed out from too much smoking and too much beer.

This was fine with everybody else.

Treb sat there looking at this young thing that couldn't be over 17 and started to slowly undress her. She put her hand on his and bent over to whisper something to him. As she bent over her large boobs hung in front of his face and he couldn't help but nibble a little bit.

"Let's go into the bedroom," was all she said.

She stood and he stood to follow. He noticed that she was wobbling a little when she walked down the hall, but it looked cute with those tight jeans over her pear-shaped ass. Treb had always been an ass man and this young thing was fine in that and all other departments.

He sat on the edge of the bed and watched her as she took her blouse off. Jesus, the young bodies were getting better and better. They couldn't have been like that when he was in school.

He reached out and kissed her on each boob, sucking on each nipple, then he dropped his mouth down to her belly button. By now she was squirming.

He undid the top button of her jeans and pulled the zipper down. She wasn't wearing anything underneath. As he slowly slipped her pants down he could see the soft down of pubic bush peek out at him and he just about lost control. He finished pulling off her pants and gently laid her on the bed. Then he stripped.

Debbie lay there watching at this monster of a man and started to get a little scared. Hell, she didn't know if she could handle a man as big as that or not. He had to be over six feet tall and his weight could crush her.

All of her fears drifted away faster than they appeared as he lay down next to her and started kissing her again. She got so turned on that all she wanted was more.

He kissed down over the small mound of her stomach and began to kiss the soft inner part of her thigh. That was it. She couldn't take it any more. She lowered her head down onto his phallus and started to suck on it like her life depended on it. As his tongue sank into her tender young crease she went wild, and for the next half hour they made love in every possible way.

Out in the living room Dick could hear Debbie moaning, but he was busy with Cindy. This young chick may not be experienced, but she was a willing learner. Her long brown hair hanging over her naked shoulders as she sat on his rigid member was enough to drive him wild, and her firm tits were just the right size. Not too big and not too small. He never imagined a better lay.

By now John had completely forgotten about Debbie. He had wanted Ann for a long time, but Debbie was more experienced, which was important in a small town. Now, as he lay with Ann in his arms, he wondered why he never tried before. He liked her a lot better.

Ann just lay there, happier than she could ever remember being, and she fell asleep.

Chapter 14

When I woke up I didn't remember where I was, all I knew was there was one of the neatest looking boobs in the whole world about three inches from my eyes and a foxy young lady with it.

I sat up and checked her out. Then I remembered last night. As my mind came back into focus I slowly got out of bed and put on my pants. I actually had plans of waking Dick and sneaking out, but my God-damned buck knife dropped off my belt and the thud woke Debbie up.

She looked up at me and smiled. Then she reached out and grabbed me by the family jewels, real soft like. Without a word she covered them with her face and started to give me head again.

You know, I'm definitely a sucker for a low blow

(sorry about that). When she was through I zipped up and walked into the front room.

Jesus Christ, it looked like I really missed out on a party. Dick had a sweet young brunette wrapped all over him without a stitch on, and John had a sweet young thing on him too, in the same state of undress.

Oh well, I couldn't complain. I was well handled.

Debbie walked in behind me and started rubbing up against me again. All of a sudden I knew she wanted a little more than a one night fun time. She was acting like she was my old lady or something.

I gently pushed her away and walked over to Dick. He looked awfully comfortable, but I had to wake him. I tapped him with the tip of my toe on the arm.

Before I knew it my foot was pulled out from under me and I was on the way to a rude meeting with the ground. Man, I had never seen anything so fast in my life.

By the time the thud of my 300 pounds echoed through the house Dick was standing over me with a surprised look on his face, but not half as surprised as mine.

He apologized all over himself and I made a mental note to wake him from afar from now on.

Pretty soon we were all laughing about it.

The girls went into the kitchen to make breakfast and Dick, John and I went outside to check out the bikes. They seemed to be okay and we talked about bikes, girls and other things that bikers talk about in the early morning.

John wanted to know where we were going and when we told him we didn't know, he wanted to come too. I almost felt bad saying no, but it was a little too hairy out there to have someone to take care of. We did promise to stop back someday to see him, though.

After a good breakfast of sausage and eggs, we started to say our goodbyes.

Or should I say we tried to. It seems that Debbie had different ideas. She wanted to go along.

Now normally I might have said yes. It's always kind of neat to have a house mouse to cook and clean up, but since we were already in trouble with the law, I didn't figure we wanted to add the Mann Act to our case history. After all, she was only 17.

After listening to her snivel I remembered why I don't keep an old lady, and we hit the road again, heading toward Salt Lake City.

The old Blue Beast was actually running pretty good as we pulled onto the interstate again. We took the speedometer up to 45, which was all she would handle, and commenced to compare notes on the last night's activities. After listening to Dick I almost wish we had stuck around so I could have tried some of that Cindy.

We stopped at a diner about 150 miles up the road and had lunch. While we were there we decided to check out the money situation.

It was pretty dismal. I had a little over $1,800 and Dick had about $500. If we planned on being on the road long we were going to have to watch it.

The biggest bummer we were having was traveling in a truck. When you are a free riding biker, you want to be on the road with the wind in your face, where you can be a part of the countryside, not all wrapped up in an iron cage looking out at it. But we decided that since the law was looking for us we would have to stay that way for awhile.

After eating we pulled over to a gas station for a fuel. While we sat there a cop car pulled in next to us. He spoke to the attendant.

"Hey Fred, you see anything of a couple of bikers on black choppers come through here?"

"No Jack, I haven't. What'd they do?"

"Oh, not a helluva lot. Some Nevada officer stopped 'em and they roughed him up a little. We're on the lookout for two black choppers, but we figure they are headed toward Denver. If they don't find 'em today, the call will be dropped. Damn Nevada cops can't handle their own problems."

Then they started talking about the weather and such, but Dick and I just sat there, quiet as two mice.

All we had to do was stay out of sight today and we would be home free. All right.

We paid for our gas and slowly pulled out of the station. We got almost a mile away when we saw the cop car coming up behind us.

Why me, Lord? As he pulled up behind us his red light came on.

I knew there was no way to outrun him, so we decided to try and play it out. As we pulled over to the curb I slowly got out of the truck with my stupid looking hat on and a weed in my mouth. Hell, I looked more like a shit kicker than Jimmy Carter.

"Yes sir officer, I do something wrong?" I asked,

all wide eyed and innocent.

"Well actually your tags are expired," he smiled. "You got your current tags for this here truck?"

Oh God, now we were in for it. All I had was a bill of sale, no pink slip or registration.

"Well ya see," I put on the biggest shit eating grin I could muster. "Actually we don't use this here truck much, and this is the first time we had it off the farm. I just come down to the station to get some gas for the tractor. My wife's got the car doing the shopping." Sweat was starting to pop out on my forehead.

"Okay, but if you are going to use it on the road, you're going to have to get it registered." And with that he got back in his car.

For the next twenty miles all we did was watch the rear view mirror and hope. At the next gas station I kept the attendant busy while Dick peeled the sticker off his car's license plate and stuck it on ours. We were legal looking again.

When we hit the outskirts of Salt Lake City I put in a call to some of the people I was told to contact by a club back in Los Angeles and soon we were heading over to their clubhouse for a little fun and games. At last we were among friends.

Chapter 15

The Sundowners is one of the larger clubs in the United States. They have chapters all over, with the mother chapter in Salt Lake City. Their clubhouse is impressive. As Dick and Treb pulled up in their truck they were met by Trona, one of the members who was on guard. The clubhouse is open 24 hours a day and there are guards on duty at all times.

They were told to park their truck around behind the large, barn-like building and then they were led in.

Entering through the back, which was the only way to get in without opening the giant barn doors, you walked through a small passageway that is completely covered with fluorescent paintings done by members and by guests and old ladies. It's kind of a thing where every member adds his own little something to the clubhouse. There are the painted names of members past and present and the names of clubs that have come to party.

After you pass through the entryway, you walk into the main room of the clubhouse. It is cavernous. All over the walls are pinups from Penthouse, Playboy and Screw magazine. The raunchier they are, the more prominent their display position. In the middle of the room, under a bright fluorescent light, is a regulation pool table that was long ago stolen from a bar. The mechanism that requires the customary quarter has been yanked out and the members play for free.

Old couches and overstuffed chairs line the walls and one section of the room is for members' bikes to be parked. It is at the far end of the room, over by the large barn doors. As Dick and Treb entered there was one bike being stripped to the bare frame. They didn't bother to ask if it was a brother's bike or just new parts being added to the warehouse in the room upstairs.

Treb stood by the bar talking to Raunchy, the Vice President of the club. He was telling of the folks who sent them there and discussing other bikers whom they knew mutually. There is a distrust in all clubs of people that nobody knows, because the police are always trying to infiltrate the clubs to get some kind of evidence on them. For anything, just so they can hassle them.

After about fifteen minutes the rules had been laid down. Treb and Dick were welcome to party, but when the meeting started that night they would have to wait down the street at a bar, with the old ladies. This was in no way intended as a put down, it was just one of the rules.

Dick nodded that this was all right with them and they were introduced around.

Meanwhile Raunchy disappeared into a back room. Treb and Dick didn't know it, but he was going upstairs to the office to call Dusty and Rat back in Los Angeles. In a few minutes there was a complete description of Treb on the desk and a complete file of what happened in Los Angeles. They knew he had killed a cop and he was running. They verified that he had been leading the organization of clubs and settling a lot of disputes between clubs. They'd seen him on the news. In all respects he was okay. They were to treat him with the highest regard.

Pretty soon Raunchy appeared back at the bar. This time he was much more friendly. He told the members there that Treb and Dick were to get full privileges, from the turnout room to the bar, and they were to pay for nothing. They were honored guests as long as they wanted to stay.

Treb felt much better now. He knew that they had been checked out and were approved. From now on they had brothers here and they were as safe as could be.

They were given a complete tour of the clubhouse including the turnout room, which was set aside for any young lady who wanted to give of herself, and the armory with enough guns to start world war three. The parts depot in the upper warehouse was elaborate enough to make any Harley dealer envious. There was a complete inventory there for the asking.

For members only.

While they were getting the tour Raunchy sent a prospect over to the massage parlor that the club owned to get a couple of woofies for Treb and Dick while they were there, and a couple of other members set up the "guest" room, which was a large, open loft at the top of the building that was furnished for visiting friends.

There was no doubt now. They were among friends, as long as they didn't violate any of the rules.

Really the rules were pretty simple. You don't talk about what you see. You don't mess with anybody's righteous old lady. And you treat the members and their colors with respect.

That's about it.

As it grew later in the day more members arrived until the place was full. About every half hour the two prospects would open the big barn doors and roll in a half dozen more of the members' bikes. Then they would be shut again.

Once inside the clubhouse you were safe. That was the feeling. Inside only brothers were there. You could smoke anything you wanted and snort anything and there was plenty of both.

Treb had laid off using anything but grass after he OD'd at a party in New York once, and Dick's martial arts training had kept him from ever being a user, but many of the members offered up some of the finest cocaine they had ever seen. A man could get snow blind there.

A little later the juke box was shut down and the meeting was announced. All the guests and old ladies left for a bar down the street. Treb and Dick were invited to stay if they wanted. They did.

It would surprise people how well and efficiently outlaw bike clubs run their meetings. When you have a club with over a hundred members, it's usually a bitch. But they have it down to a science.

In the front of the room a table is set up where the officers sit. The officers consist of the President, Vice President, Secretary, Treasurer, Sergeant-at-arms, and Road Captain. Each gives his report in turn and after each one speaks there is a question and answer period. The meeting is then opened up for general questions and new business and then any member may speak.

If anybody gets out of hand or out of order the Sergeant-at- arms (usually the biggest member) fines him. The standard fine at this meeting was $1 for talking and the same for being late.

All during the meeting a prospect was kept busy running between the bar and thirsty members, hustling beer.

After the meeting had been in progress about fifteen minutes, Raunchy stood up after being recognized by the president.

"Brothers, we have a couple of guests here tonight, and I want to introduce them to you." He smiled at Treb.

"That big son-of-a-bitch there is Treb Lincoln. Some of you might have heard of him. He is the one that settled the war between the H.A. and the Breed in New York. He is also the one who led the big protest we all read about in Los Angeles a few days ago. He and his buddy Dick are going to be staying with us for awhile. Treat them like brothers. Anything they want, they get. They don't pay for anything. If you're partying with them outside the clubhouse, pick up the tab and give it to Grease here," he indicated the treasurer. "Any questions?" He paused. All the members looked them over real close. The rest of the meeting was pretty routine, with discussions of a run that was coming up and a party they were going to have the next week.

After the meeting was adjourned a prospect was sent to the bar to get the old ladies and guests that were there and soon a party was going full swing.

Chapter 16

Karen Sweeney had been working at the Sundowners' massage parlor for about three weeks and she knew what she wanted. In a town like Salt Lake City the only way to make a buck was by hustling, and the only way to hustle was to be protected. She learned a long time back that if you're going to get rich, you can't fight the competition. Always join them.

Karen knew about surviving. Ever since she left the small town of Pulaski, Georgia, she had been a survivor. Her father had tried to rape her when she was 14, but she got loose and ran away from home. She did feel a little guilty about leaving her mother there, but hell, she made the choice to stay with the guy. Karen had been born into it.

She had been on the road almost three years now, and even though she looked like a sweet, innocent little 17-year-old, she knew the score pretty well. What she knew best of all was, as long as she played the game she would get ahead. The only time she had been hurt was the first time she tried to hustle a black guy. She thought she was being pretty smart.

She was hitch-hiking across country on Highway 40 when a black dude had picked her up in a two-year-old Pontiac. She had been on the road by herself for about a year and thought she knew all the cute little tricks. When he made his play for her she acted like she didn't know what he meant, and then she said she was hungry. All the times before, the guy would offer to buy her a meal and then she would sneak out through the restroom of the restaurant.

Well, this guy must have been hustled before. He went for the meal routine, but when she went to the head he got up, paid the check, and was waiting outside when she came out the back door.

It was just a matter of luck that there was a big truck driver taking a piss against the back of the building because when he tried to throw her into his car, the trucker punched that man up pretty bad.

Until then she was still a virgin.

But that ended the same night. The trucker offered her a lift and out there on the open road, in the back of a truck, she gave up her girlhood and became a woman.

She had wanted to for a long time, but she had been afraid. But there was something about that big trucker that made her want him to be the one. She had always been attracted to big guys. When they turned off on the side road and stopped, she was a little worried, but he was so gentle as he took off her clothes that she didn't even try to stop him. When he entered her it hurt a little, but the pleasure was much stronger. She stayed with him for a month, traveling the highways of America in that big cabover Mack. She loved the open road.

But, as with everything in her life, when she really got something she wanted, she would lose it. She lost him when a cop stopped them on a back road for speeding. When the cop found out she was underaged he threatened to put him in jail.

She convinced the cop to let him go and for the next hour she gave in to the cop's every whim. He was a real weirdo, too.

But that was all water under the bridge. She made her way to Salt Lake with some of the Sundowners who picked her up hitchhiking and soon she was making good bread at the massage parlor. She got half of the money she made giving $20 massages and she got to keep two-thirds of what she got paid in the back room. Her age and her centerfold looks made her one of the most sought-after girls there, and she stockpiled her money like a miser.

She didn't date anyone and the only time she went out was when the club needed someone special taken care of. They always offered to pay her, but she knew that if she did it as a favor she would be much better off.

When the prospect came into the parlor today and said they had a "special friend" in town, she offered immediately.

When Karen walked into the clubhouse with the

prospect she was very glad she had come. The guy they wanted her to be with was a dream come true. She liked them big, and this S.O.B. was huge. He looked like everything that she wanted in a man. It scared her in a way. This guy was different than the other Johns. He didn't seem to know she existed. When she was introduced to men, usually they stare a little bit and she could see the lust in their eyes. This guy was as cool as could be. His dark blue eyes just glanced at her, looked her up and down, and then he smiled just slightly and said, "Hi."

That was it. For the next fifteen minutes she stood by his side, as she had been directed to do, while he talked bikes and the like with some of the club members.

She could tell by what they were talking about that this guy had been around a lot. He seemed to know everybody in every club all the way across the country. Hell, he even knew some of the Bandidos, which were from her neck of the woods.

But it wasn't just the fact that he knew some bikers. He was different. He was more "into" biking. Most of the bikers she had met were a little slow. This one was quick and witty. He didn't put anybody down, but he was obviously in a different class.

Yeah, she could see she would have a problem with this one. He was getting to her and they had just met.

His friend was different too. He didn't talk hardly at all. He would smile a lot, and nod his head, but he didn't say much. The way he moved was sexy though. It was like a tawny cat was trapped in his body. He didn't walk, he glided around the room.

She wouldn't have minded being with him, either, but Esther had been the one chosen for him.

After a little while Karen excused herself to go to the toilet. She and Esther waited until they got into the head and then they didn't stop talking. They compared their draws like a couple of rodeo riders comparing a mount. They talked about the size and shape of the two guys and tried to guess how good they would be. It was a game they often played.

While Karen combed her short blond hair she tried to picture what it was going to be like with Treb. She couldn't help but compare him to her first lover. She could hardly wait.

Chapter 17

As long as I have been a biker, I still can't get off on what they call partying. It's so much like the old cocktail parties I went to when I was a citizen, it's hard to believe. The big difference is the bikers don't get as bad mouth about the other guests as the so-called citizens do.

I scoped Karen and Esther coming back from the head. That Karen was some good looking bitch, but I figured she was probably just like all the other young good looking suckies that hang around with bikers — completely empty in the head. They all are there for the same thing, the chance to impress their girlfriends.

While I checked out the suckies coming back, one of the members of the Sundowners was buying me a beer. He was about six feet tall and had a long black beard. The only thing that kept his belt from touching in the middle was his clothes. Damn, but he was skinny. We stood there talking about a run that had happened a few months earlier in Sturgis, South Dakota, and trying to discover if we were in the same bar at the same time.

We were both in Deadwood, a little cowboy town outside of Sturgis on the Saturday afternoon of the run, but we couldn't figure out if we were both in the same saloon. Just as we were narrowing down the possibilities, when it was about three in the afternoon and we were both on the same side of the street, I saw a familiar face come in through the back door.

It was Rom.

I nearly screamed his name.

"Rom, you ass hole son-of-a-bitch. When did you get here? How did you know I was here?" I ran across the room. "How's your neck, you stupid asshole? Don't ya know you're not supposed to catch bullets like that? You're supposed to use your teeth."

I couldn't believe it. He was actually here. He had a big white bandage around his neck, but other than that he looked fine.

He was well dressed, so much so in fact that I almost didn't recognize him. Stepping back to look at him, it was the first time I had ever seen him when his hair was short, not to mention clean, and he was even clean shaven.

But that didn't matter. It was Rom. Damn I was glad to see him. I took him around like a lost child and we wandered off to a sofa in a far corner of the clubhouse to talk. I had a hell of a lot of questions to ask him.

He told me how the police had questioned him for two days before he snuck out of the police ward at the hospital. That was early this morning. When he got out he called Leroy Makelray, the newsman, and Leroy told him what had happened with me. I am going to have to thank that guy someday for all he did for us.

"I didn't have any idea where you were, and then I was over at the Angels' clubhouse when a call came in from here, checking on you," he smiled a tired smile. "That was it. I borrowed the money for a flight, bought these clothes so I would look normal, and caught a plane."

It was just like him to think he looked normal with a big white bandage sticking up like a sore thumb.

"Oh, by the way, I used your name when I borrowed the money from the Angels' treasury, so you owe them $300." He smiled broadly now, "Sorry about that."

Just then Dick walked over with Karen and Esther. I introduced Dick and told the chicks to split for awhile and wait at the bar. We had some talking to do.

As I watched Karen walk away I made a mental note to check her out a little later. She had a pear shapped bottom. Definitely worthy of further study.

But for now we had some getting together to do. I told Dick about some of the old times with Rom and filled Rom in on what had been going on with Dick and me, right down to the cop we short sheeted and the young sweeties we had partied with. He smiled at both stories and laughed out loud when we told him about the kids with the Hondas.

I signaled Karen to bring us some cold ones and when she got there I asked if she could find a sweetie for Rom. She smiled and gave my middle leg a squeeze. Damn, I just might get to like that young'un.

I left Rom and Dick to get better acquainted and wandered off to find Raunchy. We had a little business to transact. If Rom was going to make it with us, he had to have a scooter. I found Raunchy stooped over the pool table taking deadly aim on the eight ball. He made a swift stroke and the ball bounced off two corners and into the pocket. He smiled, looked at the loser, who was the same guy I had been talking to when Rom came in, and held out his hand. The skinny guy planted a five in it and they shook hands.

Raunchy walked over to me.

"Yeah bro, what do ya need? Another broad, some more booze?" He smiled. "A little snort?"

I smiled back and took him aside.

"Actually Raunchy, what I need is a scooter." I let that sink in.

He looked at me for further enlightenment.

"Well, you see, my bro that was hurt in Los Angeles just came in, and he had to leave his scoot in L.A. I want to get a scoot up for him so he can jam with us. We have some bread and that truck parked outside. Can you help us?"

He smiled broadly.

"Follow me." He turned and walked away.

I followed close behind. The party had started to get pretty good by now and there were girls dancing in various stages of undress and a few bikers even getting in on the act, mimicking the girls.

We made our way through the crowds to the stairway. Once upstairs, we turned toward the office. About halfway there Raunchy stopped. He reached up and pulled on a bar that was sticking out about halfway up the wall. All of a sudden the wall separated. It was like magic. A minute earlier it was just a paneled wall in a dark hallway. All of a sudden it was a giant cavern, murky and foreboding.

I followed him into the room and he shut the door behind us. As he did, he flicked a light switch on the wall.

It was a biker's dream come true. There had to be at least twenty bikes up there and all of them were real biker scooters. Panheads, shovelheads and knuckles. All complete and in the standard hardcore black paint job. The light from the single bulb overhead glinted off all the chrome even though they were deep in dust.

I checked out some of the license plates. Florida, Kansas, California, everywhere but Utah. They had all been shipped in.

"Can we get any papers on these?" I asked.

"Right here," and he pulled open a drawer that was full of blank pink slips from all over the country. "Just let me know what state you want it for."

A few minutes later we were walking back into the clubhouse. I had picked out a real good looking panhead, about a 'fifty-four, with a small peanut tank that I knew Rom would like because it was like his old scoot back home. There was a medium height sissy bar on it and the standard rigid frame. It was a good looking bike.

Raunchy said it would be ready in about an hour, after they got the numbers doctored on the cases and the frame, and the price was just five hundred dollars. I knew they could have gotten at least a grand for the bike, so I didn't argue. These guys were really doing us right.

We walked back over to where Rom and Dick were sitting with Esther and talked about little things. I wanted the bike to be a surprise.

A few minutes later Karen came back in with a cute little blond. She introduced her to Rom as Candy and they hit it off fine from that point. Karen walked over and kind of leaned against me, testing to see if I minded. I reached around her waist and gave her a little squeeze to let her know it was all right and then dropped my hand to rest on the top of her round little butt. She nestled against me a little firmer and I started to get hard.

Damn, that chick was pretty wicked. A little rub and a little squeeze and I'm ready for the sack. Not many chicks affect me like that.

For the next few hours we mingled with the club members and with the visitors. Somehow the word got out that a "celebrity" was at the clubhouse and some of the other clubs showed up to show their respects. I guess for that part of the world even I was considered somebody special. Hell, it was actually kind of neat being treated like royalty. I might even get to like it if I'm not careful.

I noticed that Rom and his sweetie were really starting to get hot and heavy, so I told him about the turnout room at the back of the clubhouse. He smiled at me and got up with Candy and walked back there. He was ready for bed. The long day and the flight, on top of all the medicine he had taken for that hole in his neck, had worn him out.

Dick and I stayed down there for awhile and then he took Esther up to the guest room.

Karen and I stayed downstairs and talked with Raunchy and the rest of the club.

Chapter 18

Dave Harding had been with the Sundowners for almost two years now, and he knew that he had their full confidence. There were times when he felt a little bad about being a snitch, but since he did his last stint up at the Walla Walla State Pen, he didn't want to go back. The last time he had been there the tiny eight by ten foot cell seemed even smaller than usual, and he hated it. When he was picked up stealing a scoot, with it right in the back of his van, he knew his goose was cooked.

It didn't take a whole lot of thought on his part when the state police offered him a deal. He didn't care what it was. If it meant he didn't go to the slam, he was for it.

The day it all happened he was in a holding cell when the cop on duty came back and got him. They walked him into one of the lieutenants' offices and introduced him to a small man in a grey suit. The man sat there reading his folder for a couple of minutes as if he wasn't even there, and then raised grey, watery eyes and looked at him.

"What would you do to stay out of the penitentiary?" he asked, like he was asking if he wanted a cup of coffee.

Dave thought for a second. He didn't know what was going on, but it looked like he was going to have a way out.

"What do I have to do? That's what I'll do." He let it drop like that.

"Tell us a little about the Sundowners."

Back then Dave had ridden with the Sundowners, but he had never been a member. He didn't figure what he knew would be anything new to the police, so he told them. He told about the way they always had cheap parts for sale, and how they had lots of good coke all the time, and even how the girls at the massage parlor were usually under age. It took almost an hour of true confessions before they sent him back to his cell.

The next morning they brought him back to the office. The same little man was sitting in the same spot, and if it wasn't for the different tie, Dave would have thought he hadn't moved since yesterday.

"Your story checks out, so here's the deal."

He told about a group called the Omega Squad that kept tabs on bike gang activities all over the country. Dave was almost overwhelmed by what he heard. He couldn't believe the cops were that much into the gangs' business. Dave signed a paper saying that he would cooperate and was told that if he didn't, the word would get out that he was an informer and the paper with his signature would be made public to his cohorts in the different gangs. He had been trapped.

But all of that was almost three years ago. Since then Dave had joined the Sundowners and become a trusted member. Every once in a while the cops would pick him up, ostensibly for old warrants, and they would take him downtown to "debrief" him. He never had a whole lot new to tell, just some of the internal happenings of the club, like some of the guns they were dealing in, and of course the dope. Nothing to make a bunch of trouble for anybody. He didn't feel at all bad about it, in fact he almost stopped worrying about his connection with the police. In a way, it made him feel safer than he had ever been before.

But now he had something big to tell and he had to get the word out fast. There was somebody who was wanted for killing a cop and he figured if he gave them him, he might get off of their books for good and be a free man again.

But he didn't know how to give them the word. They had always contacted him. He tried calling the police from a pay phone, but when he asked for the Omega Squad they laughed at him. He didn't know it, but the Omega Squad operated out of the Federal Justice Building, not the police department. They just use the police to supply their informers. The Omega Squad was so secret that few local cops had even heard of it.

Then he had a thought. The lieutenant who was in

on the original deal with him would know. He called the police department back and asked for Lieutenant Clifton. After a couple of minutes he was on the line.

"Lieutenant Clifton, detectives," was the brisk answer,

"Yeah, lieutenant? This is Dave. Dave Harding. You remember me?"

He waited a second for the reply. There was silence.

"Well, anyway, I was the guy you set up with those fellas from the Omega Squad a couple years ago." He waited again, this time there was a grunt on the other end of the line.

"It's very important that I get hold of them, but I don't know how. There is a guy that's wanted for murdering a cop, and he's over at the clubhouse. Can you get the word to those guys?"

This time there was a reply.

"Harding. Oh, yeah. You're with the Sundowners now, aren't you?"

Dave replied in the affirmative.

"You say there is a cop killer at your clubhouse?" This time he didn't wait for a reply. "Well, we'll be right over," and Dave heard the line go dead.

"Wait a...." He let it trail off, since he was talking to a dead phone.

Damn, he didn't want some cops busting into his clubhouse. He wanted to work with the ones from Omega who had him by the balls. At least they didn't run around like a bunch of Gestapos like most cops, crashing in and playing gangbusters. There was no telling what the local police might do. Hell, they didn't even know who they were looking for.

Now he was really scared. He didn't know whether to run back to the clubhouse and warn everybody, in which case he would be suspected for sure, or just head for home and act surprised when he found out about it the next day.

He hated to think about all his friends getting hassled, but it was better than him being in on it, so he decided to take the easy way out. He hopped on his scoot and headed home. It was going to be a long, sleepless night.

Chapter 19

The party was starting to slow down a little now and I could see that a lot of folks had already split. The music was turned down a lot lower and the Coors beer clock on the wall showed that it was almost four in the morning. It had been a pretty long day and I was about ready to climb on Karen and see if she was as good as she looked. Actually I was almost too tired, but if I didn't do it I knew I would hate myself later.

I looked down at her and she looked a lot older than she did a few hours ago. Some of the mask she painted on her face had rubbed off and I could see she wasn't as innocent as she pretended.

I gave her a soft hug and told her to go on up to the room, I would be right behind her. She smiled and it almost looked like she meant it.

I watched her tight little ass wiggle up the stairs and felt a surge on my groin. Yeah, I wanted some of that, no matter how late (or should I say early) it was.

Raunchy was still awake and he was at the bar getting a fresh beer. I walked over and thanked him for everything. He said it was okay and told me that Rom's bike was parked next to our truck outside.

I thanked him again and headed for bed. Damn but I was tired.

The room they gave us was near the top of the stairs and I heard Karen in there getting undressed and walked in. There was a small lamp over in one corner and I could see Dick and Esther lying stark naked on top of the bed. Over by the other bed Karen was just taking off her boots. She had already taken off her sweater and those tight tits I had been rubbing against were hanging free in the cool September air. I just stood there looking at her. In that moment she looked like a little girl getting ready to say her prayers.

She reached down and pulled off her socks and stood to remove her pants. Then she saw me.

A smile spread over her face like she had just seen Santa Claus, and found out he had a twelve inch shlong. She was a little girl and a grown woman all rolled into one.

I walked across the small room to where she was standing and she put her arms around me. She had to stand on her tiptoes to reach. For a couple of seconds we just stood there. She smelled good and felt good in my arms. I forgot how tired I was pretty damn fast.

I sat on the edge of the bed and she reached down to take off my boots. Then she helped me take off my pants and shirts and soon I was lying there without a thing on. She stood slowly, smiled at me and walked about three paces away.

Damn, but she was good looking.

When she turned to face me she had the smile of a real vixen. She cupped her hands under her boobs and bounced them a couple of times for me. She then lowered her hands to the snap on her pants and unsnapped them. Slowly she pulled the zipper down and licked her lips at the same time. Damn, she looked sensuous.

As her pants dropped to the floor she gave a little wiggle and walked over by the bed. Now all she had on was a pair of the sheerest see-through panties I had ever seen. She hooked her fingers in the waist and dropped them, then she stood there looking down at me. I waited for a couple of seconds and then I realized she was just playing a game, to see how much I could take. I decided I had waited enough and reached up for her.

She fell into my arms as if she had been moulded for them. I could smell her and feel her warm softness. She may have looked like a little girl, but there was no doubt she was all woman. All of a sudden it was like she was in heat. She was all over me, moving like she was completely on fire inside. One minutes she was sucking on my cock and a second later she was sitting on it, looking down at me with a face of pure sex.

For the longest time we just lay there with my mouth on her vagina and hers on my cock. We hardly moved at all and I got the feeling that if I did I would shoot all over her.

Finally we faced each other, with her looking straight up into my eyes, and made love.

Making love is a lot different than fucking or just having sex. There is a feeling that radiates between two people. It can be a one time thing or all the time, but it is different than just getting a piece of ass. Karen and I were not fucking. We were making love. I knew it and she knew it. I could tell by the look in her eyes.

Each time, just as I was about to cum, I would stop. She would look up at me and smile. In a couple of seconds we would start all over again. It was like we had made love a hundred times before. It was great.

Then we slept.

Chapter 20

The clubhouse was just about empty. The sun was starting to come up and the only ones still awake were the two prospects, who were busy straightening up after the party. A couple of members of the Sons of Silence were still up. They had ridden over from Denver and had been partying with the Sundowners for almost a week now. They were hunched over the pool table in the middle of a game of nine ball.

It was hard to believe that just a few hours ago there was a full fledged biker party going on.

There were only about four bikes left inside and the outside lot was empty except for Treb's blue truck and Rom's new motorcycle, which he had yet to see.

One of the Sons of Silence was in the middle of

racking up the balls on the table for another game while the other one was into the refrigerator getting a couple of cold ones. The only time there is a Sundowner pulling bar duty is during a party. Other than that it's on an honesty basis. The biker took a couple of beers and dropped a buck into the kitty. He should have taken his thirty cents change, but he was not awake enough to realize that.

All of a sudden the big barn door in front was crashing inward. When it gave way there was a huge police van with big wooden bumpers pushing it in. The two prospects and the other bikers just stared in stunned disbelief. Soon the room was filled with police. They had all four bikers against one wall and riot guns were aimed at their backs. There were at least five cops to each biker and twice that number outside watching for those who would try to escape.

It had taken Lieutenant Clifton all night, but he had managed to round up enough men for his raid.

Unfortunately there was no one there to bust, or at least so it appeared.

The noise brought Treb and Karen awake with a start. They heard all the commotion downstairs and knew they would have to move fast. He woke Dick by throwing a pillow at him (he wasn't about to chance another wrestling match) and they crept quietly out into the hallway. Treb remembered that trap door where the bikes were kept in the secret room. He hoped the police wouldn't find it.

They walked as quietly as they could to the secret latch and opened it up. As soon as all four of them were clear they closed the door quietly behind them.

It was dark as hell in there, but Treb hoped they would be safe. He also hoped that Rom wouldn't get hassled too bad, but since he looked like a square with his new clothes, and wasn't wanted for anything here anyway, he figured he would be all right.

A couple of seconds after they closed the door behind them they heard footsteps outside. The police were checking upstairs. They searched the room they had been in just a few seconds earlier and then the office. Everything was clean.

By now Lieutenant Clifton was starting to reason that he had been conned. All he was thinking about was getting his hands on that Dave and wringing his filthy neck for giving him bad information.

After rousting the four guys downstairs and getting poor Rom up and hassling him, the police left the clubhouse with the doors hanging on their broken hinges. The lieutenant said if they didn't like the hinges, they could report it. But if they did they might find things a little tough for awhile. The bikers gave them the universal sign for fornication and a couple of Bronx cheers as they departed.

Treb and Dick and the girls stayed in the room for a few more minutes and when they were sure it was clear they went downstairs.

Rom smiled a broad grin when he saw they were all right and they all had a big laugh at the police.

Then they started to think. Why had the cops picked that night to show up? Maybe someone had said something, and if so, who was the one who did the talking? There were a lot of unanswered questions.

Pretty soon Raunchy and some of the other members showed up and they started to compare notes.

Treb figured it was probably because of them that the raid had taken place and he apologized for causing any trouble. They all said it wasn't their fault, but when he said he was going to leave they didn't try real hard to stop them.

Figuring the police had taken down a description of the blue truck, Treb made a deal with Raunchy. Instead of $500 for Rom's bike, it would be the truck and two hundred. That made them both happy. The Sundowners had a new follow-up truck and Treb got $300 for a truck he knew wasn't worth $100. Everybody was happy.

Especially Rom. When he heard that bike was his he almost cried. All he did was poke his fingers all over it, sigh and grunt and generally carry on like he was a new father.

He liked the bike.

Treb and Dick unloaded the two bikes from the back of the truck and while they were saying goodbye to their new-found friends, Karen and Esther got Candy to help them and the girls cleaned up the bikes.

Treb knew Karen wanted to go with them and he was awfully tempted to take her. She would have made a perfect old lady. She didn't snivel, she was small and easy to pack, and she even had some bucks in the bank, but he knew he couldn't. It would be too hard while they were on the run.

He did want to see her again so he told her part of the truth, about being on the run (but not for what), and said he would call her in a month and she could come and join them if everything was cool. She kissed him as warmly as he had ever been kissed and they said goodbye.

Chapter 21

Rom was riding up front, testing the new bike like a toy. I knew he would like it but I didn't figure he would go nuts over it. Dick looked over and smiled. He was just plain happy to be back on the road again.

We didn't even know where we were going. All we knew was we had to get away from Salt Lake and east was a good way to head.

I remembered that there was a helmet law protest planned for Madison, Wisconsin and figured that was as good a place to go as any other, so I made a mental note to check our map at the next rest stop.

After about fifty miles we pulled over to rest our weary butts and I pulled out a map.

"How about we go to Madison?" I said. "There is

going to be a big lid law protest up there, and there will be a lot of scooter bums there. It might be fun."

Rom was too busy wiping the dust off his gas tank to even hear me and Dick just smiled and nodded. Madison it would be. After a few minutes R & R, and after Rom finished a cigarette, we mounted up again. We had over a week to make it to Madison and the road we were headed southeast on was supposed to be a real nice ride, so we decided to stay on it over the mountains and turn east when we hit Denver, on Highway 1-40.

As we climbed higher into the mountains it started to get a lot colder. By the time the sun was going down the temperature was down into the twenties. We were stopping often to warm our hands on our oil tanks and we were looking for a place to get some coffee and warm up.

Every once in a while we would see a sign that said "Summit Inn" and a small note underneath, "Open 24 hours." We could hardly wait to get there.

While the temperature dropped into the teens the signs were regular. "Summit Inn, 30 miles," then "Summit Inn, 20 miles."

We stopped about every ten miles to warm up. I could feel the marrow in my bones turn into ice. All I could think of was getting some hot coffee in me. I thought I would freeze to death.

"Summit Inn, 10 miles." We pulled over again to warm our frost bitten hands on our oil tanks.

We didn't even talk any more. We were too damn cold. We would just pull over, warm our hands for a few minutes, and get back on without saying a thing.

We were on the last leg in and it seemed like an eternity.

"Summit Inn, 5 miles," then "3 miles," "1/2 mile" and finally, "500 feet."

As we rounded the bend we saw it.

All the lights were out. No neon sign. No warm coffee. Nothing.

I led the way into the parking lot and we peered in the front door. It was dark inside.

I could see someone at the back of the restaurant and knocked on the window, but he just stepped out of sight.

"Damn. If I don't get some hot coffee pretty soon I'm gonna ice over."

The next town was a good thirty miles away, and it was getting colder. No chance.

Just as we had about decided to build a fire out of the place, the front door opened. The guy looked us up and down and motioned us in.

I didn't know what made him change his mind, but I was sure glad he did.

"Hey, I thought you guys were open 24 hours, what happened?"

"Well, actually we are robbing the place," he wasn't smiling, "and we figured you guys might as well warm up and help yourself too."

With that he started to pry at the juke box with a screwdriver.

Dick, Rom and I stared at each other. All I could think was the guy was kidding, but I could see he wasn't. After a couple of seconds, considering the alternatives, which were freezing on the outside or sitting in here warm, we started to take off our leathers. What the hell, why not?

Pretty soon we were listening to the three burglars tell how they found out the owner of the place had been thrown in jail for bad checks, and they knew it would be empty. It was a cinch. We threw some steaks on the grill, started the coffee water heating and opened a gallon can of green beans. What the hell, might as well go whole hog.

Rom handled the cooking while Dick and I sat fascinated listening to these guys. They were nuts.

Of course they weren't as nuts as we were, sitting here with them, but what the hell, bikers were never supposed to be a whole lot bright anyway, right?

As we gulped the hot coffee the burglars were busy loading the flatware into their station wagon.

While we wolfed down our steak sandwiches we watched them loading up the canned goods out of the cupboards, and while we packed a couple of sandwiches for the road they loaded up the dishes. They weren't missing a thing.

As we sat there they all got into the wagon and started the motor.

Hey, just a minute. Let me get this straight. We were going to sit here in a place that had just been burglarized while they take off? Is that what they expected?

I shouted at Dick and Rom to get their shit together and in a couple of seconds we were out the door and on our scooters. I made them leave the sandwiches behind.

We all straddled our scoots at the same time and kicked the starters.

None of them would start. We kicked for a couple

of minutes and I started to panic. Hell, we were being set up. There was no doubt about it.

I told Dick and Rom to push their scoots down the grade until they would coast, and then try to roll-start them. This we all did. The motors refused to run.

About a mile down the road we pulled over to check out what was wrong. Those God damn thieves had ripped off our coil wires. There was no way these scoots would run.

Just as I was about to push the bikes off into the bushes, so when the inevitable cops came they wouldn't see us, I saw a red light down the road about a half mile.

After we got the bikes off the road I started walking toward it. It was the tail light of that station wagon the burglars were in.

Dick told me to wait and he continued on toward the wagon. I don't know how he stood it, but he even slipped his boots off. Damn, he must have had cold feet.

About three minutes later Dick came back with the biggest shit eating grin on his face I had ever seen.

"What the hell you laughing at?" I asked him.

He held his finger up to his mouth like to make me be quiet, and told me what had happened. It seems the crooks had stopped at one of those emergency phone booths and called the cops. They said a bunch of bikers had broken into the Summit Inn and were ripping the place off. He heard them say after they hung up that they were going to wait at a cabin up the road until it was all clear.

While they were on the phone, Dick crawled under their car and pulled some of the wiring out, including the wire that ran from their battery to the starter. They wouldn't be moving for awhile.

We cut the wires into pieces long enough to replace the coil wires on our bikes and coasted down the road.

Just as we were about to pass them we popped our clutches and turned on our lights.

The look in their eyes will not soon be forgotten. You could see they didn't know how the hell we got our bikes running.

About three miles down the hill we pulled off onto a dirt road. We had timed it well. In a couple of minutes two police cars went by with their sirens wailing. As soon as they passed we hopped on our scoots and headed down the hill. The farther down we went, the warmer it got. Soon it was almost bearable.

We pulled into a coffee shop in the next town and heard the tales of some burglars who were caught stuck on the side of the road in a station wagon that wouldn't run.

Nobody could figure out why we laughed so hard.

Chapter 22

Leroy walked out of the bathroom and entered the large hallway. "Jesus," he thought, "Who'd of thought the shitters would be so different?"

He was thinking about the John he'd just left. It was designated as the "Executive Washroom."

He knew there was a difference between the offices of KABD in Los Angeles and the network offices here in New York, but he never expected valets on duty and individual stereo speakers in each crapper. That was getting a little ridiculous.

He walked down the spacious hallway back to where the meeting was in progress. As he passed the receptionist he glanced at her short almost non-existent skirt, and wondered who she had been balling to keep her job. Behind her desk was a large window that looked out over Manhattan from the 37th floor of the ABD building.

He had often wondered why all the networks were headquartered in New York. All that dumb traffic, and the muggings on the street. But where else could you get a view like that? Nowhere.

He walked up to the large double hardwood doors to the national news director's offices. Actually Mr. Hutton's title was "Vice-President in charge of News and Special Events," but he was commonly called the news director.

The meeting had been going for almost an hour now, and no one was more surprised about being there than Leroy Makelray. In Los Angeles he was just another on-the-scene reporter. He had never even been an anchor man or anything, and all of a sudden here he was, rubbing elbows with the gods. It was scary.

Howard Harding looked up from the conference table as Leroy re-entered the room. His deep blue eyes stared holes in him for a moment, and then he smiled a little. He used to think it odd that every time he had a conference with someone from one of the stations the network owned they would always have to go to the toilet. He smoothed his steel grey hair, which was longer this season because of a poll they had taken, and looked back down at the papers he was holding.

Leroy walked self-consciously to his chair between the legal advisors and his local bureau chief, who looked as out of place here as Leroy felt, and sat down.

"Hell, the chairs are even different," he thought,

as he sank into the plush down filling with the real leather covers. He felt like he was a very special person.

Leroy didn't know it, but he was.

The network had been gathering bits and pieces of information from all over the country and compiling it. Whenever something big began to look like it was going to happen, the computer was programmed to spit out a probabilities factor, and if the readout was over 25% probability, it would go to the attention of the head of computer operations.

He would look at it and decide if it was important enough to be considered for network news, or if it should be put aside and watched.

If the probability factor got to 50%, the decision would be up to a network news supervisor. They would make a survey to see if people really gave a damn about what was going on.

Then it would go to the national news bureau, and finally to the VP in charge of news and special events — the news director, and finally to Howard Harding, the President of ABD.

That is just what had happened, and that was how Leroy was tapped to come to New York. Little did he know that it was just some little memory chip in a computer which picked him above the other hundreds of reporters that work for ABD. The chip remembered that he had filed the most stories on the motorcycle movement.

Warren Hutton looked around the table and his gaze rested on Leroy. He thought for a second and then he began.

"Gentlemen, there is a 55% probability that over

100,000 motorcyclists will ride on a political protest in Washington, D.C. on July fourth." He paused to let that sink in. "And there is an 80% chance that when they do, there will be trouble." There was silence around the table.

Leroy thought for a moment. So that was it. The reason he was here was because of the series of specials that he had done on the bikers and the helmet law protest in Los Angeles. It was his friendship with the bikers that had brought him 3,000 miles across the country and thrust him into a position that he day dreamed about.

For the next few minutes the legal advisors and the network news people talked of sponsors, coverage and problems, but Leroy just sat there stunned. He knew that if there was going to be a national protest, Treb would be there, and probably heading up the damn thing, and if he was, the police would be there too, looking for him. Then he started thinking about how he should handle the story.

Chapter 23

The Sons of Silence clubhouse just outside Denver was about the same as the Sundowners in Salt Lake. After awhile they all looked alike to me. After a couple of days there I got tired of all the partying and drinking and talked Rom and Dick into splitting. Rom had fallen in love with a little ski bunny he met at a bar downtown, but then he fell in love with anything that would say yes, or even a soft "maybe."

The protest in Madison was planned for Sunday, and it was Tuesday, so there was plenty of time to get there. No use rushing things. I figured we might as well take our time and enjoy the trip.

The two members of the SOS who partied with us in Salt Lake returned to Denver, and when we said we were going to Madison they asked if they could go too.

I figured it might be fun having more folks, so I invited them along. Snoopy, the short one, was riding a good looking fatbob with ape hangers like they used back in the late 'sixties, and Oaf was on a chopped shovelhead.

I liked Oaf because his name fit him so damn well. He was a big oaf. Not really big, but he just looked it. He weighed about 280 pounds. His hobby was weight lifting.

That was how we got to know each other. While I was staying at the clubhouse, Oaf and I would head over to Adam's Gym downtown and work out every day. I had gotten into working out while I was doing time a year or so ago for interstate transportation. It was a bum rap, but I was hung anyway. I got a year on the farm that was dropped to eight months. All eight months I worked out with the iron. I got to where I really enjoyed the challenge of trying to beat my own records. Pretty soon I was bench pressing a little over 300 pounds and dead lifting 500. It was a kick.

The first couple of times Oaf and I went down to the gym we got sore as hell. I had forgotten just how long it had been since I worked out. Every time I would do a new exercise I would find a new sore spot. After the second day it was okay.

Actually the biggest thing I missed about being on the run was the gym. But I figured now that I was back into it, I would keep it up whenever I got a chance.

Snoopy was about as typical a biker as you could

find. He had been riding for as many years as he could remember. I talked to him until the wee hours one morning while we passed a bottle of Peppermint Schnapps back and forth, which is his favorite beverage. He told me of days when he rode with the old Galloping Gooses in the 'fifties, and even back in the 'forties, at Hollister, when the Booze Fighters were the big club, but he was just a kid then, packing with his father.

As I sat there looking at him I thought it was pretty hard to believe he was old enough. He had one of those faces that just doesn't age at all. His light brown hair was worn long, almost down to his shoulders, and his beard was the same color and came to the top of his pants. He always wore this stupid looking hat that had become like a part of him. I think it was his eyes, that were somewhere between blue and green, that made him look ageless.

We pulled out onto the interstate and headed east. The five Harleys were running good and it felt great to be back on the road again, listening to the deep roar of the engines and feeling the wind blow over our bodies. I knew I had found the real reason I was a biker again: The freedom and alive feeling you get going down the road.

On the way through Kansas we were going to stop off at the Outlaws clubhouse in Wichita to pick up some of the brothers there, so we just hooked it straight down 1-40. It was a clear day and by noon it had gotten almost nice out. We still wore our leathers, but the wind didn't have the chill we rode in getting from Salt Lake to Denver.

After a good easy ride, stopping for food a couple

of times and gas when necessary, we pulled into Wichita about 9:30 at night. The Outlaw clubhouse was a small house on a farm road eight miles outside of town on the south side. We pulled up in front and parked our bikes with the eight or ten other bikes that were there.

The sounds of music and the inevitable pool balls clicking together made us feel right at home before we even entered the front door.

On the inside it was the same as a lot of small clubhouses. There were posters of Peter Fonda and Dennis Hopper flipping off the camera in "Easy Riders," and of course the old standard photo of Ann Margaret from "C.C. and Company." Whoever had distribution rights on those posters sure did get around.

The rest of the walls were covered with centerfolds and other dirty pictures. Above the fireplace was a large banner with the Outlaw patch right in the middle of it. There was no doubt whose clubhouse we were in.

The ceiling of the main room was covered with patches from other clubs that had been taken in wars and fights. The Outlaws were not one of the more tolerant clubs.

It has always been a practice, that I never agreed with, that if a member of a club enters your territory, either he gets permission first or he loses his patch.

Now, to the layman that may not sound too bad, until you consider a member will usually die to protect his patch. It's part of the outlaw code.

I knew that more than one of those patches was taken from a body that wasn't moving. I didn't like that.

One of the Outlaws walked around behind us to see if we were wearing any patches. He saw the two Sons of Silence patches and grinned. They were all right. They had a truce going and partied together a lot.

Then he walked behind Dick and Rom and myself. When he didn't see a patch he looked a little worried. He could see we were bikers, and many times warring clubs would take off their patch to infiltrate a clubhouse and then blow away some of the members before anybody knew what was going on.

The Outlaw was about to say something when Snoopy took him aside and whispered to him. The Outlaw's glazed eyes looked confused for a second, and then he just went back to his blank stare.

Snoopy walked over and explained that there had been some trouble with another club and they were a little nervous. I nodded my understanding and we walked over to the ice box to get a beer.

We dropped the customary half dollar into a cigar box that sat on top of the refrigerator and wandered over to where Snoopy's brothers were sitting by the fireplace. A number was being passed around and we took in the pungent smoke with great care. Kansas pot has never been known for its potency, and if we wanted to get anything out of it, we had to take in as much as possible.

In a couple of seconds I realized this wasn't Kansas pot. I could taste the minty bite that lets you know that angel dust was in the grass and my head started to spin a little bit.

We talked about the trip and what fun we were going to have when we got with all the brothers up in Madison. The word was out and most of the clubs from all over would be there to party. It was also going to be the place where we would plan the national helmet law rally that was set for next fourth of July in Washington.

I had gotten the idea from the Gay Liberation movement, of all things. I figured if those asshole buddies could get equality by walking on Washington, the bikers could do it too. I had already started the arrangements, and was going to make the announcement in Los Angeles, when all hell broke loose. There were those who had been partying with me who knew about it, like the H.A. and the Hessians, and they had been spreading the word. It was still set.

The more KW we smoked, which is what they call dust in the east and midwest, the deeper we dipped into never-never land. Soon we were all grinning at each other and having a hard time talking.

A couple of little foxes were there dancing to the old stereo over in the corner and soon we were all just sitting there watching what was bouncing around. It was trip time in Kansas, for sure. My head felt like it was being clamped in a vice and I decided not to smoke any more of that stuff.

All traces of time were lost. All I knew was the fire felt good, I was with some good brothers, and everything was as neat as it could be.

I looked over toward the door when I heard a little noise from outside. It sounded like some scooters pulling up. Maybe eight or ten. Nobody came in, and a couple of seconds later I had forgotten all about it.

Then three or four more scoots pulled in, and a couple of the Outlaws got up to check it out.

All of a sudden all hell broke loose. The first Outlaw to the door had a big red hole open up in his back and he was lifted through the air and landed on the pool table. At the same time there was a loud explosion. I had heard that sound before. It was a sawed-off shotgun, probably a twelve gauge.

We all got the same idea at the same time and dove for the floor as the beer bottles on the mantle shattered into a million little pieces. Then the Outlaw banner was shredded and all that could be heard was the booming of those God damn guns.

I had my 357 out and pointed toward the door. I looked over at Dick and he had his gun out too, pointed at the window. Damn, it was like he had a second sense.

I screamed at Rom to cover the hall door and we all started to crawl toward where our guns were pointed.

As I was belly crawling under the pool table I had to go through a puddle of blood that was forming under the Outlaw who had been shot. Hell, I didn't even know his name.

Then it hit me. I didn't know who was out there either. Shit, for all I know it might be friends.

But it was too late now. We were committed. Once you are in a clubhouse, you are with that club. That's it.

All of that went through my head in about a second. I saw a flash from a gun outside as I heard the light over my head shatter. I fired at the flash.

All of a sudden a loud cry was heard and I knew at least one of them was down.

A couple of the Outlaws were next to me. One motioned in the dark to Snoopy that he was moving (o the door, to cover him. Snoopy nodded and aimed at the doorway. When he started to move. Snoopy pumped two shots into the dark.

He lunged for the door and fell a little to the left, using the chair that was there as a blockade. He nodded at his bro to come ahead, and Snoopy and I both fired a couple of shots as the other Outlaw dove for the right side. Now it was covered.

I checked my pocket and found four more bullets in it. Then I realized I had about eight or nine bullets altogether. The rest were in my saddlebag on the bike.

A shadow appeared by the window over Dick's head and I fired once at it. At the same time I heard the blast of a shotgun right next to me and the window blew outward. The Outlaws had a couple of sawed-offs too.

I heard the one over by the door say "on three," and he counted fast.

"One, two, three!" We all started firing at the dark from the windows and doors.

I heard the sound of bikes between shots and we all ran to the front door. We could see the glint of chrome in the moonlight as the eight or nine bikes roared off into the night. We shot in that direction until we had no more ammunition.

One of the bikes went down and another started to swerve. Finally the one that was swerving flipped off the road into an irrigation ditch and exploded.

All I could think of was how it looked just like a friggin movie. The flame and all. I always thought that was a big put on.

We all stood there in shock. Nobody said a word. It was so quiet we could hear the bikes going at full speed down the road.

After about a minute a light went on back inside. We turned and saw Dick standing over the body of the first Outlaw that had been shot. He was just looking at him.

We went back in and a couple of the Outlaws carried their brother out in back. There wouldn't be any big funeral. That only goes on in peace time. This was a war, and it was a cold, shallow grave in back for their brother. His name was Animal. Nobody knew his righteous name.

There were three others killed that night. They were all with the Pagan Few out of Kansas. They were a crazy bunch that all had tattoos on their lower lips, to show they were bad. To me it just showed they were nuts. This proved it.

The Outlaws ceremoniously tore the patches from their foes' back and wrote Animal's name on them in the enemy's blood. They had paid.

By the time the place was almost back in order the sun was coming up. The Outlaws thanked us for helping and apologized to the Sons of Silence for getting them involved.

We all got on our bikes and headed into town. I didn't figure the clubhouse would be the best place for us to get some sleep.

We found a small motel and got some rooms. We

made sure they were in the back. After paying the motel keeper a little extra, we rolled our bikes into the rooms and crashed for the day.

I didn't sleep too well. All I could think of was about four lives that had been wasted. It made me sick.

Chapter 24

Mike Jones had been running the helmet law protest for a long time in Madison, and he didn't want anything to go wrong. He knew from past experience that handling 30,000 bikers was just as easy as handling 3,000. The big difference was with 30,000 you had to find places for them to sleep and stuff. Hell, the logistics were like getting ready for an army maneuver.

Most of the time he spent at a place he and his old lady had run for years, Jones Cycle. They had built it up into a pretty good little business, but he just couldn't stay away from the helmet law protest. It had always gone against his grain to see people stomped on by big government, and the helmet law hit closest to home, since he was a biker too.

Oh, the helmet law wasn't the only thing Mike fought. He didn't like the welfare system or the tax system either, but the helmet thing was the closest to his heart, so he spent most of his time and money on it.

A couple of years back, during a national meeting of those fighting the helmet law, he had met Treb Lincoln. That meeting left a pretty big impression on him. He saw there were others around the country like him, who would fight for their rights, and they started to get together with some of the groups that had been futilely fighting the laws at a state level.

It had been like beating their heads against the wall. The states had to enact a helmet law because there was a federal regulation set by the Department of Transportation saying that if they didn't, they would lose part of their highway safety funds. Millions of dollars a year were at stake.

That really frosted Mike's balls. What the hell could those assholes in Washington possibly be thinking? If the state didn't follow their law, then they would take away safety funds? How stupid. If they were really trying to make things safer, hold back building funds if they had to, but safety funds? That was like cutting off your head if you refused to wear a hat to protect it. It just didn't make a whole lot of sense.

But then nothing the government did made a whole lot of sense to Mike.

So he fought them. For the last three years he had been fighting constantly.

The Madison protests had begun in 1975 when, on June 29th, bikers got together and petitioned congress to repeal the national helmet regulation.

Bikers all over the country, under the leadership of the small state associations that had been working on the wrong level, protested on the same day. It had all been Lincoln's idea. Instead of fighting the state, which couldn't really do anything, why not fight the federal government? The biggest problem was that there wasn't any big national biker organization. The only one was the U.S. Motorcycle Club and they were afraid to come out strong against the helmet law because most of their members who rode street bikes already wore them.

So that left the small state organizations. Most of the bikers who were trying to fight the law were outlaws, and the people didn't give a damn what happened to them.

Then one day this guy Lincoln showed up. He made it sound so damn simple. All we had to do was pick a day, and all over the country get bikers to ride on their local federal buildings asking for freedom of choice. That was it.

So they picked June 29th. It was the Sunday before the fourth of July, and as good a day as any.

It worked. That was the first time in the history of America that all the different bikers, from outlaws to touring bikers, and even dirt riders, got together. Outlaw clubs forgot their wars for a day, and ironically the federal insistence on helmets did more to bring bikers together than anything in history.

And the bureaucrats got scared. They had created a monster. What was once a bunch of easy to handle bikers, warring and fighting among themselves, was all of a sudden a formidable enemy. A quick check of statistics showed that there were 10,000,000 American bikers, and most of them wanted freedom of choice.

When the government saw Hell's Angels and Outlaws riding side by side with the Renegades and Pagans they started to get scared. Because if all the bikers stopped fighting and got organized, they might not be able to control them.

It was then that the Omega Squad was formed.

Mike first heard of the Omega Squad through a friend he had gone to school with. They had been good friends and while Mike went into business in Madison, he had gone into police work. Soon he was working in Washington.

One day Mike got a phone call. All he said was "Mike, I owe you one and here it is. The Federal Bureau of Investigation is starting a special squad of law enforcement officers to handle bikers. It was brought about because of that protest in June. Watch out."

That was it. No goodbye, nothing.

It wasn't until almost a year later that he learned the name of the squad.

Mike's thoughts drifted back to present problems. Where the hell was he going to find a place for 30,000 bikers to sleep? Hell, the shitters alone were going to be a problem. Sometimes he wished he had stuck to his bike business and stayed out of politics.

A couple members of the Cyclops came into his office. They were good friends and Mike was an honorary member of the club. They volunteered for all the jobs that nobody else wanted. They were as dedicated to beating the lid law as he was.

Tiny was the first to speak. He had found a place about three miles out of town that would hold at least 20,000 bikers, and all they had to do was get some portable crappers.

Hell, that was simple. Why hadn't he thought of that?

He thanked them, and went back to planning the big protest. It was just four days away now, and he wanted everything to go just right.

Chapter 25

Treb squinted to keep the sun out of his eyes as they crossed the bridge from Kansas City, Kansas, into Kansas City, Missouri. He never did like this stretch of road. Why don't they finish the damn freeway, anyway?

Behind him Dick and Rom pulled their hats down a little to shade their eyes from the sun and the rest of the group did the same. When they left Wichita the group had swollen to fifteen bikers. After all the shooting, eight members of the Outlaws decided it might be a good time to ride up to Chicago and visit their brothers, and the party at Madison sounded good too.

People on the street stopped and stared as the group of choppers passed them in a roar. Little children smiled and young girls glanced nervously from under their down turned heads. There was just something about a bunch of bikes that made people a little nervous and Treb figured it was the same thing that made it feel so good to ride in a pack. It was kind of like a feeling of power, but more than that, it was also a feeling of brotherhood with those you rode with. Only a true biker could ever know the feeling.

They stopped at a stop light and Treb heard Rom shout that he was hungry. Hell, he was always hungry. Treb stood still while holding his bars and half turned around.

"Anyone hungry?" he shouted. About eight or nine heads nodded yes. Treb dropped back into his seat and looked ahead. He wanted to find a place that had plenty of parking and would be easy to get in and out of.

Up ahead he saw one of those chain franchises that served up pretty good sandwiches and he pulled in. The bikers pulled in right behind him.

As he shut down his engine he could see all the little girls who worked there looking through the glass and smiling. The guys who worked there just stood staring.

He walked in and gave his order to a little pimple-faced girl. She screwed it up twice and finally got it right. She was so nervous she didn't charge him. He had to remind her. He thought that was kind of funny.

They took the food outside to the tables and pretty soon there were two or three cop cars cruising around the block.

Wherever he traveled with more than four or five bikes the police would always be close at hand. After about five minutes a plain grey Plymouth pulled in and parked next to the bikes. He knew it was a cop right off. If the blackwall tires didn't give him away, the suit and white socks did.

He never could figure out why, but cops always wore white socks.

The cop walked cautiously over to the group and tried to smile.

"You boys passing through, or you plan on staying awhile?"

Treb didn't know how many times he had heard that same line from cops in every part of the country.

"Well, we thought we would go to your house for a party. If it looks good we might settle here." Treb smiled the same smile right back at him.

The cop didn't know what to say. He had expected a typical "just passing through" line.

"Oh, ah, well, I just thought I would see where you were heading. I, ah..." he just stood there a second with his mouth open. "Well, we'll see you later," and he walked back to his car.

As he pulled out Treb could see him talking frantically into his radio mike.

They all had a good laugh at what had just gone down, as they finished their sandwiches.

Soon they were back out on the open highway and headed toward Chicago.

They had three days to get to Madison, and it was only 600 miles away, so there was no big hurry.

They were cruising at about 60, just enjoying the

afternoon sun. Treb was riding up front with Rom and Dick behind him and then the Sons and the Outlaws. It was pretty relaxed and they started to stretch out as each biker got into his own thoughts and dreams. Riding cross country is probably the best way ever invented to relax.

Treb's reverie was interrupted by the sound of a bike pulling alongside. It was one of the Outlaws. He signaled Treb over to the side of the road.

When they stopped he got off his bike and walked over to Treb.

"Hey, Beany's got a bad cylinder," he indicated one of his brothers at the back of the pack. "You think we could stop up in Carrolton and get a new set of rings put on? We got some brothers there and we could do it in about an hour."

Treb thought for a minute. Why not? They had plenty of time. They could use a break anyway.

"Yeah, sure. You lead the way in."

With that he kicked his bike to life and waited for the Outlaws to pull in front.

For the next twenty miles they followed the Outlaws to their brothers' clubhouse.

This one was a little different than most. It was actually a bar that the club owned. It allowed regular patrons in the front, but the back, where the owners used to live, was for members and guests only.

They walked into the club and there were introductions all around. There was a little more excitement than usual, though. It seems that there was a run being planned for Saturday and Sunday at a place called The Pit. They hadn't even heard about the Madison protest. They invited the newcomers to stay for the run. Since it was going to start the next evening, Friday, they said they could stay for that, but they had to jam up to Madison for Saturday night and Sunday.

The Outlaws from Kansas called Chicago and told them they wouldn't be there, and said to meet them in Madison.

Since one bike was down being worked on, Dick, Rom and Treb decided it was time to do a little work on their sleds, too. The hawgs were getting pretty beat up from all this long distance running and could use a little care and repair.

The rest of the day was spent changing oil, cleaning spark plugs, and doing all the light things like tightening loose nuts and bolts. So far the scoots had been running good.

A little later in the day a couple of numbers of some really good smoke were passed and it started to get pretty laid back around the bar/clubhouse.

Treb was getting a little into the weed too, and in a weak moment he telephoned Salt Lake. He called up the parlor where Karen was working.

"Hey, can you get a couple of days off?" he asked.

She said she would check, and for him to call her back in an hour.

Chapter 26

It had been almost a week since Karen had heard from or seen Treb, and she was surprised how much she missed him. She couldn't remember feeling that way about anybody in her short 17 years.

As soon as he hung up she called Raunchy over at the clubhouse. She knew he liked Treb and hoped he would let her off.

In a couple of minutes it was all set. She could take off for a week and she would still be welcomed back. It had helped that there were some of the brothers from the club out there, too.

She rushed out of the salon and ran up the street to her house. She left a message that if Treb called while she was out, to find out where she should go and at what time.

It took her three minutes to run the block and a half to her room, 10 minutes to throw some things into her only piece of luggage, which she had taken from her parents' house almost an eternity ago.

She rushed back to the salon and waited for Treb's call.

A couple of her regular Johns came in, but she begged off, saying she had a headache. Hell, it was like being married.

It was almost two hours later when Treb called back, and she could tell by the dry mouth way he talked that he was smoking weed.

She didn't care, she just wanted to get out to him.

He told her to catch a plane to Kansas City and then a bus to Carrolton. He gave her a number to call when she got in, and hung up.

She rushed to the bank to draw out a couple of hundred dollars and caught a cab to the airport.

The cabby checked her in the rear view mirror and made a small pass, but both he and she knew it wasn't for real. Then he tried to set up a business arrangement. She didn't know how, but cabbies and hotel clerks always seemed to know she was a pro. Someday she vowed to find out how.

She found she was in luck when she got to the airport. There was one flight that would be taking off in fifteen minutes and would get into KC at six p.m.

On the airplane she was seated next to a man who sold farm equipment. For the whole flight he tried to impress her with how much money he made selling something to make manure easier to spread. She just smiled politely and let him buy her drinks. When she found out he had a car and was heading towards Carrolton, she even went as far as letting him lay his hand on her thigh.

He was a dumpy looking dude with a stomach that hung over his belt and an awful looking brown suit that was so shiny it almost glowed. He wore a cheap wedding ring on his finger. This guy was a definite loser, but what the hell any port in a storm.

When the plane landed she left with Murray, which was the nerd's name, and the stewardess gave her a look like, "Really sweetie, you could have done better."

They walked to a white 1967 Ford two door in the parking lot. It was pretty beat up and had Missouri plates. As he opened the door for her he made an awkward grab for her breasts and tried to kiss her. The smell of bourbon on his breath almost got her drunk.

She slipped out of his arms into the seat and started to wonder if maybe she should have taken the bus instead. This guy was going to be a pain. But she had handled guys like him before, and she knew she could handle him.

When he slipped into his seat she half turned toward him, leaning against the window. She knew he wanted her to sit closer, but the chance that he might be able to see up her dress would be the first thing on his mind, if he was like most men. In a couple of seconds she could see that she had judged him right. She lifted the leg closer to him a little bit and she knew that he was looking right up her dress. It didn't really bother her, since she had worn panties, which she normally didn't do, and besides that, with this asshole looking up her dress, he wouldn't go through all the maneuvers to get her next to him.

She smiled sweetly at him and leaned her head back against the window.

"When we get to Carrolton, I just know I can find a way to thank you," she said. And with that she moved her leg a little farther up the seat, and she could see that he was hooked.

All the way to Carrolton, which was over 100 miles, he kept glancing sideways at her. They both knew it was a game, but only she knew what the rules were.

She asked him about the town of Carrolton. Was it a big town? Did he know a lot of people? Were there any of those nasty bikers there? He kept telling her everything that he could, to try and impress her with his smarts. She almost got sick thinking about what it would be like to ball the slug.

When she asked about the bikers she made it sound like she really was intrigued by them. He told her there was only one club in the town, and that was the Outlaws.

She thought for a second and remembered that Treb had said he knew some Outlaws. She figured that was where he would be. All she had to do was figure a way to get this turkey to take her to wherever they were.

As it turned out it was a lot simpler than she thought. In his haste to impress her he told her all about this bar they had there, that the bikers owned it, and it was open to the public.

She moved her foot over to where it was rubbing against his leg and rested it there for a moment.

Just as he reached down from the steering wheel to lay his hand on her ankle, she asked, "Would you take me there for a drink, before we get a room for the night?"

That cinched it. She could almost hear the wheels going around in his head. He ran his hand up her leg to her thigh and started to put his finger under the elastic of her panties. She gently pushed his hand away and smiled at him. Licking her lips, she looked at him with the most innocent face she could muster.

"Let's wait until after we have a drink. I always feel so sexy after I have a drink. Is that okay with you?"

He just looked sideways at her and forced a smile. She could tell that he didn't really want to go there, but he wanted into her pants so badly he could already taste it.

The rest of the trip was spent in silence. She pretended to be asleep and he would slowly run his hand up her leg, trying not to wake her. Every time, just as he would get to her panties, she would shrug his hand off like she was coming awake, and roll over a little.

When the lights of Carrolton appeared in the distance, she almost let out a sigh. It probably would have been easier to take a bus, but not as fast.

He turned onto one of the small side streets downtown and she could see all the bikes in front of a bar. She didn't know Treb's bike, but she recognized a couple of the Sons of Silence's bikes and knew that this was the right place.

Chapter 27

The weed was really starting to get to my head. I didn't remember where the hell I was at times. Dick and Rom were busy in a game of pool, with most of the bikers there betting on the outcome. Either of them could have been pool hustlers if they wanted to be.

A couple of regular patrons were sitting at the far end of the bar. I could tell that they came in pretty regular just to be near the bikers. There were a lot of people like that. They like to be around bikers because it makes them feel important somehow.

For a second I had a thought. I wonder if those guys are cops. Then, as soon as the thought hit me. It left again. Good dope does that to me.

My mind kept wandering. That was what I really

liked about good smoking dope. Not angel dust or any of that other exotic shit, but just plain good marijuana. That was what I really got off on. My mind would jump from track to track, and no matter what I was thinking about, it seemed to be perfectly clear how to go about it. A couple of seconds later would have forgotten what the answer was, along with what the problem was. It was a neat mind game.

Thoughts of Karen floated in and out just as quickly. I wondered how long it was going to take her to get here. Then I rationalized that when she got here I would know, and went on to other thoughts.

I looked over at the pool table. There was a sight that I really got off on. Dick and Rom were hard locked in a game of pool, but I could see the love between them, like brothers. I felt awfully lucky to have a couple of friends like that.

Rom looked a little funny with that stupid bandage around his neck. It was so dirty it was almost black. It probably would have been better for him to take it off, but he liked to tell the tale of how it all happened, and the more he wore it, the more questions were asked. It was like a status symbol.

At the bar one of the Sons was talking with one of the Outlaws who had ridden down with us. All of a sudden my mind went on a bummer. I thought back to the killing at the Outlaw clubhouse. I hated that.

Why must bikers keep killing each other? Usually it's over real horseshit things too.

My mind started its little game again. What if? What if all bikers got along? What if we ended the wars? What if we were all brothers? It was the same old marijuana mental process.

Or was it?

I tried to capture the thought again. I remember thinking I had that thought before, when I was sober.

Oh yeah, that was it. What if?

It was something that had bothered me as long as I had been a biker. The way outlaws were always killing each other.

I remember a war back in Los Angeles between two clubs. It started over something so dumb nobody would have ever guessed it. It was at a bar in Long Beach. Two clubs that had partied together for a long time were drinking and having a good time. One member of the Talons was dancing with one of the Hawks' old ladies. It was all fun and games, no problems. When the guy from the Talons walked her back to her old man, he squeezed her butt a little. The old man took offense and punched him. It was all fair and square.

But the members of the Talons didn't like their colors being knocked to the floor. After all, that's what brotherhood was all about, they thought. Before the night was through there were two dead bikers, one from each club.

In the next few months 11 bikers were killed, and for what?

If it wasn't for an accident of birth they might have been in the same club. All bikers live for the same things: The freedom of a good ride, some good times, and the brotherhood of his club.

Then my smoky mind solved the whole problem.

If there were just one club, there wouldn't be any fights.

It sounded logical to me.

But then, everything sounded logical to me when I was as fucked up as I was now.

Just then a number was placed in front of me and I awoke from my reverie. I took a long, deep hit on it and passed it back.

Where was I? It had something to do with the freedom of riding, I think. Or was it something new I was going to do to my bike?

Oh hell, I can't remember.

A shout went out by the pool table and I saw Dick slapping Rom on the back. Dick had won the match and he was razzing poor Rom. They laughed a lot, and then a new challenger set the table for the next game. Rom came wandering over to where I was sitting.

"Hey bro, what'r you doing over here by yourself? Wanta get into the game?

He knew I wasn't much into pool, and he loved to play and almost let me win, and then clear the table on his last shot.

"I was just laying here getting fucked up. You?"

He smiled.

"Hell, if I get any more fucked up I'll be fucked down," and with that he laughed like he had just made up the funniest thing since busted crutches.

I was about to answer him when I saw Karen come through the door. She was wearing a short brown dress and a tan blouse that made her boobs look like two large, ripe grapefruits.

Some weird looking dude in a wrinkled suit came

in right behind her. He looked like he thought he owned her.

I got up from the stool I was sitting on and started toward her. She got a real big smile on her face and almost ran to me. The nerd looked a little upset.

After a kiss that I thought would smother me, I asked her who the weirdo was. She told me he had given her a ride from the airport, and she had just met him on the plane.

I walked over to the guy and thanked him for the ride out.

He looked a little surprised, and a little scared too. Oh well, that was his problem.

Karen and I walked over to the pool table and the nerd turned and left. Guess he didn't like it there.

Karen walked around saying hello to the Sons of Silence and Dick and Rom. They introduced her to the Outlaws, and then she came back to where I was sitting. She looked good enough to eat, and as a matter of fact that was exactly what I had in mind.

It had been a couple of long days since I had dipped my wick, and the memory of what her tight little body was like had been getting more and more to me.

From the way she snuggled up against me I knew that she was ready too. I walked over to Mother Trucker, the President of this chapter of the Outlaws, and asked it they had someplace "a little more private." He smiled a broad, almost toothless grin. His mouth looked almost comical through the jet black beard that was dotted with popcorn kernels that hadn't made their target.

He pointed to a blanket on a far wall.

"Go through there. There's a door about ten feet down the hall. That should do fine." His grin got even bigger.

We walked over to the cheap Spanish serape and pulled it aside. There was a long hall behind it. At the end I could see some of the members of the Outlaws playing cards. One of them was traveling with us. He smiled when he saw me come through the curtain with Karen.

"Got lucky, huh?" His smile got a little broader. "She gonna be a turnout?"

It was a logical question. Usually when a biker brings in a chick that he picked up he has his turn, and then offers her to his hosts. It's part of the code.

"Sorry Frank, this is my ol' lady. She just got in from Salt Lake."

He looked her up and down, and forced a frown.

"Damn, you big guys get all the fun," and a smile broke across his lips. "Good luck," and he turned back to his cards.

Karen looked at me and moved a little closer.

"What's this ol' lady shit?" she kidded. I stroked her on the end of her tit.

"Okay then, how about your being a turnout?"

She grabbed my balls and smiled, squeezing them real gently.

"Baby, if you don't like what you're about to get, you can turn me out to the whole damn club," and with that she walked into the small, dark room and started to take off her blouse.

I stood there for a second and looked at her. She was something else, that was for sure.

I walked into the room. It wasn't like most of the

turnout rooms I had seen. Most of them are dirty and just have a couple of mattresses on the floor. This one was carpeted and had a nightstand and everything. The bed was a double with a bedspread, and it was made. That in itself was different than anything I had ever seen in a clubhouse.

I walked over to the bed and sat down. Just as I bent my knees I saw a piece of paper on the bed where I was about to sit. I stood up and picked it up.

"TREB, ENJOY, "it said.

That was it. They knew I had called Karen and they had set up the clean bed and everything. I smiled and put away the note. Sometimes it's really pretty good being with your brothers.

The soft light from the lamp glowed on Karen's body. It gave it a sense of being unreal, like when I was a kid and walked into a girly show. It just wasn't real.

I knew the weed I had smoked had a little bit to do with it, but something about Karen had a lot more to do with it. I liked her.

I reached out for her and buried my head against her soft stomach. Not only did she look good, she felt good, too. To top it all off she smelled good.

I took one of her tits in my mouth and sucked on the tender little nipple. Running my hands up the backside of her skirt I could feel her firm young ass and the line of her panties.

"Equal time," I said, as I started to suck on her other boob, and she squirmed a little bit in my arms.

The odor of her filled my nose and I could almost

taste her.

I held her out at arm's length and just looked at her. Her blond hair was a bit disheveled and her makeup was slightly smeared, but she looked great to me. I reached out and pulled down the zipper of her dress. She wiggled a little and it fell to the floor. Then she slipped her panties off.

Just as I was about to reach for her, to bury my tongue deep in her pussy, she took the panties and put them on my head.

I started laughing so hard I thought I would choke. Then she jumped on me and started to tickle me all over.

Normally I'm not a whole lot ticklish, but tonight, with all the good dope I was smoking, a Mack truck hitting me would have felt funny.

We twisted around on the bed, me so weak with laughter that I could hardly move. All of a sudden she stopped tickling me and I felt her warm tongue on my dick. I opened my eyes and saw her soft pubic hairs just inches from my face. I reached out slowly and tangled my fingers in them. She moaned a little and slowly opened her legs. For a long time she sucked on me while I just ran my fingers over her pussy and her tits. Then I pulled her over on top of me and buried my tongue deep into her soft and warm groove. Every nerve I had was in the head of my dick.

After a couple of minutes we started changing positions.

First her on top, then me, then every variation we could think of. It was one of the most erotic nights I could ever remember. After we both came, her three times and me twice, she fell asleep in my arms. I lay there for a few minutes looking at her, wondering how anyone who looked as innocent as she could be so damn good in bed, and then I dozed off.

Chapter 28

The Pit is a large hole in the ground, just like the name implies. It sits out in the middle of a barren wasteland that hasn't been used for anything in a whole lot of years.

There are a few of these places scattered around the country. After World War II the government had a whole bunch of ammunition they didn't know what to do with. It was decided to bury it and a contract was let to dig the holes.

The Pit where the Outlaws had brought the run was one of these holes. It seems that the government, in their wisdom, decided they might as well use up the ammunition in target practice, so the holes remained.

Three Outlaw chapters had gotten together to put

on this run, and the prospects were sent out early to get things ready. They filled the potholes in the road heading down into the pit and set up the beer coolers.

A portable generator had been borrowed, but it didn't work. When the group from Carrolton headed out across the prairie towards the pit all they could see was a small glow.

As they approached they were stopped by five armed guards sitting on a hill. The strangers were checked out and then the pack was allowed to go on in.

Treb was almost overwhelmed. He had never seen anything like it in his life.

The pit was over 300 feet in diameter and almost round. The walls were 30 feet deep. There was only one road leading in or out, and it was guarded at all times. As the pack he was riding with rode around the rim, heading down into the pit, it looked like something out of a movie. There were eight or nine bonfires going and the chrome from hundreds of bikes reflected the red and yellow flames.

Over to one side a target range had been set up and there were cans and bottles lining the walls as targets. Music could be heard over the roar of the fires from a stereo playing in one of the beer trucks.

Sparks and ashes flew into the air from the fires and the whole thing looked almost ritualistic.

The pack Treb was riding with had about 50 bikes in it, since the Carrolton chapter had met another at a small bar down the road. As the bikes rolled down into the pit, most of the people who were there came over to greet old friends. Treb and his group were introduced to all within earshot and soon it was back to being just one big party.

Once during the night a sheriff's helicopter flew overhead and aimed a spotlight down on the group, but when a couple of guys who had a little too much to drink started shooting at it, it flew away.

Treb and Dick and Rom stayed pretty close to the group they came in with for the first hour or so, but then they just started to mingle. Karen was busy making friends with the old ladies around one of the fires. She liked the biker lifestyle and hoped Treb might take her with him for awhile, but she didn't want to get her hopes up too high.

Kilos of good grass were being smoked as a community stash and over an ounce of coke was snorted as fast as it could be laid out in lines.

At a club run the beer and everything is always free to members and guests, so things get pretty fucked up in a hurry. It was no exception here in The Pit.

All night long more and more bikes pulled in. When the sun started to rise on Saturday morning there were over a thousand bikes and close to 2,000 people there. It was getting to be a real blast. Some of the other clubs that the Outlaws party with had been invited to come too, and there was some real partying going on.

After a night of partying like this, it's pretty hard to get on your scoot and split, but if they wanted to make it to Madison they were going to have to hustle. It was still three hundred miles away.

They picked up a few more bikers who wanted to go, and when Treb led the way out he had 30 bikes following. Karen wrapped herself around him to keep out the early morning chill as they headed out through Burlington and up the Mississippi toward Wisconsin.

Along the road they met other bikers who were heading north to join the protest. Some were on stock bikes, Hondas and Yamahas, and others were on stone, chopped Harleys. All were invited to join the pack, and as they passed into Wisconsin there were over 100 bikes behind Treb and his group.

The gas stops got pretty hectic and Treb and his friends took full advantage of them because they were starting to hurt a little bit for money. So they would fill up their bikes and crank back the pumps. Free gas was a good way to save bucks.

At one gas stop they tried a little con. When a bunch of folks were in a small store getting food, Karen and a couple of the other old ladies faked a fight over some cookies. When Karen's top was ripped off, the guy behind the counter was so busy filling his eyes he didn't even see Treb and Rom cleaning out the meat department. They had cold cuts for lunches for a couple of days and there would be steaks that night for a whole lot of folks.

When they hit 1-94 and passed Janesville the pack had grown to almost 300 bikes, and the snake was two miles long. Treb really got off on looking in his rear view mirror and checking it out. It was a beautiful sight.

There were too many now to fuck with, so the police just pulled in front of them and turned on their lights to give them an escort into Madison. They led them right to the park that was chosen as a campsite.

Even with so many, they still made good time. They had left the pit at sun up, which was about six in the morning, and they pulled into Madison a little after three in the afternoon. Treb sent Karen to find a place to set up camp and he took off with Rom to look up his old friend Mike Jones.

They rode into town and headed right for Jones Cycle. He figured that would be the logical place to find him.

Chapter 29

Mike was as busy as a one-legged rooster in a cockfight. The protest was coming together as well as he had hoped, but all the hassle of getting the press lined up and handling all the VIPs that were coming in was almost too much. He laid a lot of work off on Tiny and the rest of his brothers.

He heard over the police radio in his office that three hundred bikes were being led in by the Outlaws and he hoped they wouldn't cause any trouble up here. That would be all he needed, a bunch of outlaws getting into a war.

He was right in the middle of a phone call from the chief of police when he glanced up to see Treb standing there. Mike smiled widely and motioned for him to sit down.

"Yeah Chief, I know there are a lot of Outlaws coming in. So what? They aren't doing anything are they?" He made a face and pointed at the phone. "What do you want from me? If you would help us get this helmet law beat we could stop all this foolishness and get out and do some riding." He finished his conversation and hung up.

For the next few minutes they talked about what was happening tomorrow and Treb asked if he could help. Mike knew of the trouble Treb was in from Los Angeles and told him he shouldn't be seen.

The talk turned to the upcoming national protest on the fourth of July. Mike agreed to get all of his people to help and said he would come to the planning meeting in Kansas in February.

Treb thanked him and got up to leave.

"Mike, I know you're busy today. Good luck with the ride tomorrow. I'll be out there if you want any help. All you have to do is holler."

They shook hands and Treb walked out into the shop. He found Rom in back talking to Patsy. Mike's old lady, and after saying hi and goodbye they went back out to the campground.

Mike walked back into his office. He had a lot to do, but he kind of wished he was just one of the bikers so he could go out there to the park and party. It was going to be a good time for sure.

Patsy walked into the office and looked at him. She looked worried. He smiled at her and told her to shut the door. There was always one way to get her in a good mood. She locked the door and smiled back at him. For the next couple of minutes they were oblivious to everyone and everything. They didn't often get as carried away as now, but what the hell, doing it on a desk top is as good as bed, and sometimes a hell of a lot better.

Just as they finished and she was getting ready to go back out and help in the shop there was a knock on the door. It was Tiny.

"Hey Mike, the beer truck can't get in until after 10 o'clock, and the guys are going to be lining them up starting at seven. What are we going to do?"

Mike thought for a second. He picked up the phone and reached for his flip up phone directory. He waited for a couple of seconds while it rang.

"John Markson please," he looked impatient.

"Mr. Markson, this is Mike Jones. Look, we contracted with your company to supply the beer for this run and if you can't handle it, we'll just have to go over to Coors. They said they could get us the 125 barrels we need by the time the group started to arrive, which was seven AM. Now what's it going to be?"

He listened a couple of seconds.

"Look, I have my own problems. Are you going to do it or not?"

His face softened a little.

"Yeah John, I know, but we are going to have 30,000 thirsty bikers out there, and your trucks have been doing good out at the park until now. Can you guarantee they will be at the meeting point by at least 7:30?" A slight pause. "Fine. We'll see you there," and he hung up.

"Okay Tiny, they will be there at 7:30. Oh, by the way. Treb Lincoln is in with some friends of his. See if those chicks that work at Jack's are tied up yet, and if not take them out to the park. They're staying with the Outlaws and the Sons of Silence."

He turned his back and started to think about other things that had to be done. The newspapers still wanted an interview, and the late news was going to do a thing with the mayor. He didn't want to miss it.

"Damn," he thought, "why can't I be out there partying?" He went back to arranging the road guards and the route for the next day's ride.

Chapter 30

It started as a humming in his head and soon became a roar. Leroy had heard that sound before. He remembered it in Los Angeles, the last time he covered one of the helmet law protests. Now he was a network newsman and he had a little better working conditions. He sat in the penthouse of the Madison Towers while two staff reporters ran around gathering the news for him to read. Damn, but it almost felt as if he wasn't doing his job.

The phone rang and he picked it up. The hotel operator asked if he wanted to speak to a Mike Jones, who was on the phone. He told her to put him through. He remembered that Jones was the one responsible for this protest event, and he wanted to find out what he knew about the ride on the national capitol that was being planned.

Jones told him of a press briefing that evening and then invited him to have a couple of drinks afterwards. Jones knew how important ABD news was to their cause and he was treating Leroy right.

As the conversation was about to close, Leroy shot the question.

"Mr. Jones, are you going to be participating in the national protest in July?"

There was silence on the other end of the phone while Mike gathered his wits. Then he spoke, "Well, how about we discuss the future over a drink later?"

Leroy grinned. This guy was pretty cagey.

"Okay, how about my hotel, in the bar, at about nine?"

That was settled. They would talk. He looked forward to it.

The conversation made him think back to Treb Lincoln. He was the same way. He never gave an inch unless you did the same. He wondered if Jones knew Lincoln and decided that he had to, since they would be working together on the national protest. He made a note to ask if he knew where Lincoln was

He got up out of the easy chair and walked to the window. He thought of all the times he had been in dingy hotels and sleazy dumps to cover some lurid story or other. Now he was on top of the world, almost literally. He looked out and gazed at all of Madison below him and the green lands stretching far beyond that, as far as the eye could see.

There was a knock at the door and he walked across the plush gold carpet and opened it. It was

Johnson, one of his staffers.

"Mr. Makelray, there are a bunch of them camping in the park and we wondered if you wanted to set up out there for a little background footage in case we need it?"

Leroy looked at him. He still remembered what it was like when he had been a staffer and he almost felt sorry for the fellow.

"Jim, how many times do I have to ask you to call me Leroy?" He paused as if for an answer. He was just thinking, though, if it might not be a good idea to get some peaceful shots in case the protest got out of hand. They might get more than a 45 second spot on national if there was violence. In that case he would need some contrasting visuals to tape his talk over.

"Yeah, that would be a good idea. Why don't you go ahead and set up around the most crowded area and I will meet you and Jack there in a half hour." He thought for another second.

"We have a press meeting with Mike Jones at eight, so we have to shift to the capitol stairs before then."

Jim almost bowed when he left, closing the door quietly behind him. Leroy almost felt sad. He had always heard that it was lonely at the top, but he wasn't even at the top and he didn't have any friends here. They were either executives he was trying to impress or new reporters who were trying to impress him. The only friends he had were back in L.A., from the early days. He felt lonesome.

Then he turned back to the picture window overlooking the city and forgot all about it. He liked it up here, even if it was a little lonely.

He went to the bedroom and opened his closet. The first thing the network did was to take him out and buy him more clothes than he had ever owned in his life. He always thought that Walter Cronkite and Dan Rather bought their own clothes. He had no idea that clothes, moustaches, even hair styles were all chosen according to viewer preference polls.

The clothes for this trip were picked to photograph well against green trees and show off the highlights of a crowd the best. Except for the gold jacket and black pants. They were for interviews. They looked best with a dark studio background.

From the closet he chose a "night" outfit, which was a light green pair of trousers with a bright lime jacket, and pulled the pastel shirt off the hanger. He took off his robe and looked at himself in the mirror.

"You haven't changed any on the inside," he widened his eyes, "have you?" He smiled and went to the dresser. He took out a pair of shorts and some green socks. Can't have anything clash on camera, he thought.

After he dressed he walked to the elevator. A couple of people got in on the way down and he looked to see if they recognized him. They didn't.

He went to the underground lot where his rented Oldsmobile was parked and climbed in. A street map was on the seat next to him.

He tuned the radio to one of the rock stations as he headed out onto the street. He always listened to the local rock station when he was covering an event like this because that was where the grass roots political news would be aired. The straight stations tried to ignore things like helmet law protests.

As he turned off the freeway and onto the road that went to the park, he could see the fires. There were a lot more bikers here than he had figured.

He wished that he had someone like Treb with him. He always hated telling people he was with ABD news. They always wanted to be on camera after they learned who he was.

He found Jim and Jack with the equipment all set up by one of the beer trucks. The bikers had befriended them and it looked like they were getting along fine. When Leroy found a place to park, he got out of his car and walked over to them.

He looked around and tried to find some good shots to fill in behind a sound track if they needed it. They got film of a bunch dancing around a fire, with their club patches showing up real good, and he even got a couple necking on the back of a chopper. Never can tell what you'll need.

He wandered over to one of the bigger fires and got ready to shoot some more lifestyle scenes when a particular bike caught his eye. It was real familiar. He didn't know a whole lot about bikes, but this one he was sure he had seen before. He walked around behind it and saw that there were California plates on it.

"Treb!" he said out loud.

He looked all around but didn't see that big fuzzy head anywhere.

He asked a couple of the bikers who were there with Sons of Silence patches on their backs, but they acted like they didn't know what he was talking about.

Just as he was about to give up he saw a scuzzy looking biker with a black bandage around his neck.

"Rom, you asshole," he shouted. Jim and Jack thought he had gone nuts. They just stared at him.

Leroy ran to Rom like he was his lost brother. It even surprised Rom.

After they shot the bull for a little while Rom took Leroy to where Treb was. He had picked a place behind a small brick wall so he could get some sleep. He had been out for about two hours. When they got there, Rom shoved Karen out of the way and woke up Treb.

Treb and Leroy walked into the dark to talk, leaving Rom and Karen to sit and stare at Jim and Jack. None of them had a thing in common and the few words that passed between them were forced.

After about ten minutes they came back to the firelight. They agreed to meet in Leroy's penthouse at 10 that night. They had a lot to talk about.

Leroy decided he had the shots he needed and he led the van to the press conference at the capitol.

Chapter 31

I couldn't have been any more surprised if God himself had walked out of the dark. Hell, I never expected to see Leroy again. He was good people, even if he wasn't a stone biker. He had a lot of the qualities it takes to make a good biker, and that's what really counts, anyway.

I was real happy to hear that he was doing good, and even happier to hear he was on the network now. He said he would work with us a little on the national protest. It just might be what we need. A way to get to the people with a positive approach instead of all the negative bullshit that they always see about bikers.

Karen looked a little upset when I told her she would have to stay at camp that night, but she understood why. She knew about the national and knew we had a lot of things to get together.

Dick came walking over with some little floozy on his arms. He said that some guy named Tim had brought a couple of chicks down for Rom and me, and he knew I was all tied up, so he took mine. He asked if I minded. I looked at Karen across the fire and shook my head. No, I was about as happy as I could get in that department. She just smiled.

Dick wandered off into the dark. I knew he was camped in that direction and figured he would be tied up for awhile.

I thought for a second and then shouted after him.

"Hey Dick, we got some business in about an hour, can you come?" He looked back for a second and stopped. He looked down at the little brunette in his arm and smiled at me.

"I'll be ready in a half hour," and he started to turn. She stopped and shouted back over her shoulder, "Make it forty- five minutes. I'm gonna teach this guy a few things," and they walked into the dark laughing.

Rom heard us and took time from his activities in the sack to shout that he would be ready too.

Karen looked at me and our eyes just stayed on each other. We didn't have to say a thing. She walked over and pulled back the sleeping bag. She slipped out of her t-shirt and blue jeans as if she were in her own bedroom, knelt on the sleeping bag and held her arms up to me.

I didn't need a written invitation. For the next half hour we were busy.

The next thing I knew Rom and Dick were standing over me.

"Well, what do you think? Can he be saved?" Dick said in mock earnestness.

"I don't know. He sure looks like a goner to me," replied Rom, equally sincere.

And then they broke up laughing, with their girls chiming in right behind.

I climbed out of the bag and pulled my pants on. I noticed that the girl Rom had been with was eyeing my family jewels. Karen saw this too.

I knew that when I got back Rom would have to find a new chick. Karen would see to that.

We went over to some of the guys we had come with and told them we would be back in awhile, to watch our stuff. They knew we meant our old ladies, and they agreed.

I straddled my bike and kicked her once. That was all it took, she fired up like she was eager to run. As I threw my leg over and got ready to pull her off the sidestand, Karen came over to me. She kissed me long and wet on the mouth.

"Baby, take care of yourself," was all she said. I nodded and put up the stand.

"You too," and I started down the path to the road.

Out on the highway there were bikes everywhere. It was almost incredible. The town of Madison looked like it was under siege.

I remembered how it was in Los Angeles, but there 30,000 bikes could be lost in the crowd. In a town the size of Madison it was a whole different story.

Leroy's hotel was easy to find. All we had to do was look for the tallest and most expensive building in the city. That was it. When we pulled our bikes up the driveway, the parking attendant looked pretty damn puzzled. He didn't know whether to tell us to leave or to try and park the bikes. We simplified it for him by stopping them in front of the main entrance and telling him to watch them.

He looked scared enough not to let anybody get near them, for fear of what would happen to himself.

We pushed through the door man and into the lobby.

There were all kinds of dressed up people in there doing whatever it is citizens do in hotel lobbies. They all stopped when we came through the door and stared at us.

We stared right back.

Fuck 'em if they can't take a joke.

We found the elevator and pushed the up button. Then we waited.

Over in one corner of the lobby were a couple of old matrons with real frilly type evening dresses on, and they were giggling like little school girls.

The registrar was looking at us helplessly, like he would like to throw us out but was afraid.

A bell chimed and one of the elevators opened. There were two couples in there getting ready to step out, but when the door opened and they saw us they took a step back. Then as if to show how brave they were, the two men stepped out first and pulled the ladies by their hands. I got the feeling if we had said "Boo" they would have lost their collective toupees.

I checked the numbers on the control panel and pressed "P." The doors closed and we waited for the long ride to the top. We discussed laughingly if we should have brought our bikes up in the elevator, and when the door opened on the top floor we were near hysteria.

There was only one door on the hall we were in, and it said Penthouse. Rom said he hoped what was in the magazine was in the room on the other side of the door, and we knocked.

In a couple seconds the smiling face of Leroy Makelray greeted us. He opened the door and I saw Mike Jones over on the couch. He looked comfortable with a drink in his hand.

We smiled at each other as Leroy walked over to the bar and started to mix drinks for the three of us.

"What would you like?" he asked as he dropped three glasses on the top of the mahogany bar.

We shrugged. Hell, if it was anything but wine we were all lost. He put ice in the glasses and filled them with something from one of the cut glass decanters on the back shelf.

Once the formalities were over we got down to business. Leroy told us about why he had been promoted to the network offices. He explained about the computers and what they said about a national protest rally. All I could think about was how weird it was to have some silly machine know more about what was going on in this country than any person. I found it a little scary.

It was honestly our intention to have a peaceful demonstration on the fourth, and I told Leroy that. He just kept repeating the 80% probability of it getting out of hand. That was a little hard to ignore.

Then we got down to business. Leroy said he would be very grateful if, when the national came down, he could get some of the best stuff first, and, if possible, exclusively. Mike and I discussed it and we decided that ABD was the biggest network anyway, so we could work it out, if, and that was the big word, if Leroy would give us some pre-event coverage on the national level. That would insure a larger turnout. Larger than if we had to rely on word of mouth. Network television had a way of making things happen.

Late into the night we discussed the ways it should be handled and eventually we had come to a bargain. Leroy said he would have to clear it with New York and he would let us know.

It was pretty late, so we thanked him and once again I thanked him for the help back in L.A., and we left.

In the elevator on the way down Mike told us about a little party he had planned for the steps of the capitol building at 2 a.m., when he planned on hanging the governor in effigy. We said we would be there.

Chapter 32

Snoopy and Oaf had seen some partying in their day, but what was going on in Madison was unreal. They had seen what it was like in places like Daytona Beach, and on this night Madison was just like it. To them it was heaven.

As they wheeled their bikes onto Williamson Street and headed up to the Freedom House, where a party had been planned for the bikers, all they could see was bikes. Wall to wall. There were all kinds, styles and sizes. Snoopy checked out some of the license plates. Michigan, Illinois, South Carolina. Hell, there were even some there from as far away as California. All he could think about was, why wasn't it always like that?

Two blocks from Freedom House there were

wooden barricades, making it impossible for cars to get through. Only bikes were allowed. They passed the barricades and cruised past the building. It was an old brick three-story building with the words "Freedom House" carved into a stone name block over the double doors. On one side of the building hung a sign. It read "Welcome Bikers. Let those who ride decide."

All along the side of the street there were bikers in different stages of hard partying. It was a mixture of the Mardi Gras and Spain's festival del toros all rolled into one. To put it simply, it was just the biggest party they had ever seen.

After they cruised by the Freedom House they turned around and found a hole where two bikes had just pulled out. Parking was a bitch here, even for motorcycles.

Walking to the entrance where the dance was being held, they could hear the music blasting from all the windows. They wound their way through the crowds, stopping every now and then to take a hit off some weed or to drink and have a few laughs with someone. They didn't know a soul there, but they were among friends nevertheless.

When they reached the door they pushed their way up and through the entry way. All they could see was bodies, bodies, and more bodies.

At the door one of the club members approached them and asked for a dollar donation for the band. They paid it gladly.

The floor of the auditorium was as packed as it could be with swaying bodies. Tight blue jeans and topless girls were everywhere.

Just as Snoopy was about to go over and hit on one of the foxier ladies out there, who looked like she was alone, a voice came over the loudspeaker. It said there was going to be a midnight ride on the federal building and all bikers were invited.

Screams and yells were all that could be heard over the sound of bikes starting their motors in the streets. As Snoopy and Oaf ran out the door all Snoopy could think about was the dollar he had just paid to get into the dance. What a waste.

Oh well, he figured, you can't win 'em all.

They climbed on their scooters and joined the parade of speeding motorcycles downtown to the federal building.

All the way there, not one signal was green, and nobody stopped. The police just sat at the intersections blocking cross traffic and watched. There wasn't a whole lot they could have done anyway.

As they approached the federal building it was a torchlight spectacle. Hundreds of burning torches were bouncing in the air as Mike Jones untied the rope on the flag pole of the federal building and hung a rag-filled dummy with the name of the governor written on it. The rags were soaked in gasoline. The crowd started to howl, and when a torch touched the dummy and it went up in flames the crowd went nuts.

Soon the sounds of sirens set up a wail in the distance and most of the bikers started back to their bikes, if only from reflex action. As they thundered away the other bikers decided that they would split too, and by the time the police showed up in force there was just a burning dummy on the flagpole and the sweet smell of Harley oil in the air.

Chapter 33

When the sun came up over the city park there were still hundreds of bikers awake and partying, but the majority had gone to sleep. Those who were barely awake just walked around looking for others who were in the same condition, and then they would stand and talk. It looked like a battlefield. Soft mist lay like a blanket over the slightly rolling hills of the park, and the bikes looked like artillery pieces that had been abandoned. The quiet figures lying scattered in sleeping bags looked like the dead of war. It was an eerie feeling.

Leroy told the guys to keep it quiet. Jim was unloading the video equipment and Jack was busy with the cable. They had managed to cut down the size of everything except that cable reel. It was still as awkward as ever.

Leroy stood in front of the camera. All the tests had been run and he was ready. He learned a long time ago that it is more dramatic when a news story starts with a shot of the reporter's back and then watches him turn around.

He turned.

"It looks almost calm now. The thundering machines are quiet and the soldiers are down." He paused for emphasis.

"In a few hours there will be over 30,000 motorcycle riders from all over the United States converging on this park."

Leroy gestured out to his right and Jim followed his hand with the camera. The sun was just coming up, lighting a line of bikers riding on the horizon.

"These people are gathering together to fight a law that they feel is unjust. This is the city of Madison, the capitol of Wisconsin. The bikers here are getting together to show their unity, that the writing is on the wall. This is just a preview of things to come. For the past few days here the talk has been of a national protest, to be held in Washington, D.C. And if it does have to take place, there will be ten or twenty times the number of people involved as there are here.

"Is that what we want? Is that what free people must do to protect their own rights in today's America?"

He paused.

"We will see. Today's protest here is a preview of what will happen if the government doesn't stop interfering in personal freedoms."

Leroy knew that this soundtrack couldn't ever be aired. The legal department would hit the ceiling. Journalists were not supposed to get emotional or take sides.

But Treb and Mike didn't know that, and he planned to play them this tape to gain their confidence and get all the information that he could on the national protest.

More bikes were pulling into the park. Leroy could never keep track of time when something of this intensity was taking place. It was as if the clocks were all turned up.

Thousands of cycles filled the park in orderly rows. People stood in small groups, unable to move about easily. The loudspeakers were booming that they would be starting in five minutes.

The only way they could get their cameras out to the capitol on time was to take the truck up over the curb and drive along the riverbed next to the park. There were too many bikes to drive out through.

When he hit the main entrance to the park, Leroy turned up the embankment and soon he was driving down the same path the bikers would take.

The townfolk of Madison were treating this like a parade. They were lined up on both sides of the streets and on the overpasses.

As they approached the capitol Leroy could see the crowds. He parked the van behind the capitol. As they shouldered the equipment the sound could be heard. A murmur passed through the crowd and then the glint of silver could be seen off in the distance.

Madison is a beautiful city, and the best part is where the capitol building sits. It is right at the top of a hill, and when you stand on the balcony of the capitol you look three miles straight out over the city. This is the route the bikes were coming up. They looked like a river of quicksilver, floating ragged people along like debris.

The closer they came the louder grew the sound that accompanied them. Soon it was overpowering. The bikes poured over the top of the grade and were led to the parking areas. Soon they were overflowing.

Mike Jones and his old lady were standing alongside on the balcony. Leroy smiled at them and prepared his words. With the bikers approaching in the background, he faced the camera and told of the reason for the meeting, the numbers, who they were, all the typical who, what. where, why, and when that good reporters make sound interesting.

As the final bikes pulled in Mike raised his hand like the Pope presiding over his people and they were quiet.

For the next fifteen minutes there were talks by local dignitaries and group spokesmen. Jim pretended to tape the whole thing, but the camera was off. Nobody at network really gave a good rat's ass about the local politicians. They wanted interesting stuff.

And they got it.

Treb Lincoln appeared all of a sudden. Mike was getting ready to introduce one of the politicians when he saw Treb coming out of the crowd. There was a nod and Mike introduced him instead. Leroy could see it was planned. He also knew Treb was taking a hell of a chance. But the newsman knew there was a story here. He told Jim to turn the camera on the audience while Jack taped what was said. Mike started the introduction.

"If there is any one man who has done more than any other to repeal the helmet laws and brings bikers together it is this man. He has stopped outlaw bike clubs from warring, and he is the national coordinator and originator of the upcoming national helmet law protest to be held this fourth of July in Washington, D.C. We didn't introduce him before because he wanted to remain behind the scenes, but we want to bring him up anyway." He waited three seconds.

"Ladies and gentlemen, Treb Lincoln."

He stepped aside and Treb took his place at the mike. The bikers applauded. Many of them didn't know who he was, but they could see he was a biker and they were tired of listening to a bunch of stuffed politicians in white shirts and ties. They wanted to listen to their own.

"The time has come for bikers to act like brothers and fight the bullshit that the government is trying to feed us."

Treb knew he was going to have to get them riled up fast and on his side. The police would know who he was pretty soon, and if there were any Omega Squad men out there, which he was sure there were, he wanted the bikers angry so he could hide in them.

"We got to make them drop the federal regulation by a show of togetherness and force in Washington, D.C. And then we are going to get them to drop the laws in every state the same way."

He waited while the bikers screamed and whistled their approval.

"The date is July fourth. We will leave the west coast in a pack on July first and make the trip across America on the interstates. You can meet us anywhere you like. All bikers are welcome. We are not going to take the horseshit from them any more, are we?" The bikers cheered.

"Are you with me?"

The cheers got louder.

"Will we win?"

The crowds went nuts.

Just then two policemen on the platform came up behind Treb and grabbed for him. He turned and swung at them and then jumped over the rail. It was fifteen feet to the ground, but the people down there reached for him as he landed and cushioned the fall. Then the bikers all started to run. It was a madhouse. People ran everywhere. All the bikers had the same thought at the same time. They were covering their man.

Treb was safe and he knew it.

Leroy stayed on the balcony with both cameras shooting every foot they could get. He knew that the news media was being used, and he knew he was being used the most.

What worried him was the fact that he liked the guys who were using him, and liked helping them. They made news for him.

Now the national could be aired on his broadcast because of the hassle it caused at this rally. They knew it and so did he.

He wondered if maybe they weren't a lot smarter than he gave them credit for.

Then his thought shifted to the tapes. He had to

get them to New York immediately. First he was going to edit them here at the Madison affiliate so he could keep the good stuff in. It was a cinch.

Chapter 34

Whoever the hell invented snow has got to be the sickest person there ever was. I mean really. Look at this stuff. It's cold, it's slippery, and it covers things like rocks and bottles in the road so you can't see them.

I figured that by as late in the year as Lincoln's birthday the damn snow and ice would have been long gone. Hell, if I'd known it would still be around I would have set the pre-planning meeting for later, like March, in Florida.

Hell, I still don't know why I said Kansas instead of Florida anyway. Just because motorcycle week wasn't until March, we could have still had plenty of time to get the word out about the national.

Oh, well. That's all a bunch of sour grapes

anyway. I knew that the only thing bugging me was that I had to go through all this ass deep snow just to get to the national planning meeting.

It was my own dumb idea anyway.

I thought about Karen sitting back at her mother's place in

Georgia. We had spent months there after the Madison protest and she was getting along real good. When she learned that her father had died, she was curiously happy, which made me feel a little uneasy, but what the hell, I was never one to butt into family business.

It was almost like being home with my own family. They treated me fine and we really enjoyed it. When I told her I had to leave she got a little pissed, but she got over it soon. Oh damn. The snow was hitting harder now. Why did I have to head over the Smoky Mountains anyway? I could have taken the southern route, which would have been a little longer, but a whole lot warmer. As I sat there freezing my ass off I really wondered why I hadn't.

But then I was never a whole lot bright anyway.

Most of the cars had pulled off the road by now. It was a real blizzard. About the only people left out on the open road were truckers and one stupid biker. Me.

I had heard the term "whiteout" before, but had never seen one. It looked like I was in for a first. I wondered if Dick and Rom were having any better luck coming in from Denver. I talked to them on the phone and they said there was a little snow there, but it was fair after they cleared the mountains all the way into Kansas.

I thought about it for a minute and figured I was the only one stupid enough to be in the snowy mountains.

Why me, Lord?

I saw the lights of a truck in my rearview mirror and pulled off to the side to let him pass. I knew he probably couldn't see me and I could just picture some road worker finding me in the spring, under a pile of old snow.

After the big son of a bitch passed me I pulled back out onto the road. I could just see his tail lights and I tried to catch up. If I could stay close behind him it would be a lot easier to maintain a good speed, especially if I could just ride in his tire tracks. The snow packed pretty tight after being run over by nine wheels.

I could see it was working. The lights were getting farther apart, which meant I was getting closer. I closed up until I was about ten feet behind him and settled in for a good ride. It was about 60 miles over the top and down to where the snow wouldn't be too bad.

The snow kept getting worse. Soon all I could see was that one red light on the back of the truck. It was all that kept me going. We were doing about 35 miles an hour and I never even had to take it out of third gear. I was just watching the light and dreaming about nicer things, like Florida and warm pussies.

I knew when we hit the top because of the tunnels. There are a series of three of four tunnels at the top of the (I was going to say "old") Smokies.

When we entered the first one I almost laughed. In the lights of the tunnel, with no snow to block my sight, I could make out the name of the truck I was following.

"Old Kentucky Frozen Foods."

On the downward side we picked up a little speed, but I still didn't need to shift.

If I had, I would have found out my problem a lot earlier than I did.

As it was I learned it soon enough.

The snow had let up a little and I figured I needed some gas. We had been putting for two hours straight now. I don't know if the trucker saw me or not, but I waved to him as I pulled off on an exit. The sign said gas.

As I made the turn I tried to step on the brake. But what was this? My feet wouldn't work.

At first I thought they were frozen, but that couldn't be. I had on a set of long Johns, my Levi's, and they were topped off by a set of very heavy leathers. I never even felt cold.

Then what could it be?

I looked down and the problem was obvious.

My feet had frozen solid to the pegs.

It seems that following that truck was not as smart as I had figured. The wet slush that it threw up was piling up on my legs and freezing solid. The farther I went, the thicker it got.

Well, after two hours, it had gotten pretty damn thick. All I knew was I couldn't shift the gears, since the gearshift was frozen in a pack of ice too, and the clutch along with it. It was one big ball of ice below my knees, and that wasn't all.

It seems that my brake pedal and braking foot were also locked in the same frozen blob. I couldn't use anything but my front brake, because the control was on my handlebar.

I passed the gas station I planned on stopping at because I was going too fast. Then I started to do a big circle in the road as I contemplated my problem.

I aimed for the station again, and as I rolled in I started to pull the brake handle. When I reached the side of the metal building I reached out my free arm and put it against the wall. Then I shut the throttle all the way down and clamped on the front brake. The engine died and I was still upright, with my hand leaning against the wall on one side and my other hand holding the brake. If I let go I would have rolled forward and fallen.

I tried to call the attendant but he was out by the island putting gas in a car and didn't hear me. The snow was still falling pretty heavy, so he didn't see me either. After mentally kicking myself for not having a horn, I tried to call louder.

Do you have any idea how hard it is to holler when you have on a ski mask, ^ helmet, two scarves and a closed face shield?

Well, let me tell you, it is hard.

Pretty soon a highway patrolman came into the station. He pulled up next to me and stared.

I guess I did look a little funny leaning against a wall in the snow on my bike.

He got out of his car and walked over to me.

"Do you need any help?" he asked almost laughing.

Sometimes I don't like cops at all.

"Yeah, asshole, I'm frozen to the pegs. Would ya break me loose?"

I think my biggest mistake was the cussword. Without that he might have helped me faster. As it was he just walked to the front of the bike and looked it over real slow.

"Ya know," he said, "if I was in a spot like yours, I think I'd be a little nicer." He put his hand on his chin and looked like he was contemplating the world.

"Yeah, I'd be a lot nicer if I was you."

Boy, he had me by the soft curlies and he was pulling hard.

"Yes sir. I'm sorry. It's just that I have been here about fifteen minutes and I'm freezing to death. Would you please help me?"

Oh shit that hurt.

But it worked. He went into the station and soon came out with a hammer and big screwdriver. He used it like a chisel and in a couple of minutes I was free.

We walked into the gas station office and I bought him a cup of coffee.

After we laughed for awhile about the whole thing, and after I warmed up a little bit, I decided it was time to hit the road again. This time I vowed to stop riding if the snow got too bad, which I prayed it wouldn't.

I guess the guy upstairs figured I paid ray dues though, because that was the end of the snow. In a few hours it was almost nice enough out to ride without a jacket. As I pulled into Arkansas it was 70 degrees. The rest of the ride to Kansas would be all right.

Chapter 35

Dick opened his eyes slowly after lying still and just listening for a few minutes. It was an old habit he learned while in the special forces in Nam. Never move until you know what is going on.

He had hated it over there. As soon as the Army found out he had a sixth degree black belt they started hounding him. Finally he agreed to teach. That was what he thought anyway. Actually they soon had him over in the jungles, killing to stay alive.

As he lay there in a state of semi-consciousness he thought back to that last patrol. It wasn't what he wanted it to do, but a lot of times his mind would wander back there.

Three of the original 10 men he had trained were still with him then. They were all Vietnamese and they all wanted to live as much as he did. Some officer had decided that if the Army didn't know what was happening on the other side of hill 819 they would not be happy, so Dick and his men were ordered out there. Dick was supposed to be going home that day, but since the supply truck had been knocked out he wouldn't be leaving until another one could be brought up.

Kimli shouted something in his native tongue just as a sniper shot was heard. Dick didn't want to look, but he knew what he would find anyway. Those damn snipers were good at their job, that was for sure. They always aimed for a gut shot so the living would have to care for the one that was shot. That could take a couple of extra men out of action.

As Dick crawled over to check out how bad Kimli was there was a pop like a mortar being fired not from very far away. He made a note to check in that direction after he saw to Kimli.

When he reached Kimli's side, he was almost relieved to find him dead. The rules were set and he hated them almost as much as he hated the Army itself. If Viet soldiers were wounded in the field they were to be forgotten until after the mission was completed. It was cut and dried. Normally that meant they would die and everybody knew it.

The two remaining men were off to the right in a low bunch of bushes that hadn't been completely wiped out by the flame throwers. Dick made his way over there and told them in their own tongue that they had to get that mortar before they could move on. They both just looked at him like a couple of small boys asking if they really have to eat all their spinach.

Dick started crawling toward the last position he heard the sound come from. It had rained and all the mud was mixing with the ashes from the burnt underbrush to make a foul slime that almost made him vomit. The worms that crawled through it topped off the sensation. There was a hell and Dick knew that he had found it.

As he slowly opened his eyes, he vividly saw the three men in the bunker with that mortar. He didn't have to keep his eyes shut to remember that. He slowly rolled over in his sleeping bag and lay there thinking about it.

The mortar was dug in. One of the three men in the bunker was talking on a field phone. The other two sat there talking and pointing to the tree tops. Dick rolled onto his back and looked up.

At the top of one of the few trees left was the sniper. Dick knew it was the one that had just killed Kimli.

Dick had lost a lot of good men in that two years, but Kimli had been with him almost a year and had helped him train three other outfits. He was almost a friend. Dick lay there in the slime and mud looking up at this guy with a gun and he wondered if he knew that Kimli had a wife and a young daughter. He wondered if that would have mattered to him.

Dick hated war and he vowed when he got out of this he would get away if he had to swim home. He was sick of killing and training killers, all to go out and die themselves.

He nodded to Wan and looked up at the sniper. Wan nodded. He knew what was meant. At a given sign he was to shoot the sniper. The other soldier just waited for Dick to tell him what to do. It was strange. A month ago he didn't even know Dick and now he let his life rely on him. Why?

Dick started to crawl toward the bunker. When he was about halfway out from the cover, and only 30 feet from the closest Viet Cong soldier, he turned and nodded. His partner started to come out too.

When Dick was less than 10 feet from the bunker one of the Cong turned and saw him. He brought up his rifle but it was too late. Dick was up and had a foot planted in his back before he could fire. The one near the mortar took aim at Dick's back as his partner arrived at the bunker and came down hard on the back of his head with his rifle butt.

A shot rang out and Dick hoped that it was Wan knocking off the sniper. All he needed now was to get a slug in his guts. When he heard the cry and the long falling thud as the sniper hit the ground, he knew it was.

The third enemy soldier was now on his back getting his throat slit. There was a look of hatred in the eyes of the man on top and Dick knew he couldn't stop him if he wanted to.

In seconds it was all over.

Dick could feel his throat tighten as he thought back on it all. He often woke thinking about that sight. As long as he was in Nam the thing that had affected him most had been the waste of lives, and that scene of a man letting the life blood flow out of another, when he didn't know him or why he was there, was the crowning thorn. That was all; he stopped fighting then and there.

On the way back to the outpost Dick took a slug in the leg. He was shipped out the next day, never to return, and even now, almost 10 years later, he still wondered what would have happened if he had made it back to the camp and they had asked him to go back out again.

He looked over against the far wall and saw Rom lying there. He wondered if he had been in Nam, or in the service at all for that matter. All the time they had spent together, about the only thing he talked about was motorcycles, women and booze, in that order. That was his whole life.

In a way Dick envied him the simplicity of it all.

The room was starting to get light now and Dick could see the bikes parked in the corner. They had been partying with the Sons of Denver for a month now and Dick was starting to get a little tired of it all. He wondered where Treb was and how he was making out.

Boy, ever since he met that Karen chick he sure did change, but it was a temporary change. He had seen it a thousand times before.

A guy meets a chick who treats him right and all of a sudden he's in love. After a few weeks, or maybe even a couple of months in an extreme case, the guy always comes to his senses and starts wanting to party hearty again.

He smiled to himself. Hell, he could think back on five or six times when he had thought the world revolved in the hips of some young suckie, only to find that he was ready to trade her in on a late model chicken plucker in a few short weeks. It's the way of mankind.

Yeah, when they all met up in Kansas he was sure Treb would be alone and it would be the three musketeers once again.

Now Rom awoke and looked over at Dick to see if he was in the same state. He smiled.

"Hey bro, how long you been up?"

"I just woke up," he lied. "Wanna get some breakfast?"

Dick knew that was a dumb question. Rom always wanted to eat no matter what the meal was called. It always amazed Dick that he didn't weigh at least 300 pounds, but somehow he always managed to stay about 15 pounds overweight and no more.

In a few minutes they had dressed and found their way out of the clubhouse. It was cool outside but they were getting used to that. After all, they had been there through December and January, and after January in Denver everything else would seem warm.

There were a lot of clouds but it didn't look like it was going to snow or anything. They hoped they were through with all that. All they could think of was getting their bikes and working on them a little and then hitting the road.

When you're caged up in a clubhouse for two months, a motorcycle is worth its weight in pure gold, or even Columbian for that matter.

That was about all that Dick and Rom talked about through breakfast. They wondered if it was time to break them out. They decided it was. After downing coffee and a couple of pieces of toast, they wandered back down the street to the clubhouse. They felt like a couple of kids. This would be the day.

To get their bikes out of the clubhouse they had to move out fifteen other scoots that were locked up for the winter. The later in the morning it got, the more bikers showed up, and since there wasn't a whole lot going on, the main show was the hassle of getting those bikes out.

Dick and Rom had been partying with the Sons since the Madison protest and they were like brothers. That was what had attracted Dick to being a biker in the first place and he had not been disappointed. It was a last stronghold of brotherhood in the old world meaning, and of male chauvinism, which he was a strong believer in.

He had never gotten into any deep philosophy about it, but every once and a while the thought would enter his head. It was like bikers were the old knights of the round table. There was a code of chivalry, just like in the olden days, and all situations were covered by a code. The code was unwritten, but nonetheless it was there, and men lived and died by it. Dick knew that code and he lived by it.

A cheer went up as the two bikes were finally extricated from the rest and they walked their bikes into the clubhouse shop for a teardown and check. Every year when a bike comes out of storage it is gone through and checked for faulty parts. It can save a whole lot of time and trouble on the road.

In less than an hour the bikes were two loose piles of old metal. Rom decided he wanted to paint his while it was down so he started sandpapering the frame. Dick was happy with the looks of his, but there was a click in the top end that he didn't like, so he decided he would replace his lifters and do a valve job on the heads at the same time.

For the rest of the day they talked bikes, drank beer, and did what had to be done. They knew their machines inside and out like a soldier knows his rifle. Each piece was checked, and if nothing else was needed at least they cleaned everything.

At about 10 o'clock they decided to break for dinner, and they walked in the cool, grey night to the diner. It was like their own kitchen over there. Everyone who worked there knew them and it was like home.

They sat down to eat and talked about their plans. They had to get to Kansas to meet Treb by Washington's birthday. They could wait around here until a week or so before the meet, and then hit the road, or they could take off and do a little light traveling first.

There was no real question. If the weather was close to being tolerable they were going to be on their bikes. It had been too long, and working on them all day had brought back the pride that a man has in his machine.

Yeah, it didn't take a whole lot of thought. It was boogie time. As they worked their way through a couple of hamburgers, they decided that tomorrow they would get on the road, then they would be where they belong again.

Tomorrow they would be alive again.

Chapter 36

John Trumble awoke early that day. He turned onto his side and looked at Ann. She was just lying there, eyes closed, and as vulnerable as anything John had ever seen.

He thought back to that day the bikers had come into their lives. The way the girls looked at them was unreal. Those two guys in that old beat up panel truck had done more to change his life than anything else. It wasn't just the girls, though. Hell, actually he had made out the best there. That sleazy Debbie that he was going with back then was a real slut, and that just showed him so. He had wanted Ann before, but she wasn't "worldly" enough for him. After that night he decided that maybe it was he who wasn't ready. That chick knew more than he ever dreamed about.

Not only that, but after that night she had made a complete transformation in his eyes. She wasn't pushy like that bitch Debbie had been. She did whatever he asked. When they needed money she went out and earned it as a waitress in the cafe. She even offered to turn tricks for him if he wanted, but he wasn't ready for that, in his head anyway. But the thought that she would do that for him made him feel deep respect for her.

He sat there a minute looking down at her and then he reached out with his hand and touched her nipple. She snuggled a moment like she was trying to get warm and then she opened her eyes. A small smile lit her face, like she knew something he didn't. Then it turned into a big grin.

"Hey, today is the day," she almost exploded. "It's your birthday," and with that she wrapped her arms around him and smothered him with a kiss.

"Hey, okay, cool it! Damn, wanna kill me or something?"

He acted like he was pissed, but they both knew he wasn't. It was kind of a game they played. He played boss, she played slave, only they both knew it wasn't really that way. They were partners. They both liked it that way.

Ann jumped out of bed and walked over to the closet. John just sat there and watched her walk. "Damn," he thought, "she sure is a sexy bitch!" Then he swung his legs off the bed too.

As they dressed Ann kept humming to herself. Whenever John asked her what she was so damn happy about, she would just smile and say she was happy because it was his birthday.

He went in to take a leak and brush his teeth. She just walked into the kitchen and lit the stove. He could hear her clanging milk bottles and breaking eggs.

"Pancakes all right?" she shouted, and he said fine.

"Hell," he thought, "I ought to have a birthday every day." He went back to the bedroom to put on his genuine badass biker boots that Ann had bought him for Christmas. He almost hated to wear them on the bike he had to ride, but a Honda 750 was the only thing he could afford, and at least it was a two wheeler.

He walked into the kitchen and watched Ann. She was busy with a couple of pancakes that were on the griddle. She was smiling to herself.

Then it came to him. Sure, it was his birthday, she must have gotten him that leather jacket he had been wanting. It cost over $100, but he knew she would find a way to buy it for him.

He stepped behind her and reached around and gave her a hug, running his hands up her stomach to her small, tight boobs. He gave them a squeeze. She leaned back and nibbled on his ear and then scolded him for bothering her while she was cooking.

He walked out to the livingroom and picked up yesterday's paper. Might as well kill some time, he figured.

In a couple of minutes Ann called him for breakfast. There, sitting on the table next to his pancakes, was a big box. She was so excited she pogoed.

"Well, damnit, come on, open it." He knew she was excited because she hardly ever swore.

He sat down and opened the box. The wrapping came off easily, but the box itself was almost unopenable, it had so much tape on it. Just as he was about to lose his temper she handed him a small box.

"Here, open this one first, it's easier," and she held it out to him.

It took but a second for him to guess. It was a buck knife. They just looked at each other as he pulled the black leather pouch out of the box.

He hugged her and gave her a tender kiss. He didn't know how he had gotten her, but he was sure glad he had.

He took the new knife and opened it. He loved the stiff action and the precise way it locked open.

Then he cut away the package.

Inside was the jacket he had been wanting for the last three years. It was almost too heavy to lift and the smell of mink oil was fragrant from it. It was all lined with quilted red satin and even had a fur collar.

On the back was a Harley-Davidson patch.

Hell, it didn't matter if he rode a Honda, he was a Harley man and she knew it.

It took a couple of minutes but soon he was calm enough to sit down at the table. He wore his new coat while they ate. She just kept smiling at him.

As he took a bite of pancakes he almost busted his teeth. He reached carefully into his mouth and pulled out a key.

For a second he just looked at it.

Then he could feel the water coming to his eyes.

On the side of the key it said "Harley-Davidson."

Ann smiled at him and she was crying too.

Chapter 37

Treb pulled up outside the motel and turned off his scoot. He could see he wasn't the first to arrive by all the out of state scooters that were parked there.

He made the same calculations in his head that he had made thousands of times before. To lock or not to lock. After considering the location (central Kansas), the number of scoots there (12 so far) and the probabilities of being ripped off, he decided he didn't have to lock it up. No one in this part of the country is going to rip off a righteous chopper with a whole group there. It would be suicide.

He took his saddlebags off and walked into the hallway. Halfway down the hall he turned into a room on the right. He stopped in the doorway.

It was a typical motel room. The furniture was

nothing special and it was obvious that this room was meant to double as a meeting room.

When Treb had made the arrangements for this room he had done it under the name of the Brotherhood of Bikers, which is a made up name, but what the hell, they needed something, and since he planned on skipping the tab he figured that sounded as good as anything.

A lot of the bikers who had worked so hard on beating the helmet laws all over the country were in the room. They were all taking big chances just being there. One of the biggest problems in working with large groups of bikers is trust. They don't have much. Bikers have been trounced on for so long they don't really trust anybody. Even if one looked like a biker he still could be planted by the heat. Since the word got around about the Omega Squad the trust had dwindled to almost nothing.

There were a lot of old friends in the room and some folks he had never seen before. Mike Jones was there from Madison and he walked over to say hi. Gizmo from New York joined him and soon it was like old home week.

Dingus was in from Virginia, Shady from Maryland, Crazy Joe from Colorado, The Wheel from Utah, Shane Harley from Washington state, and even Speedy from Kansas. They were all people who had fought hard to beat the helmet law.

Dingus, Shane and Treb were bench racing in a far corner when Playboy came in from New York along with Wino Willie from Georgia. The room was getting full enough to bring the meeting to order. Treb excused himself from the conversation and walked to the front of the room.

"Hey, hold it down a little." He paused a second or two.

"Okay, anybody not here that we are still expecting?"

"Yeah, Jewboy from Illinois and Sandra Rommel from Ohio," said Dingus. "They are riding together. They should be here any minute now."

"And Terrible from California," chimed in Shane.

"Okay, we have to get this thing started pretty soon, so I say we give them another hour and then we start, that sound okay to everybody?" Everybody nodded or said it was all right with them.

For the next hour they sat around shooting the breeze and trying to get an idea of what they should do. This idea of a national protest had been getting a lot of press and people might pay attention. They were only going to have one go round at this and it had to be right.

In the next room it was a whole other atmosphere. It was total silence. Three men sat around in their shirt sleeves with their ties lying on their discarded coats on the bed. The two with earphones on sat staring at the wall. The third one was busy turning dials on a big tape recorder.

They were with the Omega Squad.

And they weren't alone in that hotel. In the next room a biker by the name of Dave Harding sat talking with some of the bikers who had come from Utah. He was with the Sundowners, and when he heard that The Wheel was coming out here for this meeting, he talked his way along. He knew his friends in the Omega Squad would be grateful. At least he hoped so.

Treb looked up from his conversation with Playboy as a movement in the doorway caught his eye.

It was Dick and Rom. They made it. Treb jumped out of his seat and nearly flew across the room. It was good to see them and he let them know it. While they embraced, Dick looked around the room. No Karen. He was right.

They all went out to the hallway and talked about what they had been doing for the last three months. Dick and Rom talked about Christmas in Denver with the Sons of Silence and Treb told what it was like in Georgia with Karen.

Every time Treb mentioned Karen's name Dick would wince. He didn't know it, but he was jealous and it was getting worse. As they sat there just talking and passing time they started to relax. At last they were three again. They were protected on all sides. It was a good feeling.

They sat down right in the middle of the hall and lit a number of some Columbian that Treb had. It slowly passed among them. Every once in a while someone would come out of the room and walk over to take a hit. They started to get a little light headed.

The pot hit Treb the same way it always did. His mind was wandering all over the place.

He laid his head back against the wall to steady himself.

"Hey Mark, you hear what that dumbshit biker said about us?"

Treb sat upright.

"Who said that?" he asked.

Dick and Rom looked at each other. Who said what?

Treb sat still. Had he been hearing things? Was the dope stronger then he though? He didn't hear anything now. Maybe he was just hallucinating.

He laid his head back again and tried to relax.

Then he heard the voices again. They were talking about what was going on in the next room. Their room.

He waved at Dick and Rom to be quiet and put his ear to the door.

Dick and Rom looked at him oddly for a second, and then did the same.

There was no doubt about it. They were being bugged.

Treb signaled and the three of them walked outside. They had to figure out how to handle this. They couldn't have the Omegas knowing everything they were going to do, but they couldn't set up another meeting, there just wasn't time. Then Treb got an idea.

He knew there was a fink that had told about the meeting, and he probably was in the meeting. He had Rom go in and bring out one of the group at a time. As they came out, Dick would ask them point blank if they were with Omega. It was the fastest thing he could think of.

As they asked each one they would watch his reaction. If he looked confused they would tell him about the tap and have him go back in and pretend he didn't know about the tap and to go along with whatever Treb said in the meeting. They were going to set up Omega.

When Dave Harding was brought out he smiled at Treb. He was a little confused, but he didn't suspect what was going on. Dick looked at him severely and asked the question.

"Dave, you with that Omega bunch?"

He didn't know what to say.

"No man. are you kidding? Not me. I wouldn't work with them." All of a sudden he was scared to death. He was turning pale. There was no doubt about this being their man. Treb nodded to Dick.

Dick was so quick that Treb wasn't even sure he had hit him, but when Dave doubled over, he knew. Treb took him from the rear and held him. He talked real quietly into his ear.

"If you want to live to get out of here, you will do what we say," and he nodded at Dick, who threw an open hand into Dave's stomach.

"We are going back in and we are going to give some bad information to those guys on the tapes, you understand?" Treb said slowly. Once again he nodded at Dick, and once more his hand snapped out, this time into Dave's solar plexus.

All Dave could do was mumble and shake his head yes. He understood.

"If we find out you let any of this out, we will tell your brothers in Utah about your friends in there and you won't have a very long and happy life, you get my drift?"

As Dick planted three more fast blows into Dave, Treb made a mental note to call his friend Raunchy back in Utah. They had to know about this fink fast.

Then they walked back into the room, holding Dave up by the arms.

When they entered nobody said a thing. They saw who the fink was and they knew they would soon get even with Omega for the sneaking and messing around.

They all had the same thought. They were working within the system to change it and the system was breaking the law. That's justice.

Chapter 38

Ocean sounds drifted into the luxurious suite of rooms through wide open glass doors. Leroy stood like a statue watching as an incredibly gifted young broad in the skimpiest swim suit he had ever seen went bouncing by as if there wasn't a care in the world.

"Hell," he thought, "if I was her wearing that suit I'd have plenty to worry about. Like keeping it on for one thing."

He smiled hoping it would fall off.

He had been in Daytona Beach for two days now, and he was starting to wonder if maybe he had the wrong dates. Treb had told him that motorcycle week was the second week in March, at Daytona Beach, so he arrived a couple days early to get to know where the bikers would be going and such. But there weren't any bikers there.

He had called the network to see if they had heard anything, and they told him that the Mardi Gras was going on now and most of the bikers were probably there. The word was that a lot of bikers had shown up for it that year.

Leroy was starting to get a little bit worried. He had been taken up in the network because he was supposed to know the bikers and have tabs on them, when all of a sudden he has to call them and ask what they know. It was a little embarrassing.

He opened his briefcase and leafed through his notes again. They didn't make a whole lot of sense. Notes that he had gotten from Treb and Dick, along with additional info from Mike in Madison, showed the bikers would be meeting this last time, here in Daytona for final plans, and then the ride would take place on the fourth of July as planned.

But then this new info came in from a source he had managed to cultivate in the Washington bureau. They said that a very reliable source (someone in the Omega Squad) had it the protest was going to be on July 6th, and that all the bikers were going to ride to Washington in four packs, coming from the eastern seaboard in two directions, from Madison, and from Atlanta.

It didn't make a whole lot of sense that way, but that was what the Omega Squad was working on and they were usually right.

He hadn't talked to Treb in quite a while so he couldn't verify any of the plans that he'd heard, but he was still pretty sure that the original plan, to ride all in one big pack on the fourth, was the one that was going to happen.

The phone rang and he answered it.

"Hello."

"Leroy, this is Treb. How the hell ya doin'?" he asked, off the wall.

Leroy could tell from those few words that Treb was fucked up.

"Where the hell are you? I thought you were going to be in Daytona Beach."

"Yeah, we will be, but we decided to stop in New Orleans for a couple of days. Mardi Gras time, you know?"

"When are you gonna be coming in?" he asked, exasperated.

"We'll be there in the next couple of days, don't you worry," he hesitated a second. "Well, we gotta go now. See ya soon," and with that the phone went dead.

All he could think was here I am sitting in a room with nothing to do and this guy's out having a ball, and supposedly I'm the success.

He picked up the phone and hesitated.

"Hell with it," he thought. "If he can have a party so will I."

The desk clerk answered the phone.

"Hi, Jimmy? This is Mr. Makelray in 1122." He paused to let that sink in.

"Send me a couple of those tall hot ones you were talking about when I checked in will you?" He stopped again, this time a little longer.

"And have them sent right up," and he hung up. It was party time.

Chapter 39

There were people as far as I could see. Of course in my present condition I couldn't see too awfully far, but there were people there nonetheless.

A bottle of Southern Comfort was put in my hand by someone, and having a reputation of being a partier I couldn't pass it up.

Besides that, the stuff did neat things to my head. I took a long deep swig off the quart bottle and handed it back to Rom. He smiled (or at least I think it was a smile) and took a deep drink himself as he handed it over to Dick.

Dick was busy at the moment though. There was this little sweet thing that he'd fallen deeply in heat with at the last bar and he was in the middle of taking her panties off. Normally that wouldn't be a whole lot difficult, but since we were sitting on a curb in the middle of the main street, it was hard to be entirely nonchalant about it.

There were people dancing and partying everywhere and every once in awhile someone would glance down in their drunken state and see what Dick was up to. They never looked too long though, because there was some floozy with all her clothes off a half block away and she kept yelling that she was Lady Godiva and someone had ripped off her fucking horse.

Such language, and from a real lady too. You could tell without a doubt that she was female, and a whole lot of female at that.

Snoopy and Oaf squeezed out of the crowd and stumbled over to where we were. They told us that Raunchy and some of the other folks from the Sundowners had come in and were looking for me. Said something about a favor they wanted to repay or something. I guess it had something to do with that Dave creep that was finking on them.

But that's all too serious to think about now. This is a time for partying, and that's just what I'm gonna do. Fuck everybody. We will have enough shit coming down in the next few months to be serious about.

Then it hit me. I had become a biker because I liked the freedom to party when and like I wanted to and here I was worrying about whether or not it's time to party.

"Hey, gimme a hit off that bottle." I reached for the bottle in Rom's hand.

He passed it to me. I took a long hard gulp, feeling

the sweet smooth liquid explode in my head and passed it back to him. We both smiled at each other. Fuck the world. We are together, with brothers, and that's all that really counts anyway.

By now Dick was getting down to business. The sweet young Mexican chick had her panties hanging from one foot and Dick was pulling them off and putting them in his pocket. I knew we would be hearing about this for a long time after the Mardi Gras was over.

He set her down off his lap and laid her back on the sidewalk. While hundreds of partying citizens walked around and over him, he proceeded to eat her. Not just a little bit. No way. He was going down on her like she was a steak and he was a starving man.

Pretty soon she was groaning and moaning like she hadn't had any in a month of Sundays. I tapped Rom on the shoulder. When he turned to look at me I gave him a signal like, hey, let's get some of this too.

It didn't take two invitations. He started to unbutton her blouse and take her little titties out while I tapped Dick on the shoulder.

When he raised his head I made a shrug like, "Hey bro, ya wanna share?"

It didn't take any words at all. He smiled.

"Okay, you big son of a bitch, but I get in first." And with that he started unbuttoning his Levi's.

Lucy just looked up at us. She was so friggin horny she didn't care who did what just so they did it fast. She had been taking downers and man, every time I feed downers to a chick she gets a case of the super hornies. Lucy was no exception. The fact that we had been pumping some super Thai stick into her helped some too.

Since Dick was busy getting it from one end I figured I'd check out the other. What the hell, the Lord gave a woman two ends for a good reason, didn't he? Might as well make good use of them.

I moved around to her head and proceeded to get some. Rom was busy playing with her titties so he didn't care.

Dick and I were both on the verge of shooting our loads at the same time and Juicy Lucy was equally ready. The people passing by no longer just gave us passing glances. Now they were stopping and staring at us. Oh well, guess you don't see a double header on Main Street every day, huh?

I went over the top and started to get it off in her mouth. As soon as I finished I heard Dick groaning and knew he was right behind me.

All of a sudden I heard Rom moaning next to me, and saw that Lucy had been giving him a hand job at the same time.

That was a first for me. Three guys getting the same piece at the same time and in broad daylight on Main Street.

If you ain't a biker you ain't shit. I had read it on t-shirts and stickers, and now I knew it was true. If you are a biker you are.

We sat there laughing about what had just happened and listening to Lucy go on about how that was the first time she'd ever done three dudes at the same time.

Of course by now we didn't give a rat's ass

anyway. Once the shooting's over and the guns are put away it's time for a new game.

But the first thing we had to do was dump Juicy Lucy.

That turned out to be a lot easier than I had expected it to be. We were sitting there trying to light a damp doobie, which is harder than hell, when the guys from Salt Lake walked up.

"Hey, Raunchy, you motherfucker, it's about time you got here!" and I jumped up and dove for him. We wrestled on the ground for a couple of seconds, laughing like we had laughing gas in our noses.

"Hey, you guys been in long?" I asked and then before they could answer, "We heard you were looking for us. What's up?"

Raunchy smiled. "Oh, not much. Just wanted to thank you for that little favor. We took care of it. We owe you one."

"Oh yeah, well you're about to owe me two," and with that I picked up Lucy's hand and placed it in Raunchy's.

"Brother, this is Juicy Lucy. She just did us all three right here in the street, and she says it was a first. I imagine that you guys could use a little cleaning job on your pipes, right?" They all smiled. "Well, why not take her off and see if you can come up with another first."

Lucy just smiled the biggest grin I ever saw on a chick.

"Brother, you're right," Raunchy smiled, "we owe you two." Without another word he turned and the four Sundowners walked off with Juicy Lucy. All of them were smiling like they just found a new

$1,000 bill.

"Ah boys, ya know, it feels good to do good for others." And we all started to laugh.

We got up and staggered down the street. Even though my head was foggy from the alcohol and good smoke I still knew we had better check our bikes. They were about three blocks from where we were and we hadn't looked them over for about an hour. That was as long as I will leave my scoot alone even though it was locked up pretty good.

We stumbled down the street, until we saw a liquor store, that is. Then we made a slight detour. I picked up another bottle of Southern Comfort and Dick and Rom split a bottle of peppermint schnapps.

Yech, I don't know how they can drink that dreck, but that's their business.

We walked out of the liquor store and around the corner. The bikes were about a block down the street.

Then we saw it. Two of the bikes were there. One was missing. We all noticed it at the same time, and started running. Each of us hoped his own bike was still there, but one of us would be short.

It was mine.

I just stood there. I couldn't believe it. I kept expecting someone to walk up and say it was a joke, that the bike was right over there, but I knew they wouldn't. It was something that I had worried about for as long I've been riding. Here I am, a thousand miles from home, and no bike.

Not only that, but everything else was gone too. My sleeping bag, my clothes, and half my money. I never carry all my money when I party. It's too easy to lose it in a game when you're loaded. This time I wish I had.

Very soon the disbelief started to turn into anger. I wanted to kill whoever ripped off my scoot. It wasn't just my scoot, it was my life, and now some lowlife asshole was going to rip it apart and sell it. That's like raping my daughter, only worse. If they raped my daughter she would get over it. My scoot won't.

Rom and Dick checked the chain that was left there. It had been cut with a torch. Whoever lifted the bike was a pro, not some Honda jockey.

I sat down on the curb where my bike had been and rested my head in my hands. I had to decide what to do. I had less than $500 left to my name and nothing else. Rom sat down\ next to me and didn't say a word. He knew there was nothing he could say. Dick just wandered off to find some of the other bikers we knew there to see if they knew anything. It was a slim hope, but better than nothing.

After about fifteen minutes I still hadn't come up with an idea. All I could think about was killing. It was still hard to believe that I had been ripped off.

Dick came back with Raunchy and a mess of the other bikers and pretty soon Snoopy and Oaf showed up. We all stood there and nobody said a thing.

Raunchy went to make a phone call. He was calling his clubhouse to check with the club enforcer. He wanted to see who they knew down in Louisiana.

And then it hit me: The Banditos. They had chapters all over here and they were pretty tight with the Outlaws. I started to feel a little hope as I walked to the phone booth. In a couple of seconds I was talking to one of the guys we had been shot at with at the clubhouse in Kansas. As soon as he remembered who I was he got friendly.

By the time I hung up I felt a little better. He had given me the name of the president of the Banditos, and how to get in touch with them.

Now it got a little tricky. If they ripped the scooter we would have to play within their laws. This was their territory and we were outnumbered to beat hell.

Besides that, the Sundowners and the Sons of Silence were on good terms with the Banditos right now and I didn't want to alter that. We needed all the good will we could get for this protest coming up.

My first reaction was just to go to the Banditos' clubhouse and ask if they had ripped the scooter, but soon my head took over from my heart and we devised a plan. I hoped that it would work. Raunchy picked up the phone and dialed.

"Hello, is Indian there? This is Raunchy, vice president of the Sundowners from Utah."

In a couple of seconds he smiled at me.

"They're getting him."

"Indian, you don't know me, but my name is Raunchy and I'm the VP of the Sundowners out of Salt Lake City. Con Man from the Outlaws up in Kansas gave me your number."

He waited while there was a reply on the other side.

"Yeah, I know what you mean." He paused again.

"Well, to put it simply, one of our bikes was ripped off down here. We're partying on Main Street. We're here with a friend, Treb Lincoln, and some of the Sons of Silence, We were getting some good times behind us when we found one of our bikes ripped." Again he listened.

"Oh no, Indian, you got me wrong. We don't figure you guys ripped it, but since this is your territory we figured you might know who did, and maybe you could help us get it back. Both our clubs would be very grateful and so would the Outlaws. Treb is a good friend of theirs."

There was a long silence. Raunchy smiled. It was working.

"Yeah, Okay. We're on Second and Jombo. We'll be here," and with that he hung up.

He was smiling through his beard.

"I think they got it. They'll make a few calls to Kansas and Chicago to check us out and then they'll be over. Don't let on you think they might have ripped it or they'll get pissed. Just go along with whatever they say."

I nodded my agreement.

Then he added, "Hey, don't get an attitude. They didn't know it was your scoot. It's their business. Nothing personal. All we want is to get it back."

Chapter 40

Indian hung up the phone. "Jesus, what a pain," he thought and he picked the phone up again.

He made three calls. The first one was to verify Raunchy. He called the Sundowners in Utah. They said that Raunchy was the vice president, described him, and said he was in New Orleans. So much for him. When he asked about this Treb Lincoln guy, the president of the Sundowners got on the line and talked about him like he was some kind of a god. When he mentioned the national helmet law rally Indian remembered the name. Oh, yeah.

The second call was to the Outlaws in Chicago. He didn't bother calling the chapter in Kansas because he knew they were in a war. He called the secretary in Chicago. It was verified again. Treb Lincoln was to be treated right. He was under their protection in Outlaw territory, and they would appreciate any courtesy that the Banditos might want to extend to him.

"God damn," thought Indian. "This dude is big time," and he picked up the phone for the last call.

"Hello, Big Eddie? You guys rip off a scoot from Second and Jombo?"

There was a pause.

"A black chop? Yeah? Okay, hold onto it. Don't strip it. We got to give it back. He's a friend. I'll get back to you. Don't leave the office," and he hung up.

Now the whole thing was up to him. There were a couple of ways he could play it. He could say that they had ripped it off. Didn't know who it belonged to, and give it back. That was one way, but if the owner was a hothead there might be some trouble. No, that wasn't the best way.

He figured the best way was to go down and meet them. Tell them the word is out and they should hear soon. Meanwhile he could party with them and get to know them. In a while he would have someone call and say they found the bike. He would agree to act as an intermediary, and he would come out being a hero.

He figured he would wait until he got to know them before he set a price for his help.

He called Big Eddie and told him to meet him at Second and Jombo on his scooter and to leave one of the other members by the phone with the bike.

When Indian walked out of the clubhouse there were about ten of the members there, along with two prospects. He decided to put on a big show for the visiting clubs. He told them what was going on and that some of the visitors were pretty important, so to be cool. They agreed.

Indian was one of the few who didn't ride a Harley. He rode a 1946 Indian Chief. That was where he got his name. He thought it was funny that Bernie Gold would be known as Indian, but what the hell, it was better than going by the name of Bernie the Jew, which is what it used to be. He liked respect and somehow Bernie the Jew just didn't get it for him.

He climbed onto his stock Indian Chief and primed it with a couple of kicks. On the third kick it fired. He smiled. Those guys kept razzing him, but his Indian kept running.

They pulled out of the clubhouse in a close pack and soon they were skirting the outskirts of town. Mardi Gras always made a mess. He didn't like it. Made the town look too dirty. He had moved here from New York to get away from crowds and during Mardi Gras it was just as bad here.

He held his hand high in the air with one finger pointed up. All the Banditos behind him fell into a single line. The only way to get through this dumb traffic was to cut between the cars. He fired into the center lane and soon the cars moved over as they saw the approaching bikers coming down the white line. He loved the feeling of power, riding in front. It was a natural high.

They turned down Second. It was about eight more blocks to Jombo Street. He cut back to the center line and started to pick up speed.

Treb could hear the bikes coming from a distance.

It was like a second sense. You know by the sound how many are coming and what kind they are. This time he was fooled though, when the Indian pulled up. The higher pitched engine sound could only be identified by the longtime biker, those who had heard that sound when Indian ruled the roads so many years ago.

Treb stood there watching as they approached. He figured the big guy on the Chief was the president. It didn't take a whole lot of brilliance on his part for that.

Soon all the bikes were parked on the sidewalk, the only place available, and there were introductions all around.

It looked to Raunchy and Treb like the Banditos were a little surprised at the number of bikers there. They must have thought there were only five or six. They were wrong. When Snoopy and Oaf came back along with the Sundowners, Dick, and Rom there was a pretty good crowd. Now that the Banditos had joined them it was a big crowd.

Indian said they should get into a bar because his skin was sensitive to light without booze. Everybody laughed and they went into the nearest bar.

It was an old jazz bar that was just like a hundred others. The all black band was playing some jazz and the bartender didn't even look up when the twenty some-odd bikers walked in. He was ready for anything during Mardi Gras.

Treb, Raunchy and Indian found a booth and sat down, while everyone else moved tables together and chairs until they were all at one big table. The bartender brought pitchers of beer.

Indian started it all.

"I put out some inquiries, and we should have your bike back today. I'll need the serial number though," as if it were an afterthought.

Treb reached into his pocket for his wallet. He didn't care what kind of game they had to play, he just wanted the scooter back.

Indian went on.

"I think I know who got it, and if we put enough pressure on him it won't cost us much to get it back."

He was fishing to see what it would be worth. Treb knew for sure who had it now. All he had to do was figure what was the cheapest way to get it back. He looked Indian over a little. There in the dark, and then decided.

"Indian, I really appreciate what you're doing. I was without a friend here and now I feel like I've found a brother." He hated laying it on that thick, but he had to play to his soft spot. Raunchy picked up on the game too.

"Yeah brother, the Sundowners are going to be eternally grateful for your help in this. We have been awfully close with this guy, and would hate to see anything happen to him, 'Specially before this big national rally coming up. You guys coming?"

Indian hesitated a second. He was starting to like these dudes. "Yeah, we plan on making it. Let me see if anybody's heard anything yet."

With that he got up and walked over to the phone in the corner by the restrooms.

Treb and Raunchy looked at each other. They had guessed right and they both knew it. The guy was setting it up now. All they had to know was the price.

Indian hung up the phone and walked back to the table. He smiled at Treb.

"The bike was ripped by a couple of amateurs down by the docks. Our boys are having a little 'talk' with them and your bike should be coming soon."

Treb had judged right. He had played the right nerve. If Indian had come back with a story that the bike was ripped by a club, and they would act as intermediaries, it would mean they wanted some bread, but since the story was a couple of amateurs, he knew there would be no charge. It was against the outlaw code to help a brother for pay.

Treb smiled.

"Indian, I owe you one. I'll try and pay you back soon."

Indian just held up his hand in a magnanimous gesture and said to forget it.

Fat chance. He wasn't about to forget someone ripping off his scoot.

Just then one of the Banditos came in and Indian smiled.

"Your bike is here," and he rose to lead the way out.

Chapter 41

The road from New Orleans to Daytona Beach is wide open. First you cross the Lake Pontchartrain Bridge, which is a super long dude that makes you feel like you're never going to see land again, and then you plunge into deep tropical jungle settings, complete with tourist type places to stop and spend your bucks.

Treb led the group of twelve bikes on the fastest route he knew. It wasn't the best road, but it was the fastest. No cops and very few towns to go through. Just two lane road and lots of it.

The group passed through Biloxi and Mobile and before the sun set they were well beyond Pensacola on their way to Tallahassee. The miles were going good. It had been some time since they had any good riding and the warm gulf breeze was making this the first good ride of the year. Each of them was getting deep into his own thoughts. Treb was thinking how nice it was to have this kind of brotherhood. It was what hiking was all about.

Dick sat in his rigid seat and wondered if the good weather would last. The warmth was overpowering him after all the cold weather they had been through.

He glanced over at Treb and then in his rear view mirror at Rom. It was hard to tell which one was smiling wider. The throb of the newly rebuilt 1,200cc engine was talking to him through his ears and through his very being. It was beating a message into the soul of him. It made him wonder why everybody didn't ride a bike. It just didn't make sense that only he and these few friends knew the intense pleasure of it.

Indian rode near the back of the pack. He could have claimed his right to ride in the front, as the president of the club with the largest number of members in the pack, but he just wanted to ride, to be reminded what the basics were all about. He could feel the engine beating strong and hard under him and he thanked whatever God there may be that his Chief was holding up all right. He would be embarrassed as all hell if she broke under him with all these Harleys running so well. He took a lot of razzing whenever he would break, but he got to give a lot when a Harley would break, and he knew he got the better part of the deal since all the bikes were Harleys but his.

Treb looked up and saw one of the mileage

markers along the road. It said “Perry 17 miles.” He thought for a minute and no picture came to his mind. He had traveled this road many times, but this town didn’t have any memories. He figured it might be a good place to stop, and maybe next time he came through he would remember it.

The more he rode around the country the more he found himself doing things like that. He wondered why, and then, just as fast, he forgot it.

He held up an imaginary glass of beer to Dick and shrugged his shoulders, Dick shook his head very fast and furious. Yes, a beer stop was in order.

The next 17 miles flew by and soon the pack was pulling into the town of Perry. It was just a little burg, with a couple of taverns and of course the inevitable gas stations. Treb picked out the station that had the lowest prices and pulled in. The first thing they always did when pulling into a town was to gas up. You never could tell when some rookie cop might try to play big shot and run you out of town. It seems that more and more small town cops like to do that. It always seemed a little ridiculous to Treb, since bikers always spent money, but what the hell, if it made the pigs feel good, might as well roll with it. If you try and fight them they call in the fifth marines, or whoever else they can get. It’s a real standoff.

Treb walked into the head to drain his lizard. The walls were covered with typical small town graffiti. “For a good time call 355-8765 and ask for Mary,” or “John gives good head.” It was the same everywhere, only the names have been changed to protect the guilty.

He zipped up his fly and returned outside to

his bike. Rom and Dick were laughing about how they ended up with free gas by double talking the attendant.

He looked up and down the street for a likely bar. A new town was always a challenge. To pick out the right bar the first time was a real talent and Treb did it a little more than half the time, so he was ahead of the game.

About two blocks down the street there was a place called the Banana Room. He figured any place with a name like that was after the tourist trade, since this was the semi tropics. He passed on that one. Across the street and about a half block farther down was a little dive called Charlie's. That was what they were looking for he was sure. With a name like that there was little doubt it was a place for the locals. If they were after he tourist set it would be called the Tropical Inn or some other horsehockie name, but Charlies's place was for locals. He knew it.

After they loaded up again he swung his fist in the air with one finger held up. The rest of the riders in the pack started to kick their bikes to life. The roar of Harleys filled the downtown street.

Treb led the way out and headed toward Charlie's place. There was only one car parked in the lot next door and Treb led them in. When all the scoots were parked and locked, they walked in. It was dark.

Chapter 42

Margo Hamming hadn't slept well the night before and she really didn't feel like opening up the bar this morning. She had been stuck with the night shift last night and that always left her pretty damn tired.

She looked into the mirror behind the bar. "What the hell are you doing here?" she asked herself out loud.

"Hell, look at yourself, not only are you talking to yourself, but now you're so crazy you're even answering yourself. Christ almighty, you've finally slipped your cogs. Lady, you're nuts!" and with that she stood up and walked behind the bar again.

She picked up a bottle of Scotch and poured about a triple into her glass.

She had been there all day and the only customers so far had been a couple of alkys that were passing through town on their way to Miami. They had sat there for an hour and downed ten drinks apiece and then got up like they hadn't had a drink all day.

No matter how long she worked in the bar business, she couldn't get used to how some folks could drink.

She took her seat again on the business end of the bar and looked back at the mirror. She didn't like what she saw. When she had come to Perry two years ago, she was 21 years old and full of fire. She had been picked up by a salesman at a bar in Sharon, Massachusetts, and when he said he was heading for Florida she said she'd like to go. It was all that simple.

She stood up and looked into the mirror. "Hell, you're still good looking," she said to herself as she checked out her long, wavy hair that was so black it was almost blue. She cupped her hands under her breasts and marvelled at them poking hard against her white sweater. "Hell, even without a bra they sure stick out where they belong."

Yeah, she knew she still had the right equipment, but the reasons were all gone. She didn't give a good damn what she did or where she went.

It hadn't been the salesman dumping her that hurt the most. Hell, she planned on dumping him anyway, but it was the people that she met. No one cared. They all wanted the same thing. A quick roll in the sack and that was it. Nobody cared what she was like inside, they just wanted to play.

She knew that fact very well by now and it made

her about as cynical as a person could be.

Even Don, the guy who owned Charlie's, he didn't want anything except a good looking bar maid that he could trust. He let her live with him at his house and pretended to care about her, but she knew that every night she was working late he was out screwing some little teeny bopper. That was the way he was.

As she sat there deep in her thoughts, she heard a rumbling coming down the street. It was the sound of motorcycles and lots of them. She remembered when she had ridden a few times with an old beau back in Sharon. She really liked it but the guys that rode them kind of scared her.

From the sound coming down the street she could tell there were a lot of them out there. She got up off the stool with her drink in her hand and walked to the door. She looked out into the warm afternoon sun and waited for her eyes to adjust. The brightness of the day almost blinded her.

In a couple of blinks she was able to see. There was a group of about a dozen choppers and she could tell from two blocks away that they were outlaws. She hoped they wouldn't stop at Charlie's. She didn't want to hassle all those dudes. Besides, they scared her more than any other type of people. They never seemed to give a damn about anything. They just lived as they pleased.

A sudden smile crossed her face. For a couple of seconds she imagined herself as a biker's old lady, cruising down some open highway with her arms around a real man, and nothing but freedom in front of her. No more early openings and beds full of strangers.

Maybe they weren't a whole lot of nuts after all. She watched as they filled their tanks and wandered around, then she turned and went back into the bar. She liked the darkness inside. She didn't want to face herself again.

The thought of her riding with a bunch of bikers couldn't be dropped from her mind no matter how hard she tried. She kept seeing that vision of her and a foxy dude on a long, low chopper cruising the countryside and being free. For the next few minutes she filled in all the little details in her mind. The guys would be a little on the slender side and about six feet tall.

He would have blond, curly hair and deep blue eyes. He would be a fox, no doubt about it. And to top it all off, she would control him completely. Yeah, she thought, that's the way it would be.

Her thoughts were shattered as she heard the bikes starting up from the station. They were getting ready to take off. Now she was almost hoping they would stop here. She wondered if she should go outside and lean up against the doorway and try to attract them in, but then she decided against it. She might as well just dream.

As the bikes could be heard pulling out of the station she raised her glass to her lips and started to drink. As she took her second sip she heard the bikes slowing down. She knew it. They were pulling into the lot next door.

She jumped from her seat and ran behind the bar where she left her purse. She took out her makeup and started to put it on hurriedly.

Usually she didn't bother with makeup for the locals, but she had a dream and now she wanted to see if it would come true.

She put on her lipstick and brushed her hair as fast as she could.

She checked in the mirror. Her hair was fine, make up okay, and lipstick wasn't smeared. She brushed her nipples hard and fast to get them to stand erect. She figured she might as well go whole hog. In a second they were sticking out like two raisins.

She was ready.

Chapter 43

Dick walked in the door right behind Treb. It looked like Treb had picked a good bar for drinking. As he stepped through the curtain it was dark, but he could see with what little light there was that the place was empty. He didn't like full bars in strange towns. It usually made for a fight and Dick hated to fight. The rest of the guys pushed their way in behind him. They wanted out of the afternoon sun. He thought it was funny that bikers waited so long for warm weather, and as soon as it hits, they're running into bars to get cool. Hell, they can't ever be happy. He walked over to the bar. His eyes were getting adjusted to the dim light. Then he saw her standing behind the bar. He punched Treb in the side. "If I ever got in bed with that, I'd never get out," he whispered. Treb just smiled at him. Margo walked over to where the four biggest guys were standing. She knew from a couple years behind the bar that the big ones are the ones you want to make friends with first. They will handle the rest.

She approached Treb. He looked like a giant to her. She stood there at five feet two in heels looking at this six foot four inch giant. She was impressed.

If this guy was skinny he'd be my dream, she thought to herself as she spoke.

"Hi, you guys look thirsty. What'll it be?" she smiled up at him.

The guy next to him spoke first.

"Let's have a couple of pitchers.'*

For the first time she looked away from Treb and at the voice. He was about six feet tall, but he wasn't blond and he didn't even have blue eyes, for that matter. But there was something about him. He was built the way she liked her men, tall and thin, but he looked a little bit mean.

"Coming right up," and she turned to walk away.

Dick just stared at her. She turned as he noticed the nice tight pants and the way they cupped her butt. He wasn't an ass man, but he could tell by the way Treb was staring that he was, and he liked it.

"No you don't, brother, this one is mine," and he was all smiles,

Treb looked at him. "Okay if you think you can handle it," and he walked over to the pool table where the rest of the bikers were.

Indian looked up. "Hey, Treb, I put a quarter up for you. You're next with the winner. I wanna play you and see if you're as good as they say."

"Okay Indian, but I'll bet you don't even win this one, so I'll be playing Rom." He smiled a broad smile.

"Oh yeah? You think so, huh? Well I'll bet ya five you and I have the next game. I'll whup this guy in a minute," and he slapped Rom on the back good naturedly.

Treb winked at Rom.

"Okay Indian you got a bet, but let's make a ten spot. I'm getting a little low."

Indian nodded, still with the big smile on his face, then he hollered. "Hey serving wench, a little brew for the crew," and with that he started laughing like a hyena.

Margo looked over at the loud one who had just hollered. She didn't like his type. The guy sitting at the bar was more her style. He was quiet but confident. She filled a couple of pitchers and carried them to the table where Indian was standing. He threw a five dollar bill on her tray.

"Keep the change" he bellowed and then reached for her butt. She dodged out of his way and smiled sweetly back at him. She didn't want him mad, but she didn't want him grabbing her, either.

She walked back over to the bar.

She looked at Dick.

"He always as loud as that?"

"I don't know. We just joined up with him a couple days ago at the Mardi Gras. He's okay though."

She thought a second.

"You and the big guy good friends?"

"You might say that. We been together a few months now. Been in some good times together, and some bad. He keeps his shit together. Makes a good riding partner. Why?"

"Oh, I don't know. You just don't seem to fit with these guys. You seem more like a loner. They're all loud and putting on a big front. You just don't fit," and she turned to fill another pitcher.

"Well if you want to talk about not fitting, what the hell are you doing here? You look more like Miami Beach than Perry. How did a nice girl like you... and all that shit?"

She smiled at him. She liked him. He seemed like good people.

"You don't really want to know. I just ended up here after a little affair. I've been here two years. I think I'm ready to travel on, though. The small town life is getting to me."

All of a sudden there was a shout from the pool table. Dick turned and saw Indian laying a ten spot in Treb's hand. He didn't have to guess. They had hustled Indian with Rom's pool playing.

"He was sure lucky with that last shot," Indian was saying. Treb and Rom looked at each and started laughing.

"Yeah," Treb said, "he sure was lucky."

Dick turned back to Margo.

"You wanna go for a ride when you get off?"

She thought a second. It went through her head like a cool breeze. She could see herself on the back of a long and low chopper with her arms around this strong, mean looking dude. It was her dream of a few minutes ago.

But could she handle it? Dreams and reality are two different things. She learned that a long time ago. She had heard about how gangs of bikers take girls out and gang rape them. She didn't want any part of that kind of action. She decided to feel him out a little before she agreed to anything.

"Let me think about it a few minutes. I don't get off until six. I'll let you know in a little while."

He watched her as she walked toward the back room. "Damn" he thought, "she sure has got'a nice body." And he turned to watch the pool game. Rom was playing Treb. That was a joke game. There was no competition at all, but Rom was obviously planning on doing a little hustling. He was letting Treb get close to winning. When there was just one each of their balls left on the table he sunk his and the eight ball with one shot. He laughed like it was a joke, but Treb and Dick knew he could do it again, and probably blindfolded.

Snoopy had the next game and he started racking the balls. He knew how good Rom was, but they never bet. They just played for the fun of it. Rom was out after the Banditos and they were the only ones he would bet with at this stop.

Outside the local sheriff was checking out the scooters. He had gotten the word over the radio that a bunch of bikers were headed this way, but every year just about this time thousands of bikers passed through on their way to Daytona. He sometimes wished that Daytona was somewhere else so people wouldn't come through this nice quiet town on the way there.

He checked the license plates of the bikes. They were pretty scattered. The majority were from Louisiana, but there were a couple from Colorado, some from Utah, and even some from California. Boy, this was a real gypsy group. Just as he was ready to get in his car and take off he noticed something else. On one of the gas tanks of the bikes from Louisiana there was a Bandito patch painted. All of a sudden his attitude changed. He had been hassled by the Banditos from Alabama and he figured this was the same club.

The first thing he did was run a make on all the license plates through the computers in Tallahassee. He asked them to run the out of state plates through Washington, too. He knew that would take about a half an hour, but figured they would be in the bar at least that long.

He eased his car out of the driveway and cruised back to his office. He was hoping something would turn up against them. The last time he had dealt with the Banditos they had left him beaten up on the side of the road. He hated to think about it.

It all started out pretty simple. He was a patrolman with the Florida State Patrol when he pulled over two bikers for speeding. He was new with the patrol at the time and it looked like a simple citation.

After he pulled them over he got out of his car and asked for their licenses. He noticed the patch on the back of their vest jackets and as he checked their licenses for restrictions and wants he asked what the Banditos were. He hadn't heard of the club before.

For some reason they got upset about that. At first they thought he was kidding, but when they found out he wasn't they really got angry. He started to reach for his gun but they were all over him. They wrestled him to the ground and started to beat him, shouting that the next time he would remember the Banditos.

He did.

It wasn't so much the beating or the pain, but the embarrassment of being cuffed with his own cuffs and having to wave down a passing motorist to get loose. It was humiliating and he vowed he would get even.

That was almost ten years ago. He had stopped many bikers since then and never hassled any of them unless they wore a Bandito patch. Then he would do everything in his power to legally hassle them. He boned up on all the motorcycle safety requirements, like what year bikes have to have front brakes and how high the handlebars have to be. He knew them all by heart and he used them to their fullest advantage whenever he met up with a Bandito. They would pay for his embarrassment.

He walked up the stairs to where his office was and turned on the radio. His deputy was off duty and he didn't want to bother him unless he was really needed.

Margo was sitting next to Dick at the bar and looked pretty comfortable there. Treb smiled to himself. That Dick, when he wanted something, he went for it. No doubt about it.

He picked up the beer and downed it in a gulp. The cold, sparkling fizz felt good going down. If there was anything that Treb hated it was warm, stale beer. He wouldn't drink it. He could never figure how those guys could drink it that way on runs and when they were on the road. He would rather drink water.

He motioned to Dick that they needed more beer at the pool table, and he nudged Margo to ask her to get it.

They were just waiting for Margo's replacement to show up so they could go puttin'. The sun was still up and it stayed warm out. Dick was thankful that it was almost summer. That was his favorite time of the year.

The curtain at the front door was pulled aside and a girl in a short skirt was silhouetted against the bright outside. The pool game stopped and everybody checked her out.

She wasn't bad at all. About 22 years old, short red skirt and tight pink sweater. The clothes looked a little used, but the fit was about as perfect as could be. Her red hair hung down to her shoulders.

She stood there for a second while her eyes adjusted to the dimness. As they did, she got a little scared. All she could see were outlaw bikers. She had seen the bikes outside, but all the cut off Levi's and tangled beards really gave her a start.

She saw Margo sitting by the bar and walked to her side. She noticed that the guy she was with was also wearing a cutoff so she was careful what she said.

"Hi Margo. Looks busy. Been this way long?"

Margo smiled. She could tell by her voice she was a little on edge.

"Don't worry Carol, these guys are okay. They've been here almost three hours now and I haven't been raped but twice."

She looked at Dick and smiled. Carol relaxed a little and slipped behind the bar.

"Don been in?" asked Carol as if she was unconcerned.

"No, but he called. He said he'd be in around ten," and she turned back to Dick.

"You ready for that ride you promised me?" She was all smiles.

Dick just smiled back at her and stood up.

"Hey," he spoke to the table where Treb was sitting, "I'll be back in a little bit." And he started for the door with Margo two steps behind him.

Treb looked at Dick, then at Rom, who looked at Snoopy. Then they all looked at each other and started to laugh. But by then Dick and Margo were out the door.

The sun was just going down as Dick fired up his scoot. Margo fumbled a little, looking for where her feet were supposed to go, and when he showed her, she felt a little foolish. They were so high. When she sat down her knees were almost beside her chest. She felt like she was at her gynecologist's.

After they started riding she got used to it though, and after a couple of minutes it felt good.

Margo knew of a neat road she wanted to ride on and told Dick about it. She didn't bother to tell him it was where she and Don used to go skinny dipping, just that it was a neat road. It went along the banks of the Fenholloway River and it looked like a jungle. It was only five miles away so they decided on that as their destination.

Chapter 44

Sheriff John Martin sat in his comfortable swivel rocker and put his feet up on the desk. He liked it in Perry. He had been Sheriff for two years now and the people there were pretty friendly. He had heard that when a sheriff was elected to a town the size of Perry, with a little over 7,000 people, he would not be able to make friends because he would always be enforcing laws against the people who lived there. But Perry was different. The people didn't break the law much.

Oh there was the occasional speeding ticket, and the Markell boys were kind of hard to handle, but all in all it was an easy job.

His deputy was a big help too. Jerry had been the town hero about seven years ago when he graduated high school there. He got a football scholarship to Florida State. There he majored in law enforcement while he played ball.

When he finished he could have had his pick of jobs, since he finished in the top ten percent of his class, but he wanted to come home to Perry.

The Sheriff thought to himself, hell, if it wasn't for Jerry, I'd probably have to work for a living. And he smiled.

The radio came to life. The bikes from Louisiana were clean. They were the Banditos. He knew that he could stop them for illegal handlebar height on the Fatbob chopper, but that wouldn't be good enough to really hassle them. He wanted something good.

It wasn't until almost an hour later that the good stuff started to come across. And it was better than he hoped for.

"California 6R78659. Registered to Robert Bruce Lincoln. Wanted Los Angeles County, murder one. Police officer."

The Sheriff wrote the information down, but his mind was speeding.

Jesus Christ almighty damned... a fuckin' cop killer!

But his thoughts were shattered in another second.

"Nevada RM6754. Registered Richard Bondano. Wanted, Coconino County, Arizona. Assault on a peace officer. Interstate flight."

He didn't even bother writing down the small traffic warrants on the other bikes. He had what he wanted and more.

The first thing he had to do was make sure he had

his back covered. He called Jerry at home.

"Jerry, we got some bikers in town and they're bad dudes. There are thirteen of them. Two are wanted on some heavy warrants. One's a cop killer from California and another is wanted for assaulting a cop in Arizona. We're gonna need some help. Call me back after you call up some of the volunteer boys. Tell 'em to bring their guns." He waited while Jerry asked the questions he expected. Was he sure of the identity and did he want the volunteers to carry loaded weapons, and he told him yes to both.

After he hung the phone up he started thinking. He wanted to get them legal, but he wanted those Banditos more than the other guys, and if they just gave up the Banditos would be home free.

After about an hour he decided on his final plan. Jerry arrived, and he had ten volunteer officers with him.

In a town as small as Perry a volunteer police force was kept on call like a volunteer fire department. About the only time they were ever used was when a child was lost, but it gave the citizens a feeling that they had a hand in running the police department, and that was the real good that it did. Good community relations.

But now Sheriff John had a plan.

He told Jerry about where the bikes were and when he heard they were in Charlie's, Jerry got visibly upset.

"Sheriff, Carol's in there. She just went to work a couple of hours ago. Is she in any danger?"

The good Sheriff thought for a second. Why did Jerry's girlfriend have to work at the same friggin bar? Now he would have to change his plans.

What he wanted to do was to set up the deputies all around the bar with their guns out and then hope the bikers would try a shootout when he talked to them over the bullhorn. He figured he would sneak around to the back door just before it started and get a couple of the Banditos first. He wanted them that bad.

But not badly enough to endanger a girl, especially Jerry's girlfriend. Hell, he was almost like a son to him. He couldn't do that.

He started thinking again. The more he thought about it, the more he realized he'd better handle this by the book. It was too big to take out any personal vengeance.

"Okay Jerry, here it is. We got thirteen bikers, who are probably armed, in Charlie's. You call Carol on the phone and tell her what is going on. Have her make like she's going to the head and come out the back door."

He paused a moment, collecting his thoughts.

"When she is out and clear, we have the deputies all around the building all ready. Then we call the one out that is wanted for murder. If he doesn't come out, we just wait 'em out."

Jerry considered this for a moment.

"Sheriff, I know you've been on the job longer than me, but maybe I can help a little bit. There was something like this that happened in one of my textbook cases in school."

The Sheriff frowned.

"Well anyway," Jerry continued, "the police in Harpertown, Pennsylvania, had something like what we have here. They figured which way they would be leaving the bar and set up a road block, out in the open, where the police had the protection and the advantage." He paused.

Sheriff John thought about it for a minute. Yeah, it would be a hell of a lot better that way. Then he could get some of them Banditos.

He smiled at Jerry.

"Good thing you went to school. We'll do it your way. Call Carol and see if she knows which way they're heading. I'll get on the other phone and call the gas stations. Hell, somebody must have talked to them when they hit town."

He dismissed Jerry with a wave and picked up the phone.

As he dialed the number for Tom's Service Station on the main highway, his thoughts started drifting again.

He remembered vividly the way those damn Banditos had beat him to the ground. The way they kicked him as he lay there in the street. And most of all he remembered what it was like going to work for the next three years and hearing the name "Biker Baby," as they called him around the station house.

He would get them back if it was the last thing he did.

There was an answer at the other end of the line.

Chapter 45

Margo draped her hands lightly over Dick's shoulders as they cruised along the winding road that led back to Perry. It was better than her dream had even hinted at. The freedom of flying down an empty road with her hair blowing in the wind was beyond all description. She kept closing her eyes and concentrated on remembering what it feels like,

She leaned back hard against the sissy bar and thought of what it had been like down by the river. The way Dick had looked as he took off his clothes and swung from that long rope into the softly swirling water. He was built better than she could imagine with his clothes on. He had the body of an athlete.

When he surfaced in the river she stood on the bank looking at him. He had a wide, childish grin on his face. There was no lust, nothing dirty or unclean. Just that boyish smile.

"Hey, come on in! The water's fine," he shouted, and then he disappeared under the dark surface only to pop up a couple of seconds later halfway across the river.

She peeled her sweater off over her head and saw his expression change a little when her large breasts came into view. She had always been proud of them, but the look in his eyes made her feel extra good. She smiled down at him and began to unbutton her skirt. She stepped out of it leaving just her panties. Those were gone in a second and she was diving into the water.

As the cool water rushed past her body she felt fantastic. It was like being born all over again. It was a lot more than a bath, it was casting off the bonds of normalcy and doing what was free. She loved it.

Before she knew it she and Dick were on the bank. His clothes were the blankets and hers the pillow. For almost an hour they made love.

After they were through he lay back and looked at the sky. All she could do was look at him. He was a better lover than she had ever been with. She liked to think she had been around, but she knew different. She'd only known four men intimately and none could compare to this drifting biker.

After more minutes of just plain lying quietly and listening to the sounds of the night and the river, they got dressed. There was something between them. She knew it and he knew it, but neither one said a thing. It was just there.

Dick kicked his bike to life and as she stepped

alongside to get on, he took her around the waist.

"If you want to ride with me for awhile I'd like that," he said sincerely.

She knew he didn't mean just for the night. She smiled at him and got on the back of his scooter. She had a lot of thinking to do on the way home.

The Harley turned onto the paved road and soon they were headed back to Perry.

About three miles out of town the road joined with the main highway that headed east out of town. Dick turned left and started into town.

About half a mile down the highway he noticed a lot of cars on the side of the road. There were men sitting in a couple of them and he could see rifles.

As he rounded a sharp curve he saw a police car on the side of the road too.

He turned his head and shouted to Margo, "What are they doing, having police training out here tonight?" He laughed, and they headed down the road.

Margo saw John Martin and his deputy Jerry, but they were so engrossed staring at the bike as they passed that they didn't even see her.

She wondered what they were up to, and then, just as soon as she did, she stopped. All she wanted to think about was whether she should take off with this scooter bum that she had just met a couple of hours ago, or stay here.

There was no contest. She knew she would go. She didn't care if it was just to Daytona, at least she would get a chance to live a little. It had to be better than another week in Perry.

When they pulled into the parking lot at Charlie's

and got off the bike she noticed Al Tuttle across the street. She had dated him once, but all the bullshit about volunteer police had gone to his head until he was like a cop all the time. He never even got loaded. She couldn't stand him.

As they walked into the bar she wondered why he was sitting in his car across the street. It wasn't like him at all. Why wasn't he out on the road with the rest?

Oh well, she figured, that was his problem.

As they entered the bar nobody said anything. There were a couple of bikers asleep in a booth at the back, but other than that the place hadn't changed at all.

Then the big guy hollered from one of the back tables, "Hey Dick, we're gonna get some pizza sent over, you want some?"

Dick looked down at her, questioning. She shrugged her shoulders.

"Yeah, why not?" as they seated themselves at the table,

"Boy, this town is dead. Not a damn thing going on anywhere." It was Treb. You could tell he was bored.

"You bet it's dull. But what the hell, it beats a dirty campsite," chimed in Dick. Margo walked over to Carol at the bar.

"How's it been? Anyone been in tonight?"

"No. They're scared of the bikers," she snapped. She seemed very much on edge,

"Hey, anything wrong? You look terrible."

Margo had worked with Carol for three months now, and in a small town like Perry you get to know each other fast. Carol was a little weird, dating that deputy and all, but not as weird as this. At least not usually.

"Margo, come in the back room a second, will ya?" and with that she turned and walked through the office door.

When she closed the door behind them Margo figured it was just that she was on edge about the bikers and wanted to swap nights off with her or something.

"Margo, Jerry called me. There are a couple of these guys out here that are wanted. One is wanted for killing a cop in California. He told me not to be scared or act odd, but I'm scared to death. I'm supposed to find out when they are leaving town, and what way they're going. Sheriff Martin is setting up a road block. I'm really scared," and she started to cry.

Margo thought fast. So that was what all the cars were doing out there, and what Al Tuttle was doing across the street. It was getting pretty clear now. All she had to do was figure out whose side she was on and what she would do.

It didn't take a whole lot of figuring. She liked that Dick guy. He was definitely not the killer. She wanted to go with him. Besides that, most of the people in this town made her sick.

Of course, his traveling with a murderer wasn't exactly her idea of the smart thing to do, but she figured if it was like most cop things it wasn't as bad as it sounded. She decided to tell Dick what was going on and see where he fit in. Then she would play it by ear. She wasn't committed to anything yet.

Margo walked out of the office and closed the door. She left Carol in there and told her to stay put until the bikers left. She said she would handle it.

She walked back to the bar. Dick was sitting at the table with that real big dude. He waved her over.

"Margo, this is Treb. He's my best friend and more like a brother than any one else alive."

Then he turned to Treb.

"Treb, this is Margo. She's gonna be traveling with me."

Margo was stunned. They had said so little, but so much was settled. He knew he was right. She was going with him, but how did he know?

Treb started making some joke about a girl in every state when Dick noticed the look in Margo's eyes.

"Hey babe, what's the matter? You don't have to go if you don't want to, you know."

"Dick, that's not it." She searched for the right way to say the next part.

"You remember those cars we saw, out on the highway?" she didn't wait for an answer. "Well, they were the volunteer police. Across the street is one of their cars too. Somehow they figure there is a cop killer and some other wanted people in here, and they are going to wait for you to leave and arrest you at a road block."

By the time she finished, she was talking so fast it was hard to understand her.

All of a sudden the place got real quiet.

Treb was the first one to speak.

"Hey Indian, could you come here a minute?"

Indian was standing by the pool table talking with a couple of his brothers.

He walked over and sat down on a chair he brought with him.

"Yeah brother, whataya need?" He was smiling. You could tell he was having a good time, and Treb didn't want to ruin it, but he had to.

"Indian, we got trouble. It's not your trouble and you aren't involved at all right now."

He waited for a second while he took a long hit of cold beer. He needed it. "I am wanted for killing a cop in Los Angeles. Dick here is wanted for assaulting one trying to help me escape." He noticed Margo shoot a long look at Dick, but Dick didn't even move an eyebrow.

"...We don't want to get any clubs messed up with our shit. If you and the Banditos want to split, you have no ties. We understand." He turned to Snoopy and Oaf, "The same goes for the Sons of Silence and the Sundowners," he looked at Raunchy.

"It's our beef. We'll handle it." With that he got up and Dick did too. They walked over to a corner table and sat down. Margo went with them.

"Margo," said Treb, "you didn't have to tell us this, but we are grateful. It would probably be better if you went over by the bar or something. They could get you as an accessory if you know what we're doing and don't tell." He stared sharply at her. So did Dick.

"I've been bored to death in this town for three years. I don't care what is going down, I'm with my man," and she grabbed Dick's arm, "and hang whatever happens. I'm with you guys." Then she stopped a second and looked at them, almost afraid. "That is if it's okay with you guys."

Dick and Treb started to laugh. Hell, she almost had them scared of her for a second.

They knew they had to work fast and come up with a plan. They didn't know what to do. Then it hit them. All of a sudden it was clear as crystal.

Indian, Raunchy and Snoopy came over to the table.

Indian spoke as the president of the club with the most members present.

"Dick, Treb. We've been riding with you for awhile and you've treated us with respect. We want to do the same for you. Whatever we can do, count us in. That's what brothers are for."

It was quiet for a minute. Treb broke the silence.

"Margo, get us a few pitchers. We're gonna have a party."

She jumped up and ran to the bar.

"Okay boys, belly up to the bar. The drinks are on the house and that means everything!" She started putting the bottles on the bar along with plenty of glasses. In a few minutes everyone was partying.

Everyone, that is, except Treb and Dick and Indian. They were working on the plan.

It was a good plan and they knew it would work. Not only that, they figured it would be fun, too.

Chapter 46

Al Tuttle was sitting in his car as the sheriff had told him to do. After all, he was a volunteer deputy and he had to do his job.

He had his twelve gauge on his lap and he was watching every move the bikers made, which wasn't a whole lot since only one bike had arrived and none had gone.

Every twenty minutes or so a biker would look out to check the bikes, but other than that, no problems.

It did kind of shock him when Margo came up on the back of that bike, though. He wondered where she had been. She was a good looking bitch, but when he took her out she wasn't too impressed with his police stories. He couldn't understand it.

He was getting ready for his regular fifteen

minute call to the sheriff to tell him everything was all right when Margo came out the front door. She started walking straight to his car.

"Damn," he thought, "here I am on a big case and she wants to talk." He figured he better not say anything to her because it might scare her.

"Hi Al, haven't seen you for a long time." She smiled brightly at him. "How come you haven't been in to see me?"

He couldn't help but look down at her boobs. The nipples were sticking straight out because of the cold and he thought about all the times he wanted to grab them when they were having a date, but how afraid he'd been.

"Oh, I've been busy with my police duties. Actually I'm on duty right now, so I shouldn't be talking to you." He tried to sound official, but that was difficult because he was getting a hard on.

Margo leaned farther into the window until her lips were almost touching his.

"Aw, come on Al, don't be so stuffy. Just because you're on a big case doesn't mean you have to ignore me, does it?"

Now she was so close he could smell the perfume in her hair. How was he supposed to keep his mind on his job when this sex pot was leaning all over him?

It made him think about all those detectives like Matt Helm and Kojak. They always had a couple of foxes trying to get them into bed and at the same time they would save the world. Hell, if they could do it why not Al Tuttle?

He tried to surveil the parking lot but all he could

see were her boobs and her dark brown eyes staring at his. Damn, but she looked good!

"Hey Al, how come you never tried anything with me when we were going out?" She batted her eyes at him. "Didn't you like me?"

Now he was really on edge. If she had been like this when they had gone out he would have lost his virginity for sure. Damn, he was so excited he could hardly cover up his hard on. He twisted around in the seat trying to cover it with his hands.

"If you'd've told me how big you were," she stared right down into his lap, "I wouldn't have let you get away." Now she was really smiling.

"Hey Al, why don't you take your hand off there and put it here," and with that she took his hand and placed it on her boob. Then she closed her eyes and started to hum a little bit.

"Damn, Al, that feels so good." She lifted her sweater and put his hand on her bare tits now. "Why didn't you do this before?"

He asked himself the same thing.

If he'd been able to see through Margo he would have seen Treb, Dick, Snoopy and Raunchy steal out the front door and push their bikes around back.

There was also the matter of time. The longer he stayed there squeezing Margo's boobs, the farther down the street they got.

When they reached a safe distance they stopped pushing. They were beat.

There was no doubt in any of their minds that motorcycles were meant to ride, not push. After a couple of minutes they were ready to get started. Treb started his engine and Raunchy started his.

They pulled up behind Dick and Snoopy and put their feet against the passenger pegs. The sound of four bikes can be heard a lot farther away than the sound of two. Treb and Raunchy foot-pushed the other two bikes for almost a mile before they too started the engines.

Margo had told them of a small gravel road that wound around town and joined the main highway about thirty miles down the road. They knew that the man might try a radio call ahead so they had to get pretty far out before they would be safe. With the thousands of bikers coming into Florida the cops would be pretty hard put to stop all the bikes, so Treb knew they would be safe once they hit the main arteries of traffic.

They decided that St. Augustine would be the best place to join the flow, right on Interstate 95. There would be so many bikers on that road that it would be like hunting for a needle in a haystack.

When they hit the open highway they turned on the throttles and by the time they made their next gas stop it was over 70 miles down the road and less than an hour since they left.

With any luck they wouldn't be missed.

Margo pulled her torso out of the window of the car and smoothed her sweater. She had let that nerd play with her tits for over half an hour, and when he made a grab below the belt she figured she'd done enough. If they weren't out of range by now, by damn they could stay there. She wasn't about to let some little baby like this feel her up on a main street. No way.

She turned and walked away, back to the bar. Al

just stared after her.

"Hey, what'd I do? Did I do something wrong?"

She kept walking for a moment and then turned around.

"Yeah, you asshole nerd. Since when does a gentleman grab a lady's tits and play with them on Main Street, and then make a grab for her pussy? Jesus Christ man ain't you got no class?" She was almost shouting and poor Al was so embarrassed that he just wanted to hide.

"And besides that, your puny little dick wouldn't fill a needle's eye. I probably wouldn't even feel the little thing. Man, you police should bone up on your law books. There is such a thing as rape you know!" and she turned and strode into the bar.

Al sat there turning red. When three or four of the bikers came out and started laughing at him he turned the ignition on and hit the gas. He just wanted to get out of there.

As he went around the block he realized he hadn't called in. He had missed a check-in. He wondered why they didn't call him to see if he was okay.

There was no way he could have known that the Sheriff just put him there as an added precaution. The police knew which way they were leaving town and Carol was going to tell them when they left. Al was only placed out of the way so he didn't interfere.

But he didn't know that.

He picked up his CB.

"Hello Sheriff Martin this is Tuttle, over."

He waited a second, then the reply came over the air.

"Yeah Tuttle, everything okay there?" He sounded

a little bit bored.

"Ten-four Sheriff. Everything is fine. I'm sorry I missed the last check-in, but I thought something was going on and I didn't want to check in until I was sure." It was a small lie, but it was better than the truth.

"Okay Tuttle, don't worry about it. Check in in fifteen minutes ten-four?"

"Ten-four," and he put the microphone back on its hanger.

He felt a little better. At least he didn't get caught screwing around on the job.

He pulled around the corner and parked a half block from the bar. He didn't want to go through the razzing from those bikers anymore.

From where he was sitting he could just see nine of the bikes, but he figured the rest of them were on the end of the parking lot where he couldn't see.

He was wrong.

By now four were well on their way to St. Augustine.

About an hour later the bikers started to leave. He noticed that Margo was riding behind the guy on the Indian.

"Jesus," he said out loud, "I thought she had more class than that," and he made the call.

"Breaker for Sheriff Martin, this is Tuttle, come in?"

He waited a couple of seconds and the reply came.

"Hello, Sheriff? This is Tuttle, the bikers are leaving now. They are heading west out of town on route three ninety. Any instructions?"

"No Tuttle, we know they... wait a minute! West? Don't you mean east? They are heading east, aren't they?"

Al sat up straight. It was the first time anyone ever got excited about something he said.

"No sir. Sheriff, they were heading west as could be. They just passed the city limits, traveling fast. You want I should stop 'em?"

The Sheriff had a terrible vision of Al Tuttle with a shotgun being run over by a bunch of choppers.

"No Al, you stay where you are. On second thought you better go into the bar and check with Carol, see if she's all right. She was supposed to let us know when they were leaving." "Ten-four Sheriff. I'll call you back and let you know." At last he had a real job to do. He drove the car into the parking lot and ran into Charlie's.

As far as he could see it was empty. There were a bunch of empty bottles on the bar and on the floor and it looked like a real party had gone on. He kicked some of the empties out of the way as he walked into the hall that led to the offices and the Johns.

In the office he found Carol. She was sitting in the chair by the desk and she was tied up.

For a second he was stunned. This was the first time he was ever confronted with a real crime and he was scared. He didn't even stop to untie her. He ran out to his car and turned on the CB.

"Hey Sheriff! Carol's been tied up!" He didn't use the ten code or anything, he was so confused.

The Sheriff came on the line.

"Okay Al, what did she say when you untied her?"

Al hesitated a minute.

"Untie her? Oh, I forgot to." He dropped the microphone and ran back into the bar.

The Sheriff just shrugged. "What an asshole."

Sheriff John Martin was down. He really wanted those crumbs and now some other sheriff would get them. He picked up the police radio and called the sheriff in Hampton Springs.

"Sheriff Harper, this is John Martin down in Perry." He waited impatiently while the sheriff of Hampton Springs exchanged pleasantries with him.

"Well Sheriff, we had some suspects in a bar up here and when we set up a roadblock on the east end of town they must have found out about it. They went west instead. They will be coming through there in a few minutes. There are thirteen bikers and they are all on choppers. You better get set up."

"Aw, Sheriff Martin? What are these here boys wanted for anyway?"

"One of them, with California plate 6R78659, is wanted for murder, one count, police officer." He let that sink in. "His name is Robert Lincoln, wanted in Los Angeles County. Another one is Nevada license RM6754. Dick Bondano. Wanted in Arizona for felonious assault on a peace officer. Both of them should be approached with extreme caution."

By then The Banditos and Oaf had just about made it to town. They knew something would be happening pretty soon so they throttled down a little. Didn't want some trigger happy deputy blowing their heads off before they realized they had fucked up.

Indian held up his hand and motioned the rest of the bikes to slow down. As they pulled into the bright spotlights on the deep Florida overgrowth he felt like he was playing a part. He was The Wrongfully Picked-on Biker. He had the role down cold.

When they were within range of the flashing blue lights and spotlights he halted the group.

Then he shouted.

"Hey man, we ain't done nothing. We aren't armed or anything. Don't start shooting or anything." He waited for their reply.

A loudspeaker drummed out of the darkness.

"Okay, this is the sheriff. You are covered by my deputies. If you can hear me hold your hand in the air." Indian raised his hand.

"Pull your bikes up into the light and stop in front of the cars. All of you. No stragglers. We are watching you.'*

Indian nodded to his men to do as they were told. He had a slight smirk on his face.

They pulled the bikes into the island of bright light.

Indian didn't feel a whole lot good about this, but it was kinda funny knowing they were pulling one over the cops so he was almost giddy inside. This was a neat game. The kind he liked to play. He knew the rules and the police didn't.

Ever since he was a little kid he had always been on the receiving end of the police night sticks and now, in his own way, he was getting back at them. He was making them look foolish.

He smiled at the man, holding his hands high in the air.

"Yessir, whatever you want. Should we turn off our motors?'*

The sheriff nodded yes and then walked over to the group.

"Put your hands on the hood of the cars. All of you." He kept his gun trained on them while the other officers searched them. Then he started to check out the license plates.

The farther down the line of bikes he got the worse he felt. There wasn't one bike from California or Nevada. They were all from Louisiana, Utah and Colorado. Not a one from the wanted states. He started to boil. That fucking sheriff in Perry had made him look like an ass to these bikers.

The deputy walked over and told him they were all clean.

"You boys seen any other choppers out there on the road?"

He didn't really expect an answer, but he figured he might as well ask.

Indian looked almost convincing when he replied.

"Oh no, sir, not a one. We were up in Perry having a few brews but that was all. Now we're heading back home to New Orleans. Why, did we do something wrong?"

The sheriff shook his head.

"No, I'm sorry about this. We heard there were some wanted men on choppers coming through and we had to check. You can go on your way." The next part really hurt him.

"We are sorry if we inconvenienced you."

The bikes started up and as soon as they were out of earshot they were laughing like all hell. They had pulled it off without a hitch.

Margo sat on the back of Indian's bike and laughed the hardest. She couldn't remember having this much fun in her whole life.

Now she looked forward to seeing Dick when they hit St. Augustine and having a real party.

Chapter 47

As we walked into the darkness of The Godfather, which was a bar just off the interstate in St. Augustine, we saw we had misjudged the place. Since I had done the picking it was my fault and I was ready to take my razzing. There were plush upholstered chairs, done in a deep rich red velvet placed just right around dark wood tables. The clientele were wearing ties, and the bartender even wore a red velvet vest.

Yeah folks, there was no doubt in my mind: I had fucked up for sure.

Dick, Raunchy and Snoopy looked the place over and then they all smiled at me at the same time. Yeah, they were going to give it to me real slow. We fit in this place about as much as Maurice Chevalier belonged in a biker clubhouse.

From the looks of the place it was way overpriced to begin with and the looks we were getting from the barkeep were just plain indecent.

It was probably the looks that we got from the customers that did the trick though. All I could think as I walked up to the bar and waited for the bartender to take my order was, "Where the hell do they get the right to look down their noses at us? Fuck'em."

Dick walked over and sat down.

"Kinda quiet in here ain't it bro?" and he smiled a real broad smile.

"Yeah, it sure is. Here," I flipped him the change from my drink, "why don't you put on some of that funky Hawaiian music?" He smiled and ambled to the silent juke box.

"And make it loud," I said.

In a moment the sounds of "School's out" by Alice Cooper were filling the place. Dick reached behind the box and suddenly the sound filled every crevice in the room.

Dick came back to the bar and took his place between me and Raunchy. Snoopy had gone back into the head.

We listened to the hard rock sounds and started to feel a little more at home. When Snoopy came out of the John he had a big smile all over his face. We asked him what the hell he was so happy about. He just looked at me and laughed a little.

"Brother, let me put it this way. You definitely did not fuck up when you picked this as a place to wait for the others. I don't care if it is a little uncomfortable," he shrugged his shoulders like the place was cramped, "I think we are going to like it here."

The three of us questioned him but all he would say was, we would see. That was it.

He was right. We soon saw.

The bartender went to the juke box and turned it off. We were about to say something about it when Snoopy put up his hand. He was still smiling.

"Wait a minute. Let him kill the music. I'm sure there will be more in a minute."

The bartender ducked back behind the bar and flipped a switch on a panel next to the cash register. The lights in the club went dark. When he flipped another switch, music started to come out of two large speakers next to the stage. I could tell it was a tape because of the loud hissing sound.

One more switch was flipped by the red-vested barkeep and the red velvet curtain against one wall pulled itself aside, and the stage behind it was floodlighted.

And then we saw why Snoopy was smiling. From almost out of nowhere a little brunette appeared. She was twisting and turning to the music. If she wore what she had on at the beach she would probably be arrested. Even though there are laws in Florida about topless and bottomless dancing, the two little covers she was wearing were just about a half inch too small to cover her nipples and the G-string she wore was less than an inch at the widest and just flat disappeared between the cheeks of her very nice tush,

Snoopy had taken up a prime seat at one of the front tables next to the stage. By now we had figured out what he was so damn happy about. I picked up my drink and joined his table. Snoopy was too busy watching the dancer's boobs bouncing up and down to even notice me. Pretty Soon Raunchy and Dick were seated at the table with us. There was no doubt about it, this place was all right.

The dancer, whose name was Mary (we could tell because it was tattooed on her left cheek inside a little rose) danced like we were the only ones in the place. That was probably due to the fact that all the other nerds in the place were acting like she wasn't there. I guess they were embarrassed to be seen staring or something. Didn't bother us a bit though. We loved it.

After the first song ended she stood there waiting for the tape to come back on. She smiled down at us like we were old friends then she squatted on the stage next to our table.

"Where you all from, around here?"

I hardly heard a thing. I was too busy looking at what the posture did to her G-string. It was positively obscene.

Pretty soon Snoopy and Mary were in deep conversation. Dick and Raunchy and I didn't hear a thing. We just kept staring at that nice little jellyroll looking us in the face. I couldn't have even told you what color Mary's eyes were, but I can tell you she has a small mole on the inside of her thigh.

Damn, that was some outfit for sure.

The music started again and she stood to dance. It was like we were the only ones there. It was a real trip.

I thought about Indian and the rest of our group and figured they couldn't be in until very late that night. And if they stopped to sleep tonight it would be tomorrow before they got here, so there was plenty of time.

Since none of us knew St. Augustine too well we had decided to meet in the parking lot of the Holiday Inn. We knew there had to be one of those in town because they were everywhere

After Mary had danced to a couple of numbers a replacement came on stage. She was a little stuck up. She danced like we weren't there most of the time and like we were scum the rest of the time. Besides that, her costume wasn't anything compared to Mary's.

Mary came out from backstage wearing a robe and walked straight to our table. She sat down when offered a chair and soon we were partying pretty damn good.

After awhile we walked out to the parking lot and gave her some good coke to get her up. I never used the stuff myself, but I knew what it did to women. Good for what ails 'em.

By the time she had to go back on stage she was loaded to the top. We topped off a couple of toots with a couple numbers of dust. That was all she needed. By the time her music started she was in another world. We all sat at our table as she played to us like we were the only ones there. We loved it.

The booze was starting to get to me a little and a couple of the other guys had snorted a little snow themselves so they were feeling no pain either. When Mary's second number started she was so far into her dance that she was oblivious to everything.

Then Snoopy started into it.

"Hey Mary, why don't you take those pasties off? Hell, we all seen nipples before."

Mary looked out like she was dancing in a fog. I don't think she heard what he said. When she bent down close Snoopy just reached up and popped one off. She squatted there for a beat and looked at him, and then smiled.

"Yeah," she said out loud, "why the hell not?" and she pulled the other one off and threw it on our table.

I noticed a little movement out of the corner of my eye and saw the bartender sidling down to a guy who was sitting at the end of the bar. After a couple of seconds the guy walked over to the far side of the stage and signalled for Mary to come over there.

She got a big smile on her face and started to dance his way, swaying her hips like she was trying to seduce him.

He didn't look like he was going for it. She bent down and he whispered something in her ear. She just looked at him and then over at us. Then she straightened up and danced back over to our table.

"Hey fellas, that guy is the owner and he wants to put the pasties back on. He says he can lose his license if a cop comes in now."

Raunchy stood up. "Hell, if that's the only problem I'll watch the door for cops," and he started for the door.

Then Snoopy told her to take it all off since the door was being watched anyway. What could it hurt?

She was so fucked up that if we had told her to jump off a bridge she probably would have done it. She stared at Snoopy for a second and then she stripped her G-string off and flung it in my face.

The owner of the place got up from his seat at the bar again only this time he didn't walk over.

"Okay Mary, get off the stage. We don't want any trouble."

She flipped him off.

"No man, I wanna dance for my friends." And with that she started to do the splits right in front of us.

I think I fell in heat about then. By the looks of Snoopy he was long gone and Dick was in the same shape.

The boss man started shouting then.

"If you don't get off that stage and into some clothes, you're firedl" His face was deep red and his fists were firmly on his hips. He was obviously at the boiling point.

"Well this for you," said Mary, and she turned around and bent over, spreading her cheeks as wide as she could.

"Fuck you, short dick," she smiled. "You can't fire me because I quit" and she walked off the stage as naked as a plucked .bird and twice as cocky.

The three of us sat there watching the owner. He was boiling, that was for sure.

Mary came out of the dressing room wearing a long coat and carrying an overnight bag.

"Hey, you guys give me a lift? I haven't got a car,"

Jesus Christ, does the pope shit in the woods, is a bear catholic? You bet your sweet little butt we'll give you a lift (as a matter of fact, that's what she had just done).

Raunchy was outside having a smoke. When we walked out the door he smiled at us. When he saw Mary with us his smile turned into a chuckle. He didn't ask any questions. He didn't have to.

Mary walked over to the bikes.

"Which one is yours?" she asked Snoopy.

He pointed to it.

"Can I ride with you?"

"If you promise you won't rape me," he answered. Mary looked very serious.

"No promises. These things turn me on," and then she broke into a broad smile. We all laughed.

This chick was going to be all right.

We started our bikes and set out to look for the Holiday Inn. As we swung out onto the highway I pulled up next to Snoopy's bike and asked Mary where it was.

She said she knew, but asked if we would mind stopping at one more bar first. After all it was only ten o'clock and a little early for beddy-bye.

After a little eye talk, which is the way bikers communicate on the road, we agreed. One stop. Maybe we would get a couple more girls.

We rode down the street and looked for a promising bar.

Chapter 48

Indian led his group out past Hampton Springs about ten miles and then made a right onto State Road 14. The road wasn't in very good condition what with all the potholes and rubbish, but it was the shortest way to get up to Interstate 10 about 20 miles north of where they were.

His Indian was running pretty good and the only regret he had was running the stock seat. It was great for one-up riding, but with Dick's girl on the back, it was uncomfortable as hell. He decided to make her ride with one of the other dudes at their next stop.

When they hit I-10 they aimed the bikes eastward and soon they were trucking through some pretty dismal looking swamp land on their way to Jacksonville about 80 miles off. From there it was just a short 25-mile ride to St. Augustine. No problem.

They pulled off the Interstate for gas in Hopewell. It was a small town and Indian hoped there would be some gas stations open. He was running pretty low.

The two stations at the offramp were closed so they started around some of the back roads hoping to find a gas station that was open.

It was no use. There were none.

They rode back to the station nearest the interstate and stopped their bikes. As they expected, in a couple of minutes a police car pulled into the station alongside them. No one was worried. Whenever a bunch of choppers stop in a town that size there is no doubt they will soon be checked out. Add a club patch on the back of the jackets and it is even more certain.

The cop got out of his car and approached the group of bikers.

"Nice night. You guys going to Daytona for the races?" He had a smile on his face and Indian could tell the guy was all right. He didn't have the "Okay you scrungy bikers" attitude that a lot of cops had.

"Yeah, but we're about out of gas and we can't find any open stations. We want to get into St. Augustine tonight, too." Indian hesitated. "You don't know where there might be a gas station open around here do you?"

The cop thought for a second. Then he smiled. Indian liked the guy already but he put off the feeling because it was a cop and he knew no cop could be trusted.

"There isn't a gas station until you hit the 1-75 interchange that would be open at this time of night, but I've got a pump over at the stationhouse and I'll let you have what you need to get back on the road. How's that?"

Indian didn't even have to consider.

"Yeah, that would be great. We'll follow you." He signaled for the bikers to start their bikes.

On the way to the police station Indian wondered about the cop. He couldn't figure why he wanted to give them the gas they needed unless he was just a nice guy. If he could have seen into his mind he would have known the reason.

Officer Fred Bender was not feeling as amiable as he pretended to be with these bikers. He hated bikers. They scared him.

It wasn't anything that had happened to him, but he had heard rumors about these guys and what they do to cops in small towns. He didn't want to be a statistic. If it meant giving them all his money and an hour with his wife he probably would have done it just to get them out before the townsfolk started to get up and jump on his case about their being in town. Sometimes folks expected you to do stupid things just because you're a cop.

He turned down the small street to the office and looked in his rear view mirror. The bikers were right behind him. Actually it looked pretty neat. All those bikes with their headlights blazing following him down the street. It looked fine.

He drove around to the back where the gas pump was. It had been put there so the police cars wouldn't have to depend on the gas stations' hours.

He got out of his car and took the key out of his pocket. Then he signaled the leader over to the pump.

Indian pulled up and took his gas cap off. He filled his tank and pushed his bike out of the way. Each of the bikers did the same. It only took about ten minutes and they were ready to go. Indian walked over to the cop.

"According to your pump it was 27 gallons. The price at the station was 70 cents a gallon*, here's twenty. We really appreciate your help." Then he smiled at him. "Really we do."

With that he twirled his hand in the air and all the bikes started up at once. The sound was loud and dreadful. As the bikes pulled out onto the tree lined street Fred just stood there and listened. It sounded good.

Much of what he had heard about bikers was probably a bunch of horse shit. He made up his mind right then. Those guys were Banditos, which were supposed to be one of the baddest clubs around, but they treated him fine and never gave him a problem. He hoped they had a good time on their ride to Daytona. In fact he kind of wished he was going along. It looked like fun.

He walked back to his car. As he sat down he felt something strange. The seat was damp.

He put his hand down and found that there was a beer sitting on the seat and when he sat down it fell over. He picked it up. It had been full.

The bikers had left it for him.

He smiled and took a long swallow.

**Footnote: This book was written in 1979, when gas $.70 a gallon!*

Chapter 49

I had a feeling something was wrong, but I never expected anything like this. I mean, shit, I ain't no friggin prude or anything, especially since I was raised in Hollywood, but who would have figured a gay bar in the middle of Florida? Not me.

When we pulled up to the place it looked normal enough. It was a little classy, but that didn't bother us. After the Godfather we figured we could go in any place.

As we walked in, there was a chick (or at least we thought it was) doing a pantomime to Carol Channing's "Hello Dolly." The patrons were getting a hell of a charge out of it. As the number progressed she kept taking off more clothes.

It wasn't until the end of the song when she

dropped her top to expose her non-existent tits, complete with pasties, that we knew we'd fucked up.

But by then we were so into it that we really didn't care.

After a few beers Mary stood up and climbed onto the stage. There was some fag out there doing a striptease to Sound of Music. Actually, the fag looked pretty good if you didn't know he was a boy.

Mary walked out there with nothing on but her rain coat. In a couple of beats it was off.

All of us were hooting and hollering having a hell of a good time and so were a lot of the straight customers who were there for the show.

The fag that was dancing was getting pissed. Not only that, but a bunch of the fag patrons were getting pretty loud about it too. They didn't want some real girl on the stage. They wanted a man up there. That was why they came.

The cheers and boos were getting a lot louder. All of a sudden I figured the odds. There were four of us and a room full of them.

It was time to bogy. I stood up and waved to Mary to come on. She just looked over and smiled and waved back, still dancing.

What a time to get coy.

Just then a big muscle-bound jerk came out of nowhere. I might have laughed at him in his skin tight, form fitting Levi's and his pink tank top if it weren't for the fact that he was built like he lived in a gym. This guy was a giant.

"Hey fella, you better get that female out of here. This is our place. If you want to look at crusty holes that smell like clams, go somewhere else."

I had two choices, neither of which made a whole lot of sense. One, I could laugh out loud at this guy. Hell, he even talked with a lisp and it was funny: Or I could belt him first and hope he goes down so I can get out of there in one piece.

As my knee came up in his groin I brought my fist up into his face, which was on its way down as he doubled over.

All of a sudden hell broke loose. I saw Dick behind me twirl in a movement that looked like it was out of a ballet and land his foot right in the solar plexus of a guy that was coming in on him, and at the same time he swung his right hand out, almost faster than the eye could see into the balls of another who was about to get him.

I made a fast mental note to have him teach me some of those tricks. Snoopy and Raunchy were back to back and moving fast to the door. They had broken a couple of bottles and were holding them like weapons to keep anyone from getting close. It was working.

During all this fooferaw Mary was having a ball. She was dancing like nothing else was going on. It made me almost wish I had snorted as much as she had, but when I felt a bottle glance off my head, I was glad I hadn't. I need whatever sense I had all together.

I spun and caught the bottle swinger in the neck. I was aiming at his face but he stood up too fast.

The neck worked just as good anyway. I think I collapsed his wind pipe because he grabbed his neck and started gasping for air.

By now most of the patrons had split. I hollered at Dick and we made for the door. When we got to our bikes Snoopy and Raunchy were already there. We were safe now. I hopped on my scooter and started her up. Just as we were about to pull out Mary came running out the door stark ass naked with her raincoat over her shoulder.

"Hey you guys, wait for me!"

All I could think was if it was all worth it.

From the look on everybody's face, it was. The fight had been fun and no one was hurt. Except for my poor head which felt like it had been used by Muhammad Ali for a punching bag.

Mary jumped on the back of Snoopy's scoot and we hooked it. We passed the tie talking about small things like what we were going to do in Daytona and how we would handle the meeting we were going to have there. I had come to depend on Dick pretty much. He made a damn good lieutenant. After awhile we paid our check and walked out to our bikes. I told him about the three motels and he agreed that the one farthest north would be the best bet. I hoped that Snoopy and Raunchy would find it too. We started our bikes and made it out onto the interstate heading north.

Chapter 50

After Snoopy lost the cop he turned through a series of side streets until he knew he was clear. They stopped to let Mary put on her coat. It looked a little weird riding around with a naked broad on the back of your scooter trying to cover herself with a coat.

Then he asked her where the nearest Holiday Inn was. She thought for a second.

"Well, there's one over on 27th Street near the beach and another by Highway 207 where it comes into town." She thought further. "Oh yeah, there's another one north on Interstate 95."

Three of them, Snoopy thought. How was he to know which one was the place to meet?

"Listen, we're supposed to meet at the Holiday Inn. Nobody said which one. There are some more people coming down from Jacksonville. Which one do you think they would stop at?"

Mary tried to think. The cocaine was starting to wear off and she began to wonder if she had chewed off more than she could swallow.

She didn't mind taking on one biker, or maybe even two, but if there was a whole club on the way she didn't want anything to do with them.

"Probably the one over on Highway 207. It would be the closest," she lied.

"Okay, lead me there," and he started up his scoot.

It didn't take long, about ten minutes, and they were pulling up in front. Snoopy rode around the parking lot once.

"We must be early." Then he added, "Oh well, might as well make the best of it," and he smiled at her.

She smiled back. She knew she could handle one dude even if he was a biker. She'd been on her own for quite awhile and knew all the tricks.

Snoopy took her by the hand and walked into the office. It just took a couple of minutes and they were registered. There were no vacancies on the first floor, which is what Snoopy wanted so he could pull his bike in, but there were a couple on the second. He locked his bike firmly to the sign post in front so the others could see it when they came in and they went up to the room.

It was a typical Holiday Inn room. Clean,, orderly, and a little too tidy for his own taste. He liked things more homey. Whenever he would go into a motel like this he was always afraid to put his feet on the bed. It made him uneasy.

As they walked in Mary turned to him. She put her arms around him and gave him a kiss like he couldn't believe.

All of a sudden he was glad they were the first ones. Now he would get it at this own pace. He didn't give a damn what happened after that.

He walked over and turned on the television. He like making love and watching TV. It was relaxing.

After he found a channel that was on that late he walked back to the bed and sat down. Mary was sitting there undoing her sandals. She let them drop to the floor.

For the next few minutes they talked about her life in the outskirts of a small town in Missouri. She was a hillbilly that had migrated to the shores of the Atlantic to get in on the big time. She had been dancing for two years so she knew her way around pretty well.

Snoopy sat there and parted her raincoat as she talked. He took one of her boobs in his hand and fondled it gently .He was starting to get turned on.

She stood up and took the coat from her shoulders and let it fall to the floor. Snoopy sat there on the edge of the bed watching. Then he sat up and started kissing her belly. She squirmed a little bit.

Then she said, "Hey, I'm thirsty. I want a Pepsi. Do you mind?"

Snoopy wanted to yes, he minded, but he figured that wouldn't be nice. He reached into his pocket and found a quarter. He remembered seeing a couple of soda pop machines down by the office on the first floor.

She just looked at him.

I can't do down like this," and she did a pirouette.

Snoopy thought for a second. He didn't like fetching for a girl, but if it meant a piece of ass what the hell? After all, he was still dressed and she was bare-ass naked.

He gave her a big kiss and she returned it just as hot. She took his hand and put it between her legs. He rubbed her mound and really started to get turned on. He pushed her down onto the bed. "Fuck the Pepsi," he said. But she wasn't going to let it go that easy.

"Hurry up," she said, pushing him away. "I can hardly hold back, but I'm really thirsty."

He got up and walked to the door. When he looked back she was lying on the bed with her legs wide apart and she was diddling herself.

He turned and walked quickly down the corridor.

He took the stairs at the end of the hall three at a time going down. He was anxious. At the bottom of the stairs he went down the long hallway to the machines.

He dropped his quarter into the slot and punched the Pepsi button. Then he thought for a second and put in another quarter. Might as well get something for himself, too. He got a Seven-Up and started to walk back up the stairs. He walked up about two steps and then turned around. There was an ice machine under the steps. Might as well go whole hog and get ice too.

Now he was ready.

He walked back up the stairs and down the hall.

When he got to the door it was closed. He thought he had left it open.

Oh well, He was so damn horny hi might have closed it without knowing. He put the bucket down and took the key out of his pocket.

He opened the door and walked in.

Mary wasn't lying on the bed.

"Oh," he thought to himself, "she must be in the head." He went to the bathroom and heard the water running. "I'm back," he shouted. "Hurry up," and he sat down on the bed.

He opened up the drinks and poured them into plastic glasses full of ice. Then he turned up the TV, kicked off his boots and peeled his socks off.

Then he waited.

After about fifteen minutes he went to the bathroom door and knocked.

Hey, you about ready to come out?"

There was no response.

He tried the handle and the door opened. Inside, the water was running in the tub, but the stopper was up. It just went down the drain.

The room was empty.

Finally it hit him.

"Why that dirty bitch," he said out loud. "She planned this."

He ran out the door but he knew it was too late. He was pissed. He had been made a fool of and he didn't like it. Not at all.

He walked back to the bed and sat down. Then he started thinking some more.

"What if she led me to the wrong Holiday Inn?

Hell, Treb and the others should have been here by now. He looked at his watch. It was almost five in the morning.

He picked up the phone book from the lost in the night stand and turned to motels.

Sure enough, there were three Holiday Inns. He picked up the phone and dialed the first number. They didn't have a record of any Lincoln staying there. No, they hadn't seen any bikers there either. They sounded relieved.

He dialed the other number, of the one out on I-95. That was it. He asked to be connected.

It only took him a few minutes to get up to I-95 and then ti was about ten miles farther to the off ramp.

When he got there the parking lot had all the bikes in it. It looked like Indian and Oaf had come in with the rest of the Banditos.

He went to their room.

When he opened the door the laughter started. It wouldn't stop for the next few days.

Chapter 51

It had been three days since Leroy had heard from Treb. The town of Daytona was starting to look like it was under siege by bikers. The people at City News Service estimated that there were over 80,000 bikers in town already and the total this year was expected to go well over 130,000 by the weekend. This was still only Monday.

Leroy watched the local news from the lunge chair in the bedroom of his suite. It was interesting watching how the small stations in town like this got their coverage. There wasn't an owned-and-operated in the bunch.

A movement in the bed caught Leroy's eye. He glanced over at the mound in the bed. She was good, no doubt about it. In the four days he'd been in town he'd tried six of the better hookers that the desk clerk could find. This one was the best, so last night he asked for just one. Usually he like two at a time.

Her same was Sandy, and she had the look of a little girl, with long brown hair that was as straight as a sable brush. And an innocent look like she should be sucking lollipops instead of cocks.

He watched as she rolled over, and he knew she was waking up. The blanket pulled up as she rolled and she lay there almost completely exposed.

Yeah, she was all right, even if she was a hooker.

She rolled back over and looked at him. She smiled.

He like the way she smiled. It wasn't as if she was smiling like a hooker to a customer. It looked sincere. He smiled back.

"Feel like some breakfast yet?" he asked.

"I think so," she threw the covers off and spread herself out on the wide bed. "How about you?"

He smiled at her.

"No, I meant the eating kind."

She placed her hand on her tunnel and looked at him.

"So did I." They both broke into laughter.

A few minutes later they were dressed and on their way downstairs to the coffee shop.

He could have sent out for room service, but it made him feel good being seen with this foxy young thing. He just hoped that everyone didn't know she was a hooker.

It was then that he decided to go somewhere else for breakfast. If they were away from the hotel, there was less chance folks would know her profession.

They stepped out of the main lobby and the parking attendant ran to fetch his rent-a-car. It was a blue Lincoln town car. He like those better than the Mark models, because there was a lot more room. They didn't stick out like a sore thumb, either.

He slid into the leather seat and sank in. Sandy slid over until she was right next to him and rested her fingers lightly on his leg about two inches below his crotch. He liked that. Not to push, but there if needed.

As he pulled out onto the main street, dodging some of the bikes that were everywhere, he turned south. He knew of a little place called The Cove that was well out of town, and very attractive.

They drove, watching all the bikes. They were there from everywhere. The license plates read like an atlas. All the states were covered.

Leroy checked every bike with a California plate to see if he would find Treb. He didn't really expect to, but it was a good game to pass the time. At the Plaza he made a left under the bridge and in a second he was driving on the sand of the beach.

It was about 11 a.m. and a lot of folks were already out there in their bathing suits. He checked out a couple of the foxy young woofies on the beach and decided he had as good a fox as there was right next to him. He put his arm around her and dropped his hand to her boob. He gave it a gentle squeeze.

She moved her hand up a few inches until it rested on his crotch. Yeah, she knew how to move. And when.

They continued south toward Ponce Inlet. After

about five miles the beach started to get a little less crowded. There were some private homes on the beach, but not many big hotels.

Just before they reached the end of the inlet Leroy noticed a lot of bikes on the sand. As he got closer he could see there was a drag race going on. He had heard that somewhere on the beach the bikers had set up a drag strip, but he didn't know where. Now he knew. He pulled the big Lincoln over to the side and watched.

Two bikes at a time would line up and a girl wearing a red bikini would wave a T-shirt in the air. When she dropped it, it was the sign to take off. They would race down to where two bikers were waiting on their bikes. They would announce the winner by one of them holding up his arm in the lane of the winner. It was that simple.

Leroy started the car and made a note to send Jim and John down here to get some shots. This was a good side of the Daytona scene to show: Bikers racing in a safe, organized manner instead of out on the street.

He aimed the car inland and soon they were at The Cove.

The Cove is a small restaurant on stilts in the Ponce De Leon river. There is a dock for the fishing boat that they send out and they specialize in fish dinners.

They picked a booth by a window overlooking the cove and had a leisurely breakfast. Sandy was a pretty good conversationalist and after a while he forgot she was a hooker. It was just like they were going together. She seemed to like it too.

After breakfast they went back the same way they came. He liked driving on the sand. The speed limit there was fifteen miles an hour, but he floored it for almost five miles and got well over 100. He slowed down when he saw the bikes ahead. He didn't want to hurt anyone.

When they got back to the hotel there were a bunch of choppers in the parking lot. One had a California plate. Leroy gave the car to the attendant and walked in. Sandy was right behind him.

If it was Treb he would probably be in the coffee shop. He searched all the faces and didn't see anyone familiar. Just as he was about to figure he was mistaken, he saw that the lounge doors were open. They would be in there.

He took Sandy by the hand and they walked into the lounge. It was dark, but from the noise that was going on he knew there must be some bikers in there. As his eyes adjusted he looked around.

"Hey, Leroy, over here!" It was Treb's voice, no doubt about it. He was sitting with about a dozen of the scruffiest looking bikers he had ever seen. He could feel Sandy's hand tighten on his. Obviously she was a little shaken by all this.

"Do you know them?" she asked, quietly as a mouse.

"Strictly business. They're not as bad as they look." He gave her hand a squeeze to reassure her and they walked over.

For the next hour Treb and Dick told of their harrowing escape from Perry. They were laughing so hard when they hit the part about Margo that they fell on the floor.

Sandy looked over at Margo and smiled. She thought it was pretty cool too. Maybe these folks weren't as bad as they looked.

After awhile Treb and Leroy told everybody to wait there and they went up to Leroy's suite. They had some talking to do.

It took about an hour, but when they were through Leroy knew the route that the bikers would take for the national protest rally and the time schedule. He was also let in on the meeting place there in Daytona for the others who were working on this and he was invited to film it all if he promised not to show any of it until after the protest. That way he got the exclusive story of the planning stage, but the bikers still had their secrecy as to what route they would take. That was essential for the moment.

When the run started ABD News would be the only station to have the route, so their camera crews would have the exclusives all across the country. It was a well thought-out plan.

Chapter 52

After three days of heavy partying, Treb and his group headed over to the campgrounds that had been picked for the meeting. It was 20 miles up the beach in a little place called New Smyrna. The campground was chosen because it was out of the way, cheap enough for a lot of the bikers to stay there, and they had a recreation room which would be perfect for the meeting.

There were about three hundred bikes in the parking area when they pulled in. It was a little difficult finding a place to park, even for a motorcycle. Treb could see the ABD News truck right in the middle of it all and he knew Leroy was around somewhere.

Most of the folks who were at Kansas meeting were there, but there were a lot of new faces also.

Chains had come all the way from Oregon with his old lady and there were others whom Treb knew by sight, but not by name.

As he and Dick were walking to the meeting room he saw another familiar face.

"John, how the hell did you get here?"

It was John Trumble from Utah. He introduced him to Raunchy and they walked off. John wanted to run prospect for the Sundowners. Since he had a Harley now, they would accept him.

Inside the meeting room was a ad house. The bikers had been partying for a long time and it was going to take some real doing to quiet them down.

It was almost noon and that was when the meeting was to start. Treb and Dick went into a corner and discussed what was going on with Wino Willie and Gizmo. They had been handling things on the easy coast pretty much themselves, with Giz in New York and Wino in Georgia.

Treb glanced down at his watch. It was noon. Time to start.

Treb asked for quiet and much to his surprise, he got it. Maybe these guys were here for business after all, not just to party and fiddle-fuck around.

He got right into it. The plans were all set for the national. He introduced Leroy and told all who were there that he could be trusted. He was going to get them all the publicity they needed when the time was right. He was with them. The bikers looked him over, but most were busier looking over Sandy, who was wearing a pair of shorts that were three sizes too small and a top to match.

Then they got into it. Times, places and people.

Who were responsible for what and how it all would be handled. It took over six hours to get it together and even then five or six of the coordinators had to stay on late into the night to finalize all the plans. This would be the last meeting before the fourth of July and they had to have their shit together.

Dingy Dave had been acting as the up front coordinator of the run so he was very much into what went on.

By three in the morning all the bikers who were still there were ready to get in some party time. They had been working for over fifteen hours and that was enough. All of the plans were set.

Outside the sound of partying was carrying into the building. Finally Treb stood up.

"Okay, fuck it, that's enough. Now let's do a little party hearty time," and he walked out the door.

Outside there were still about a hundred bikers partying like crazy. The news truck and gone with the daylight ad the bikers really let go. There were big bonfires all over the place and numbers were being passed like they were trying to get rid of their laughing tobacco before it went out of style.

The colors on the backs of the bikers read like a how's ho of the biker world: Hell's Angels, Mongols, Vagos, Desperados, Banditos, Widowmakers, Outlaws, Pagans. They were all partying together. There were a lot of clubs there that Treb hadn't even expected. The Warlocks, Renegades, and Chosen Few along with the Gypsy Jokers and the Heathens. They were all there.

As he watched them all, drinking and dancing together, he realized what the national helmet law had done for the bikers. It had given them a common enemy. A year ago all these clubs could never have gotten along. They were too busy fighting among themselves. But now that they had a common cause, to beat the damned government out of a law they didn't like, they were all like brothers. It was a good feeling.

Treb also realized that this protest was going to be a lot bigger than he had expected. If there were this many coordinators already, by the time of the run, still over three months away, it would be enormous. Hell, Mike Jones from Madison had almost guaranteed that all of the bikers who were at his protest would go on the national. Add to that all the clubs that were here and it was a guaranteed success before it started.

Or so he hoped.

He stopped at a picnic table where some of the folks were sitting and took a hit off the number they were passing around. He could tell by the minty taste that it was dust. He didn't like to smoke angel dust because he knew it was bad for him, but he wanted to get his head off the fucked up government and beer wasn't fast enough. He took a couple of deep hits and wandered back to his bike.

He sat down sidesaddle and tried to think.

"I wonder what Karen is doing now?"

His mind was wandering again. He kept thinking about what it had been like for those months in Georgia.

Then it hit him.

"Hell, Georgia's not that far. Why not?"

He pulled out the map that was tucked under the

bungee cords on his sleeping bag and checked it out.

"Not more that 150 miles." It was harder to think because the dust was getting to him by now.

"Hell, I can make it in tow and half hours easy."

He straddled his bike and kicked it over.

As it fired Rom and Dick came running over.

"Where are you goin'? I thought we were going to stay here tonight," Rom said.

"I'm going up to pick up Karen. It shouldn't take me more than a couple of hours each way. I'll see you guys tomorrow." He waved as he popped the clutch, "You guys party hearty."

Dick and Rom watched as the dust cloud moved out of the parking lot.

"Oh well," said Dick, "he's a big boy, I guess he can take care of himself."

After they started back to the party Rom added, "Yeah, but he was fucked up. Hope he doesn't get hurt out there."

Then they started to party.

Chapter 53

The offices at Daytona Beach were not at all like the federal building that Charlie Bainbridge was used to working in. When you are the Captain of something as secretive as the Omega Squad, you get used to priority treatment. Hell, the police department in Daytona only had enough space to give him a desk in the corner of the squad room. Not exactly plush, but he'd see better days.

Since the Omega Squad dealt strictly with gang activities, and since Daytona attracted most of the bigger gangs, this was a natural place for Charlie Bainbridge ad his crew.

A long time ago the Omega Squad had invented an outlaw biker club, which they called the Widowmakers, and it was made up of all their officers that were used as undercover agents but weren't on specific duty. The club had become accepted by the other outlaw clubs. Through the Widowmakers, Omega Squad members could get into the other clubs. They would party with them, wearing their Widowmaker colors until everybody knew them and then they would say they liked their host club better. The unsuspecting club would figure they were all right because they were accepted by the Widowmakers, and soon they would become members of the legitimate clubs.

Here at Daytona they had decided to ring in every man. They were looking for the guy who had shot Mike Brandi out in Los Angeles during that helmet law protest. Treb Lincoln. Charlie knew he would be here and it was just a matter of finding him.

It was past midnight when one of the Widowmakers came into the office. The Daytona cops looked at him like a spreader of the plague. They didn't know about the Widowmakers' real identity. Nobody did. If the word ever got out it would ruin their whole plan.

Charlie saw the man standing there and walked over.

"It's about time you showed up. Get your ass over to my desk and sit down!" He sounded like he was coming down on him. It was all preplanned.

The bogus biker informed Charlie that Treb Lincoln was at the campgrounds in New Smyrna. Omega knew about the meeting and had sent some of the Widowmakers there.

Charlie worked fast. He didn't want to lose Lincoln.

He went to the big map on the wall in the squad room and studied it. If Treb was in New Smyrna he would have to come one of two ways back to Daytona. Either by the beach route or by Highway One. They only needed to bock two roads.

He didn't want to be overt about it. It might upset the bikers to know that the police were coming down on one of them.

He walked into the Captain of Police's office and sat down.

He explained what was going on and asked for four unmarked cars; that would be all he needed. The captain had been told to cooperate in every way with this official so he agreed.

A half hour later they were all set up. One of the Widowmakers was back at the camp watching Treb. If he left it would be radioed in.

At the split where Treb would either go the beach route or the highway route, an undercover Daytona cop was sitting on his motorcycle, looking like he was just relaxing. When Treb went by he would radio to Captain Bainbridge which route he took.

Then it would be a simple matter to move his men either to block one road or the other. Simple.

Treb was so fucked up from the dust he'd smoked, that they could have put out a sign saying, "Treb, stop here to get busted." And they would have had no trouble. He was wasted to the max.

He was approaching the turnoff for the beach route. He decided that he wanted to take that way so he could open up his scoot on the Daytona Beach raceway, which is what it used to be called, and see what she could do. The wind in his face felt good and he wanted more of it.

As he turned into the narrow entrance to the beach he saw a biker sitting off to one side. He looked like he was resting. Treb took his hand off the bar and gave him the closed-fisted biker's salute. He like the brotherhood involved in biking .The biker didn't wave back, but that didn't bother Treb. Hell, in his condition nothing would have bothered him.

When he hit the hard part of the sand he wound the throttle full on. He could feel the back wheel losing traction as it spun in the sand. By the time he shifted into fourth gear he was going over a hundred miles an hour. He could feel the front wheel hunting on the sand.

It was a little hard to see with the sunglasses on, but he couldn't take them off without getting a lot of sand in his eyes from the tire. It was times like this he wished he had run a fender. The beach was flying by him. His headlight gave about fifty feet of good visibility, but he knew the road was open so he kept the throttle wide open. It felt good.

Then all of a sudden he was in a panic. Some asshole was waving a flashlight at him about three hundred feet ahead. He had his car parked right across the hard section of the sand meant for driving on. He knew it was too late, but he slammed on his brake anyway. As his bike slid over onto its side he wondered why the nerd had parked like that.

It all happened in less than three seconds but it seemed like a lifetime. When the bike went down it was still a good fifty feet from the car. It went down on its left side and the shifter caught in the hard sand causing the bike to flip in the air. The gas tank caught

Treb in the middle of his chest as they tumbled in the air at about 80 miles an hour. The exhaust pipe broke off and jammed through the gas tank. That was all it took .The crushing of the tank compressed the gas fumes, and when the red hot pipe broke through into it, the tank exploded like a bomb.

To Treb it was all like a dream. He was blown up, off the bike, and that was all he remembered. He was out cold. The force of the explosion blew pieces of hot metal all over the place. One piece of the gas cap shot into the leg of one of the police. The bike continued to climb until it reached its apogee, and then it fell in flames onto the top of the car parked in the center of the beach road.

Stunned, Captain Bainbridge watched it all. He hadn't expected it to happen like this. He didn't want to kill the guy, not yet anyway. He wanted to take him in and find out more about this national protest thing.

He watched to see where Treb Lincoln's body landed. All of the officers acted like they were in a trance. It had all happened so quick.

He ran over to where the body was and looked down. He didn't know the guy was such a big son of a bitch. He tried to roll him over so he could hear if there was a heartbeat, but he had a lot of difficulty. One of the Daytona police ran over and gave him a hand.

He was still alive, but he was burnt and broken up pretty bad. The explosion had done a lot of damage.

"Call an ambulance, fast!" he barked to the policeman and he took off his jacket and covered the body. He would have to be very careful to keep him alive.

He propped the head on a piece of the bike's seat that was lying nearby and made sure that his prisoner kept breathing.

Damn, but ambulances take a long time.

Chapter 54

Treb heard voices nearby. He tried to remember where he was, but for the life of him he just couldn't he just lay there trying to recognize the voices, or at least try and make sense out of what he heard.

Most of the words didn't make sense, but some of them he did recognize and they scared the living hell out of him, terms like "whole blood" and I.V.'s" Talk like that on y went on in a couple of places. Stockyards and hospitals. It didn't smell like the first, so he knew he was in the second.

All of a sudden he felt a powerful itch on his knee. He tried to move his arm down to scratch it, but it was being held. Probably some kind of cast or something, he figured.

If he had opened his eyes he'd have seen just how

right he was. Both arms were in casts as well as the whole upper portion of his body. His right leg was broken in three places and he had fifteen fractures in all.

That was the easy stuff. The force of the tank exploding had pushed his ribs in so hard and fast it had broken some of them and in doing so had punctured his lung along with some other damage that only the doctors could describe.

In other words he was in pretty bad shape.

Treb opened his eyes finally. The first thing he saw was the butt of some big black bitch in a short nurse's outfit with little red and white stripes on it. She was bending over the patient in the next bed and all he could see was her big black ass and a pair of cotton bikini panties.

All he could think was that he had died and gone to hell.

He tried to look around, but his head wouldn't turn. That was because of the neck brace. He was one big stone cast from his waist to his chin. There were minor scrapes on his head, so they just shaved him and cleaned them up. He looked kind of like a golf ball on a mountain of whipped cream.

The big black butt finally turned around and she saw that his eyes were open. She smiled broadly at him.

"Oh, we're finally awake." She stood there staring at him.

He wanted to say something like, "No shit, really?" but when he tried, his mouth was too dry for words. He almost laughed as he figured the best lines are always lost.

"There's been somebody waiting for you for three days. I'll send them in if the doctor says it's all right," and with that she waddled out of his sight.

Then it hit him.

"Three days!" he tried to shout. "What the fuck do you mean, three days?" But all that came out were some unrecognizable guttural sounds. Shit, but he was thirsty!

After what seemed a lifetime he heard the door open behind him. A doctor walked round into his sight and bent over to check him out. He looked like a cross between Dr. Welby and Ben Casey. He had the age and graying hair of Welby and the pissed-off look in his eyes like Casey. He was quite an odd looking dude.

He bent over and peered into Treb's eyes through a little gadget that had a light to blind you with. Treb figured he knew the score then. The cops had him and they were going to blind him, and then as soon as he could walk they were going to use him for a dart boards.

But he found out he was wrong. Everything was cool. After the doctor checked him out he was allowed to see his visitors. They were Dick, Rom and Karen. She had flown down as soon as she heard what had happened. All Treb knew was some asshole parked in the middle of the street he was riding on. That was all he remembered.

In the next hour he learned the whole story. After the accident, which was with a cop car that was trying to catch him in a trap, he was brought to this hospital and put in intensive care. He was under arrest though, so he called a lawyer friend of his and asked what they should do. That's where it got a little tricky.

It seems that since it was the fault of the police that put Treb into jeopardy, and finally into the hospital, and even though he was wanted as a suspect, he was still "innocent until proven guilty," so, if you're still keeping up with all this, the police would be responsible for all the medical bills as long as he was still in custody.

He understood all that just fine, and even some of the other legal crap that was going on. Like the bail setup. Since he was wanted in California on a murder warrant, if he had been captured there they could hold him with no bail. But, (he loved all the buts) since he was captured in Florida, he was just being held for extradition, so bail could (and had been) set. It was $50,000.

Treb almost choked on his flex straw when he heard the amount. In fact, he was almost as surprised to hear the amount as he was to hear that the $5,000 needed to get it from a bondsman had been raised by the bikers in Daytona already. Not only that, but ABD had guaranteed the bail to the bondsman, after a little talking with the head folds in New York.

It seems they wanted to keep the national protest as their own little exclusive, so they decided it was a good investment.

So what it all boiled down to was this: As long as he was in the hospital under care, he was a prisoner. All the food, medicine and care were taken care of by the arresting agency.

As soon as he was well enough to go out on his

own, he was ready to go with bail. No jail at all. Al he head to do was agree to appear in California on the trial date.

That bothered him a whole lot. He didn't want to show up to get a life term. Not for killing some undercover cop in biker's clothing. That didn't suit him at all.

Then he got the kicker. It seems that Leroy had rerun the tapes they had shot during the Los Angeles protest and it was plain obvious that Mike Brandi, the dead undercover cop, had at least partially instigated the trouble. Not only that, it was all on videotape how Brandi had pulled his gun and fired at the podium before Treb even took his gun out of his jacket.

It was clearly a case of self-defense.

The only offense that Treb could be convicted for was carrying a concealed weapon. And that was a thirty day sentence, if anything.

After all the information was ingested by his aching head, he went to sleep. Actually he passed out. His body needed a lot of healing.

For the next couple of months, that's all he did. Dick and Rom had rented a small room with Karen and Margo. The two girls got jobs as dancers and Dick and Rom were getting to know some of the local clubs.

As Treb's body healed, he worked in the exercise room with the therapist almost every day for as long as he could stand. He didn't want to lose any time getting back on the road. The court case had been set for June and he wanted to be ready as he could be.

The gym they had for therapy was a dream come

true. The closest thing he had ever seen to it was Gold's Gym in Santa Monica, where all the Mr. Americas work out. It was equipped with weights, machines and even saunas and therapy baths.

Treb felt like he was at a country club. If he had known being arrested was like this, he never would have run.

The only after effect of the accident was his leg. It just wouldn't set right. He would limp for the rest of his life. That didn't bother him a lot, but what did concern him was the fact that he would have to put an electric starter on his bike. No more kicking.

Dick and Rom were working on getting his bike back together, but it was gong to take a lot of bucks. The frame was bent beyond repaid and the engine was almost a wreck. The cases were cracked and the cylinders were pretty bunged up too. A lot of the internal stuff was good, but not all of it.

Everything else was junk. The front end looked like a pretzel and the wheels looked like two infinity signs.

While Treb worked on getting better, they worked on getting his bike up. They all had one goal, to get to Los Angeles by June. For the trial, and for the start of the national on June 30th. They were to be the first bikes in the procession.

By the time mid-May came around they were all ready. The doctors released Treb, the police arrested him, Dick and Rom bailed him out. It was just like clockwork.

Chapter 55

Had it only been two days since I got out of the hospital? Shit, it seemed more like a month. I really wasn't ready for all the partying, but I sure as hell wasn't about to turn down a bunch of good Columbian smoke.

A whole pound for just the five of us. It was unreal. All I can remember about the whole thing, as I look back on it now, it either I had a number of my mouth or was stuffing food into it to satiate the super humongo munchies, which came on like clockwork. Other than that all we did was listen to some good sound, clean the bikes and get ready to putt, or screw. It was heaven.

But all good things must end and it was already well past the time for us to split. Dick and Rom had done one hell of a good job fixing my scooter, in fact it looked just like new. It was as if I had never crashed except for my bum leg and of course a court date we had waiting in Los Angeles.

Karen came into the room carrying the leather saddlebags. I could tell she wasn't happy. I told her that she would have to stay at her folks' place until after the trial and then she could fly out and be in the big protest. She wanted to putt out there now, but she was a good old lady and kept her pretty mouth shut. The only problem was an occasional snivel, but hell, I got used to women sniveling before I could ride. It's a way of life.

Dick decided he wanted to hang around Florida for a couple of days before he took off, to clear up some dope deals he had going, and then he was going to meet us in Los Angeles, hopefully before the trial started.

Rom was busy packing his bike for the trip. He was ready to go. No doubt about it. You could tell we were about to set for the road when he started pacing back and forth in the living room while Karen and I said goodbye. She didn't want to walk outside because she was sniveling and they would see her. Hell, as if they didn't know she was sniveling in the room. Some broads ain't a whole lot endowed in the head department, ya know?

We walked out to the bikes and I strapped the saddlebags on with a couple of bungie cords. As I got ready to walk around to the side of my bike so I could kick the starter with my left leg, Dick walked over to me and smiled.

"Hey, brother, why not do it the easy way?" and

with that he touched a little button that I hadn't noticed on the handlebars. I heard the unmistakable grinding of a Harley electric starter and in a second the seventy-four coughed to life.

"Well, I'll be a son of a bitch," was all I could mutter. Those bastards had gone and installed an electric start on my scooter so I wouldn't have to kick her with my bad leg.

I switched off the bike and swung my leg over. As Rom started to kick his bike I smiled and hit the button. That was all it took.

I grinned so hard I thought my face would break. Those guys were all rights. No doubt about it.

We pointed our bikes out of the driveway and soon we were out of sight of the apartment. For a couple of seconds a picture of Karen lying on the bed crying filled my mind, but it was soon replaced by the pictures of all the country we were about to cross. This was the tenth time I was going to cross America on a bike, but that didn't matter a bit. You never get used to it. It is always a thrill.

Heading out of Daytona itself is a real trip. We decided to take the shortest route to California and so we headed across Florida. It was about ten in the morning when we left town and soon we were heading through the Ocala National Forest. This is a unique place in America. It is a cross between your typical forest and a tropical paradise. Wildlife and exotic birds would scare us half to death when they would fly or jump out of the deep underbrush. Our pipes would echo into the forest and it was almost eerie as the sound came back to us muffled and mixed with bird calls and other sounds of the forest.

It was a trip.

As we approached Perry we realized that there was no good road that bypassed the town. Unlike when we came through on our way to Daytona, now all the bikers were gone. A couple of choppers traveling the highway could be very suspicious to a sheriff who lost much face just a couple of months back.

When we were about ten miles out of the town we stopped at a gas station and asked if there were any little "scenic" roads that weren't on our map. The friendly attendant took his time as he explained a nice little road with "just a little dirt" that headed over to the Gulf, about ten miles off.

After we topped off our tanks we headed onto the small road he showed us.

The road was beautiful, like the guy said. Soon we forgot that we were trying to avoid Perry and were lost in our thoughts putting down a road that was unreal.

Soon it turned into the "just a little dirt" part.

I noticed it as my front wheel left the road and started bounding like it had a mind of its own. Long springers were not made for a bad road putting, rule number one.

Rule number two, don't look over your shoulder to see how your buddy is doing unless you know what is in front of you. I made that mistake about a half second later. By the time I got turned back around where I belonged, I had bounded off the road and was heading springer first into a swamp. The road went off somewhere to the left.

Why me, Lord? What did I ever do?

As soon as I realized what was happening I dropped the bike to the right and pulled my legs out from under it. Fortunately I was going very slowly so the bike didn't go all the way in. Just up to the rear wheel.

For the next few minutes I sat there looking very disgusted as Rom laughed his fool head off. He tried to stop but he just couldn't after a couple of minutes I saw the humor in it too and we sat there like a couple of demented fools for the next hour, alternately laughing our heads off and trying to get the bike out of the slimy mud it had gotten stuck in.

It was after two p.m. when we finally broke it loose and almost three by the time we were back on the road with all the wire ends dried out and the carburetor working fairly well.

If it weren't for the thick coat of mud all over the bike you would have never known how dumb I really was.

We finally found our way back to the blacktop and we started to hook it once again. We had a little time to make up. We had called ahead to the Outlaw clubhouse in New Orleans, telling them we would be in that night, and we didn't want to keep them waiting.

We didn't stop at all except for gas and soon we had made it past Pensacola and Mobile and were heading into Biloxi. There we stopped just long enough to get a cup of coffee and by one in the morning we were crossing the Lake Pontchartrain Bridge into New Orleans.

We made our way to the clubhouse and were relieved to see there were only a couple of bikes out in front. We were beat and didn't really feel like partying all night long. Especially since we had a long ride in front of us the next day.

We walked into the clubhouse. Indian and Fast Eddie were playing a game of pool and there was one prospect with a broom in his hand over by the bar. That was it. Indian smiled a broad smile when he saw us and ran over. He hugged us like long lost brothers.

"Man when I heard about your accident I thought you were a goner. You probably don't even remember, but I was at the hospital the first week. When we knew you were all right we came on home." He smiled again. "Damn but it's good to see you."

I could tell that he meant it. It was typical of the biker way of life. We just met a couple of months ago when his guys ripped my scoot, and now I would trust him with my life. What a strange world.

Rom and I took the beers that were offered to us by the prospect and sat down on one of the old sofas that surrounded the room. Then I sat back as Rom told the whole story of our trip, including the running off the road and the bike full of mud. Indian and Eddie took turns running outside to look at it. They couldn't stop laughing.

Hell, I had to admit the bike did look pretty funny all caked in dark grey mud like that.

Indian could see we were pretty tired and so he cut everything short. We talked for a couple of minutes about the national, and he assured me they would be there. Then he assigned the prospect to watch us that night and we said our goodbyes. We wouldn't see each other again until July second. All the plans were set.

I walked out with him as he got on his old Indian and made the normal wisecracks about the bike's age and he took off smiling. I really was starting to like him.

I walked over to our bikes and took the sleeping bags off the sissy bars. When I got inside Rom was putting a couple of cold ones down by two of the newer looking couches and it wasn't a long time before the beers were empty and we were asleep, with the prospect staying awake to watch our bikes. I didn't wake until I heard a bike start up outside. I looked over and saw Rom still asleep. The prospect was standing by the front door looking out.

"Everything all right?" I asked him.

"Yeah, just one of the members taking his bike. You can go back to sleep."

"Naw," I glanced at my watch. "It's after seven already and I want to get an early start.

I guess Rom heard me because he opened his eyes. One of them was almost all red. He looked like a lopsided stop light.

He must have known it, because he turned to me and held the eye open real wide with his fingers.

"Gory, isn't it?" and he made a face with his eye wide open.

"Yeah, what's the matter?"

He laughed.

"Every time I get real tired I got some blood vessels that break in my eye and it looks like this. It will go away in a day or so."

Hell, if it wasn't going to bother him, it sure wasn't going to bother me.

Soon we had our bags rolled up and we thanked the prospect for watching our stuff. He said he'd probably be a member by the fourth, and he would see us on the national. Then we left.

The next 100 miles west are over water. A bridge covers the swampland. Usually when I cross it the rain is falling and I never really liked it, but for some odd reason now it was bright and sunny. The tropical vegetation was really cool and comfortable to look at and time flew by as we cruised on the interstate.

We passed through Lake Charles, and soon we were crossing the Sabine River into Texas.

Now folks, I don't really have anything against Texas except it takes so long to get through it. Especially when you enter through Beaumont. It is almost 1,000 miles from there to El Paso and that is one long putt. For sure.

The good part about it is the highway. Interstate 10 cuts a wide path through east Texas and before you know it you are heading into San Antonio, land of the Alamo. From there you take a cut north over some hills and soon you are putting out into flatlands.

It was getting pretty late by the time we passed through Boerne, a small town about 30 miles out of San Antonio, so we decided to look for a place to drop it for the night. After searching high and low for a gas station to fill up at, we pulled into one of the roadside rests that dot the interstate system of America and threw out our sleeping bags. We were beat.

Before it seemed possible, the sun had come over the horizon and it was time to move again. Time does weird things when you are trying to really hook it.

As we pulled off the interstate in Junction to get gas and a little food at one of the local rip off joints, we saw a lot of clouds coming in. That was just what we needed, a little Texas rain.

After wolfing down some ham and eggs, we got back on our bikes. From the look of the sky we could tell we were in for it. It was going to rain, and soon. Over to the west it was so dark that it looked like night.

Rom and I pulled out the rain suits that we carry, and a couple pairs of goggles. That was all we had. Then we hit the road.

The rain didn't get really heavy until we got to Sonora. Then it decided to take a big douche right on our heads.

Now folks, let me tell you the second worst feeling in the world. That is riding across Texas in the rain. Wanna know what the worst of all feeling is? No? Well I'm gonna tell you anyway. It's riding across Texas in the rain without a front fender.

You see, the front wheel picks up all the road oil and dirt that countless cars and trucks have dropped, along with who knows how much cattle shit, and it is nearly deposited right smack dab in your face. Sounds like fun, huh?

If we had any intelligence at all we would have pulled into a sheltered spot right there and stopped to let it go by. But no, we're bikers, and everybody knows bikers are the dumbest clods on earth, so we just press on.

What fools we bikers be.

We crossed the Pecos River and it actually had

water in it. A first in my experience. Then we rounded the bend into Sheffield.

Sheffield is a little town with four gas stations and an auto repair shop. That's about it. It's a real burg.

I'd apologize to anybody from there that I might offend, but I know no one who lives there is smart enough to read, so this can't offend them.

After a fast stop for gas we started to pull out of town. As we made the first turn I heard a loud clang.

"Clang?" I thought, "why clang? I don't like clang. Maybe kerthud or something, but not clang."

As I tossed what it might be around in my head I felt the bike jerk as the rear wheel locked up. The bike stopped in the middle of the highway.

I got off and inspected the back wheel. It seems that the drive chain had decided to take a crap, and it picked this particular spot to do it.

As if that weren't enough to get me into a very anti-social mood, the chain also decided to jam between the rear wheel sprocket and the frame, making it impossible to push the bike to the next town to get it fixed. First we would have to get a hacksaw and cut the chain away. Oh boy.

It didn't take a whole lot of figuring to decide that Sheffield was the place to get the hacksaw since it was just a quarter mile back. I hopped on Rom's scooter and headed back into town.

First I tried the station we bought gas at.

"Hey, could you loan me a hacksaw for a second?"

The guy just looked at me.

It took him almost five minutes to tell me he didn't have one.

Then I hit each of the four stations. None of them had a hacksaw.

I went over to the auto repair shop. They must have one, right? After asking twice, the guy finally told me to go away.

By now I was getting desperate, so I offered him $20 cash money if he would just rent it to me. He could keep the twenty and I would bring him back the hacksaw. He couldn't lose, even if I ripped it off.

He still said no.

Just as I was about to persuade him I should have the saw by knocking him on the head with a number three Harley tool, the local highway patrol pulled in.

Why me Lord?

I explained our trouble to him. He just smiled as I explained it all. The he told me life was tough here in Texas and he hoped I found what I wanted in the next town.

Nice folks.

I walked back over to the station we first stopped at and asked how far the next station or town was.

It seems the next town was Fort Stockton and that was 80 miles away. I could just see us trying to push the bike with a locked up rear wheel all that way.

I rode back out to where Rom was waiting. He looked wet and cold and not a whole lot happy. He looked even worse when I told him what happened.

As we sat there about four vehicles passed us and we both noticed the same thing. They were all pickup trucks, it seems that the goat ropers of Texas all drive pickups.

Then the thought hit me. We would try to flag down a truck and offer to pay for a lift to the next town. Hell, they have to be going that far since there's nothing out there but Fort Stockton, so they should do it cheap.

Or so we thought.

After about an hour a truck pulled over. They guy looked over the bike and then agreed to take us "For $20 and a full tank of gas at the other end."

Rom and I thought about it for about two seconds and as the rain turned to hail, we decided the price was right.

Besides, since he was ripping us off I figured we'd just short him at the other end. Maybe we'd give him the $20, but he could buy his own damn gas.

Rom followed us on his bike and for the next 80 miles I rode in style listening to some off the wall shit-kicking music tapes and a CB that blared loud with static.

Just before we pulled into town the dude called on his CB to learn if there were any bike shops in town.

There was one so we headed for it.

After we pulled in we started to unload the bike. I was just getting ready to tell the dude that he was going to get shortchanged when he pulled out his card to give me "In case we ever needed" him again.

There ought to be a law against sheriffs driving pickup trucks.

There also ought to be a law against forty gallon gas tanks. Especially when they're empty and I have to pay for the fill-up.

That ride ended up costing fifty bucks.

Chapter 56

The road was still west as Rom and Treb made the crossover where I-10 and I-20 met. They both thought it a little weird that even though they were staying on the same highway they had to change roads, while folks coming west on I-20 stayed on the same road and it just became I-10.

Oh well, thought Treb, it was never taken for granted that highway engineers had a whole lot of smarts anyway.

He thought back to Fort Stockton and the guy who had fixed his chain. He didn't have a master link to fix it with, so he had to repair his old one, which was pretty mangled but it seemed to be holding. It was after five when they pulled out, but at least they were on the road again.

The traffic was heavier now that the two interstates had become one and they were passing cars and trucks like they were standing still. There was a strong wind out and the cloud cover had brought a real cold front in. Treb and Rom both had on all the clothes they could get into. It was well down in the thirties and they were both hoping the road would dry before it got below freezing. Nothing is worse for a biker than frozen roads.

About thirty miles before Van Horn, Texas, they were passing a big truck when Treb heard the same sound he heard earlier that day. Clang.

This time the rear wheel didn't lock up though. Treb coasted over to the side of the road. Rom stopped way behind Treb and picked up the drive chain. It seems the Mickey-moused master link didn't do the trick.

The master link was all messed up this time. They didn't know what to do. As they looked for alternate ways to fix the bike Rom found an old master link in his tool kit. They got real excited.

It was starting to get colder out now and the wind was blowing stronger too.

They worked and worked, but the master link was too thick to fit through the chain. The only way it would work was if it were filed down. It just couldn't be forced.

After hours of working on it, Treb lost the flip of a coin and he mounted Rom's bike to go into town for a file. Van Horn was a big town and it wouldn't have been hard to find tools there.

He putted the 28 miles to town in a hurry. He could picture poor Rom freezing his butt off out there.

As he made it to the turnoff he started to slow. Then he saw it.

There was a stupid red light in his rear view mirror.

All he could think was, “Why me Lord?”

He pulled over.

The cop proceeded to tell him about the laws in Texas and how anything over 55 was speeding. He had been clocked at 75.

Treb took out his license and got ready to get a ticket.

In Texas, if you’re from out of state you don’t just get a ticket. You get taken to the local Justice of the Peace and you pay your fine there and then.

Even this didn’t bother Treb and he followed the cop to the offices.

Then he got upset.

It seems that the JP was off duty and wasn’t due until the next morning. Treb would have to spend the night in jail.

All he could see was pictures of Rom with icicles hanging from his nose as he was found frozen stiff the next day. There was no way they were going to keep him overnight.

He really started to get pissed and he was soon hollering at the cop.

Finally, more to protect his hearing and his sanity than anything else, the cop agreed to call the JP and see if he would set the bail over the phone. It took about half an hour but it was done. Treb paid $25 and was out the door.

Then he made his way to a gas station to find a

file. He couldn't get a regular file, but they had some emery cloth so he took that and then he headed back out to where Rom was. He had been gone almost two hours by now.

By the time he pulled up to where the bike was parked poor Rom looked like a snowman. It had rained and the rain froze on his blanket, which he had wrapped around himself to keep warm. He looked like an old Indian sitting in the snow.

Rom didn't see the humor in it though.

They started working on repairing the bike. Al they knew was they wanted to get on the road and out of the dumb state of Texas. It had been a jinx to them.

It took almost an hour for them to realize that you can't sand cold rolled steel with ice cold fingers and do any good. It just wasn't getting any skinnier and it still didn't fit.

Finally in a fit of rage Treb grabbed a big rock that was lying nearby and started to beat the thing in.

It worked. It popped right in. That was all it needed.

It didn't take a minute for them to finish the job and pack up again. They wanted to make some time and get somewhere warm, but out of Texas.

It was almost 11 p.m. by the time they got their bikes started and they didn't even stop as they went through Van Horn. From there it was 100 miles to El Paso and another twenty to the border. They only stopped once for gas.

And then they were out. They were tired as hell, but they were out of Texas. It was just a little after one in the morning.

They pulled into a small truck stop in Demming, New Mexico, and poured some hot coffee down their throats. They either had to find a place to crash or a way to stay up.

Now here we must interject a little dope data. There is only one segment of America's society that is as into the drug culture as are bikers, and those are your redneck truckers. They know every type of speed and upper known to man and a few that haven't been let out yet.

Treb had been around enough to know that, but for a couple of long hair bikers to score good speed from a redneck trucker is always a bitch.

In this case it wasn't hard at all.

Treb and Tom were just sitting in a booth sipping their coffee when this big trucker came sauntering over.

"Those your choppers out there?" he motioned to their bikes.

"Yeah," was the tired reply.

"Boy ya'll sound tired. Been on the road long?"

"We sure have, and we got a long way to go. I don't think we're gonna make it either. We're both pooped out."

The trucker reached into his pocket and came out with a small plastic vial.

"Here, try this," and before they had a chance to say anything, there were little piles of white powder floating in each of their coffee cups. Treb and Rom looked at each other. Then they shrugged their shoulders. Hell, what did they have to lose?

They thanked the trucker and slowly drank their

coffee down.

Treb sat there looking at Rom. He just stared back with that one red eye and one regular one. He didn't look any different. They sat there for a couple more minutes. Then Rom had to go take a leak. He stood up and slowly walked back to the head. Treb looked at his empty coffee cup and signaled the waitress for a refill.

Halfway to his booth she seemed to slow down. It was almost like she was in slow motion. She poured the coffee into his cup and then into Rom's. He just sat there fascinated watching her. She was moving so slow. The coffee poured like cold crude oil. All of a sudden Treb didn't feel tired anymore. In fact he felt great. Rom came out of the head and he was smiling.

"Well Treb you ready to ride for awhile?"

"Ride hell," Treb snapped. "Fuck it, let's just tuck them bikes up under our arms and run for awhile!"

The next few hours were crystal heaven. It may have been cold out when they pulled in, but it felt just fine as they trucked out of New Mexico into Arizona.

As the sun came up they were pulling into a little place called Texas Canyon, which is just a roadside rest, but it has the most beautiful scenery and rock formations in this country. They were in such a good mood they just sat there looking at the rocks. They were tripping.

In physics there is an old saying: "What goes up, must come down."

We all know it was disproved by the space flights, but it still holds true for white powder freaks.

One minute they were flying high, and the next they were crashing. Everything was bad. The bikes were too loud, the seats too uncomfortable, and they were so tired they could hardly keep their eyes open.

The only problem was, it was now daylight and sleeping just didn't seem right in the middle of the day. So they kept riding.

They crossed out of Arizona and into California at Yuma feeling about ready to die. As they passed over the mountain range east of San Diego they knew they were dying for sure and as they came down into the rump of San Diego paranoia was setting in. They just knew every car was a cop and were afraid they were speeding or something. It was awful.

Somewhere along the highway to Los Angeles, just about in San Clemente, they stopped in a roadside rest. It was about 11 a.m. They looked at each other balefully. Not a word was spoken. Both reached for the sleeping bags and in three minutes they were sound asleep as thousands of cars drove by.

Chapter 57

People just gawked as they passed, but Leroy was used to that. They had set up their cameras in the hallway outside the courtroom where Treb Lincoln's trial had been going on for the last week. It was noon and at one p.m. the jury would announce its verdict.

The trial became a big story after ABD ran it on the evening news. It took two days to get it together, but with a little bit of pressure Leroy had managed to convince the national network boys. The fact that the victim had been an undercover cop and was assigned to disrupt the event made the difference. The official view was, why were the police inciting a riot? Secondly, as Leroy was quick to point out in his broadcast, how could a man know that another man is a police officer when he is dressed like an outlaw biker? This and the film that ABD News supplied the court from footage they had shot at the Los Angeles protest proved that Treb was shooting in self defense. There was no doubt about it.

Leroy was just about ready to start his taping. He was gong to do his intro now, while the halls were relatively empty. Then they could put it all together later.

He nodded to Jim to start the camera rolling.

"Testing, one, two, three…Is that okay, Jack?" He waited until Jack nodded that the sound was right and then he was ready. He turned his back to the camera and looked down the hall. He could hear the faint whirr as the camera started. Then he turned and looked into the camera. He didn't say a word for a full three seconds. Then he began.

"Last week a trial started in this courtroom and there was very little commotion about it. A hard core biker named Robert "Treb" Lincoln was accused of killing a police officer and charged with interstate flight to avoid prosecution. It was a simple case, or so everyone thought."

He looked into the camera like he was staring into a person's eyes and continued.

"In the course of the trial the defense attorney asked for some file footage that we had taped at the helmet law protest here in Los Angeles when the death had occurred. That was when we came back in to the picture. It seems that the officer that the biker was accused of slaying was working undercover. Now we find no fault in that, but we do ask the question, how can he be accused of murdering a peace officer if there was no way he could know that he was one?"

Once again he let that sink in slowly.

"As the case progressed for over a week now, it became obvious that the policeman had not only been the first one to fire a shot, but that he had been ordered to disrupt the lawful protest. That was when the case started to draw national attention."

He paused again, this time to run his fingers through is hair. He was ready for the biggie.

"Since when is it the job of the government to interfere with political rallies? Not only that, but this case has brought out the existence of a motorcycle club called the Widowmakers that is made up completely of undercover policemen. The club has been operating for over two years now."

Leroy held up a photo that was taken in Daytona of two of the Widowmakers walking down Main Street. They looked like worse outlaw bikers than most outlaws did.

"Here is a recent photo of these policemen," he verbally underlined the word, "and, as you can see, they are not your average-looking peace officers. It was a man dressed like this that fired at Treb Lincoln and whom he is accused of killing. The question is, was he acting in self defense? After seeing this film clip we about to show, can there by any doubt? Now the trial is over, so the public is ready to see it."

He paused again. Here the tape would be spliced and they would drop in the action footage that the jury had seen. Then he continued.

"What bothers us is the fact that Treb Lincoln is the coordinator of a political rally that will be held in the nation's Capitol in just a week, and the undercover police were trying to either prevent or totally disrupt the event."

That was it. He was sure the jury would find Treb innocent, but he wanted to wait until after the jury's announcement before he taped it.

The sight of all those bikers jumping up and down in the background would be a good touch and as they rode off he could probably work in another plug for the national. He had already mentioned it four times in his earlier broadcasts, and that publicity had gotten a .5% additional participation factor from the computer, which figured to be about 100,000 additional bikers in the protest.

Chapter 58

I opened my eyes when I heard the noise outside. It sounded like someone was rolling their bike out of the garage. Karen was lying in my arms so I didn't want to move too fast.

Hell, with my head as big as it was from the last few days' partying it was surprising I could open my eyes at all. It was just a good thing I stopped early enough last night. I knew we had a big couple of days in front of us and would need some sleep.

After the trial had ended it had taken two days to get the route down on a map and all the times scheduled right. It was going to be a real feat if we brought this thing together. Ever since the word got out on Leroy's broadcasts the response had been phenomenal. It looked like every biker in the country was going to get involved. Not because of the helmet law, but because the police had been spying on bikers and that was getting real personal. The helmet law was unpopular, but it took something like the police interference to really get folks riled up.

The more I thought about it the more I figured we really owed Leroy a lot. From the beginning he had helped us keep it together.

Karen rolled over and looked at me. I could tell by her eyes that she had been awake for awhile. She just smiled at me.

"You ready to get up?" I asked. I was ready, and actually a little anxious. This was a big day.

"Yeah," she said as she grabbed my balls softly, "I'm ready to get up. You?" She smiled like she had just found a $20 bill.

I softly pushed her hand away.

"Yeah, but not that way. We got a busy day to look forward to. No time for that," I winked, "kind of foolishness."

She forced a pout and then broke into a smile.

"Promise me we'll do it tonight."

She never lost an argument, just postponed the victory. I nodded yes. Tonight we would. I figured by then she would be too tired.

I pulled my Levis on and put on my best black T-shirt. My cutoff was hung over the back of the chair so I threw it on too. As I walked into the head I checked my buck knife and wallet and made sure my keys were clipped securely to my belt loop. All I had to do was strap on my boots and I would be ready. As I bent over the sink to rinse my mouth, the 357 Magnum made a clanging sound against the sink. I had almost forgotten I had it in my jacket pocket.

I remember when I first got the damn thing whenever I would wear it I felt like it was pulling my cutoff down on one side. Now I was used to it.

The clock said five a.m. so we still had over an hour before we were to meet. The starting time was set for six-thirty at Griffith Park, the same place the Los Angeles protest started a year ago. It was symbolic. A little twist that Leroy added.

We had packed the bikes the night before so I walked out to see who else was up. It was Rom. He was wiping down his bike. I pulled up a milk crate next to his bike and we sat talking about a bunch of little things. This was almost like the old days when we would kill a whole day just sitting around in a junky garage talking bikes and broads. It had been a good life. Sometimes I wonder why we ever changed.

Karen came out the back door and handed me a cup of coffee. She asked Rom if he wanted one too, which he declined. She said breakfast would be one in a minute. Then she went back in. Somehow women didn't belong in a man's garage. It was like a sanctuary not to be invaded or desecrated with the female touch.

Pretty soon I got up and wandered into the house. I wanted to make sure everything was all set. We wouldn't be back for at least three weeks and I didn't want to forget anything.

After breakfast we pulled the bikes up in the driveway. We thanked Rom's folks for letting us stay with them and said we would see them when we got back. Then we started the bikes. It was time to go.

We wound our way out of San Pedro and onto the Harbor Freeway. From there it was almost a straight shot to the park. Traffic was light for a Saturday morning. Almost all the vehicles on the freeway were motorcycles. There were bikes riding in the same direction we were for as far as the eye could see.

When we made the transition onto the Golden State Freeway we saw a camera crew on the overpass. Looked like we were going to get some coverage on this deal.

We swing off the freeway at the Griffith Park offramp and made our way to the gathering area. It was over by the merry-go-round as always.

We pulled around the bend and into the parking lot. As we passed through the bikes we knew we had underestimated. I had figured only a couple of hundred bikers would want to ride al the way to Washington D.C. for a protest, but I was obviously wrong. There was already well over a thousand bikes and it was 45 minutes before we were to leave.

I saw a couple of the Omega Squad lieutenants in an unmarked car and I walked over to them.

"Sorry we had to blow your cover like that," I lied, "but next time pay more attention to the rules." I stroked my finger at them.

They didn't smile at all. They just sat there with stone faces. "You really think you can get this many bikes in one pack from here to Washington?" They didn't even wait for an answer. "You're crazy."

I smiled at them and turned back to the crowd.

I knew it was gong to be a problem and that we would lose a lot of them along the way to breakdowns and the like, but I figured enough would get through to count. To make an impression. To beat the fool helmet law.

We had arranged for a big flatbed follow-up truck that one of the motorcycle accessories manufacturers had donated and I saw it pulling in. On the back were a lot of boxes. I knew they were the printing that we had ordered. It was a route map showing where the group would be stopping each of the two nights on the road and the final night, on July 3rd, in Washington. Every biker who went would get one, so if he had to drop out of any reason and the follow up truck couldn't help him at least he would know where to go.

It was a simple plan. It called for us to cover 800 miles a day, give or take a few. It would mean hard riding and long hours. I figured at least sixteen hours a day. We would stop three times during the day for fifteen minutes only. Other than that they would have to stop on their own and then catch up.

It sounded harsh, but I knew that before long the pack would stretch out over many miles and it wouldn't be any problem for any of the bikers to pull off, get gas and a hamburger, and then be back on the highway before the pack had all gone by.

Leroy had set up his cameras and was filming some of the activities. He saw me and walked over, pulling Jack along by the microphone cord.

"And here is the man who started all of this, Treb Lincoln." He nodded and Jack panned the camera over to me. I tried to smile.

"Treb, what are the plans for the run to Washington?" We had rehearsed that question but I wasn't quite ready for it this fast.

Well, I…ah," I stopped. I don't usually get camera shy, but all of a sudden I was. I took a deep breath, and started again. I knew Leroy would cut out the pause.

"We are going to leave here in Los Angeles at six-thirty this morning in one pack. We will head out the Golden State Freeway to the San Berdoo. From there it will be all interstates. This group will head up through Las Vegas…"

From there on it was just a stream of details. I had gone over it so many times in my head it was easy. The way each city had its own meeting time and how they would all join into our one group along the way. The large field we had picked outside Grand Junction, Colorado, for our first night's stay and a campground next to the Missouri River for the second night. All the plans were spelled out. By the time this aired on Network TV tonight we would already be in Utah, but we would still pick up additional riders in the east.

By the time the interview was over about a thousand more bikes had shown up. The crowd was well over two thousand now with only about fifteen minutes to go.

I walked around talking with some of my old friends. All the clubs were represented here. The Angels, Mongols, Chosen Few, Hessians, Vagos, Defiant Ones, more than you could ever imagine. It was great. All wars had been called off for the next four days no matter in what state or what city. They were all on friendly terms. If nothing else, that alone would scare the hell out of the politicians.

Chapter 59

It was cold out in the desert. Dog stood in the middle of the highway and looked out over San Bernardino toward Los Angeles. He couldn't see anything. It was already a little after seven-thirty, and they should have been in sight by now.

Dog had been in the Diablos for a long time and he like the feeling of belonging. This was the first big national run they had participated in since he was a member and he was looking forward to it.

All of a sudden he could see something glinting far down the road. Then he heard the unmistakable sound of bikes riding together. It was a sound he loved.

There were about eight hundred bikes gathered outside of San Bernardino Most of them were from outlaw clubs. Berdoo had been a haven for outlaw bikers for many years. It was a safe place because of the low density of population and the high population of bikers.

By now Dog could see the pack. It was more than just long. It was more bikes than he had ever seen. He couldn't even estimate it, but the line was double wide and as far as the eye could see. It had to be over ten miles long.

The newscopter flying overhead had just estimated the pack at three thousand, but that was before he saw the bikes waiting on the hill, they would sell it to nearly 4,000 people.

Treb was riding in front and he was just getting settled for the long roll ahead. He expected more bikes to join them at Las Vegas. Dick had a group there and that was the first planned stop, for fifteen minutes. Treb gave the bikers the high sign as he passed and he heard them starting their bikes to fall into the pack.

At about five o'clock that morning Sportster and some of the other members of the Grants Pass, Oregon chapter of the Nuggets had been on the road with the Choosey Beggars. They were heading south to join with the pack forming outside Reno, Nevada. All of the bikers from Salinas California, to San Jose and Sacramento, the Wheel Lords and the Easy Riders. Hundreds of clubs and outriders would be meeting there to cut across US 50 and join the pack that was forming in Salt Lake City as they dropped down to meet the main pack at the I-70 intersection.

At the Sundowners clubhouse in Salt Lake the bikers were ready to take off by early morning.

Raunchy walked among the bikes. He knew there would be a lot of bikes going. But he never figured over a thousand would ride just from Salt lake. The route was all laid out and he was ready to lead the pack down to the meeting area. There they would join with Treb and the rest of the pack.

It had been a month since Raunchy had left Treb at the hospital in Daytona, but he had talked to him a couple times on the phone and the plans were pretty simple. He just hoped that the large pack of bikes would be able to keep up the fast pace Treb had planned.

The bikers in Tucson had left early too and they joined with a lot of the Banditos and other bikers coming out of El Paso and the Big Bend area of Texas. They met at the I-10 and I-25 intersection and made their way up to Albuquerque, where they would join the bikers out of Flagstaff and Phoenix. The Dirty Dozen and the Rightful Agents were meeting there too.

It was noon when the main body dropped off the interstate and headed down Las Vegas Boulevard. Treb was happy with the time so far. He was staying right on schedule. The gas situation was working out pretty well so far. Each biker was responsible for his own fuel and would pull out of the pack whenever he wanted to get some. Then he would pull back in at the end of the pack.

The rules for the pack were the same as for any pack. You were partners with the rider next to you and if anything happened to your bike only your partner would pull off with you. If it was serious he could get whatever help you needed. That way the pack could keep going instead of stopping for every bike that broke down.

As they pulled into Las Vegas, if Treb could see behind him he would have seen over a hundred bikes already strung out making minor repairs. But their loss wasn't at all noticed because the pack had swelled to over 6,000 after the smaller packs from central California and the Colorado River area had joined them.

He led the pack right down the main drag of Vegas. It was planned that in most of the large cities they would parade before the people to let them know just how many bikers were involved. It gave the bikers a chance to break the monotony of the interstate pace they kept up. Now that the pack was large enough, they had taken it up to sixty miles an hour. If the man wanted to, he could try to stop them for speeding, but Treb didn't think they would.

In a large vacant lot next to Caesar's Palace on the strip there were over two thousand bikers waiting for the pack to pull in. Dick Bondano was at the lead. He had left Treb to organize this area and he did a damn good job of it. Since this was the first stop for the main pack out of Los Angeles, Dick had gotten some of the local bike shops to chip in and there was free coffee and donuts for all.

When the pack could be heard, long before they could see it, Dick got the driveway area clear. He had been listening to the news on one of the radios that was in a follow up trick and he knew there were a lot more bikes than they had expected.

Dick saw Treb and Rom at the head of the pack and waved to them as they pulled in. He ran over and they embraced. It had been awhile. They all walked to the coffee and donut tables and hurriedly discussed the route out of town. This was Dick's town and he was to lead the snake out.

The fifteen minute break went fast and soon Treb was waving his hand in the air for the bikers to load up while the bikers were still rolling into the parking lot. Only a couple of hundred could see him, but the sound of their bikes starting alerted the others and soon they were ready.

Dick pulled out first with Treb and Tom right behind. Then all the clubs and outriders started to pull in behind. Dick led them down to Fremont, right through "Glitter Gulch" where all the big neon lights were, and out to the interstate. The gamblers lined the street for over an hour to watch the pack go through.

They headed out of Las Vegas and into the desert again. Treb and Dick both had the same thought. Less than a year ago they had met here and they had taken the very same route.

They headed out of Glendale, Nevada, where a lot of bikers pulled off for gas, and Dick and Rom led the pack. Treb had stopped for gas and would catch up as fast as he could.

In the gas station Treb stood like a m an in a trance watching the pack go by. He was there just a few minutes, but for the whole time he was being passed by the pack. He estimated the pack now at over 8,000 bikers.

He cut through the pack after getting gas and held the throttle wide open as he passed down the double yellow. He was doing over a hundred and it still took a long time for him to get back to the head.

He reached it just as the snake was heading into the Virgin River Gorge. Dick and Treb grinned at each other as they passed the spot where they had tied up the cop.

Their next break was planned for the little town of Richfield, Utah. It was at the beginning of the I-70. There they would meet the Sundowners and all the other clubs from Washington, Oregon, Idaho, Montana and Wyoming. Raunchy would be leading the group.

Treb was pretty well settled back into riding as they pulled through St. George and made their way out of town. As they turned the bend ten miles north of St. George Treb was a little surprised. There were almost a thousand bikes waiting there led by John and Ann, the folks he had met on his last trip through here and whom he hadn't seen since Daytona. He remembered that John had gotten a Harley but he didn't know he had already run prospect and was now a full-fledged Sundowner. John waved as he passed and Treb motioned for him to come up in the front. John motioned for the pack he had gotten together to drop into the back and he was proud as he started his Harley and pulled out to catch up with the front. Ann was smiling broadly to, but she didn't want him to know it. She just wrapped her arms around his neck and gave him a squeeze. She knew what this meant to him, to ride up in front with Treb and the other organizers.

With the new group that was added and with the stragglers that there were picking up a long the way, the news broadcasts were estimating over 10,000 bikes already in the pack and they weren't to meet the next big pack until Richfield. It was working better than Treb had expected, but he didn't know the half of it yet. All he knew was that as far as he could see behind him were bikes and that was all he needed.

Raunchy was busy leading his group down through Redondo and Salinas and he was the first to arrive at the meeting point. He checked his watch and saw that he was almost half an hour ahead of schedule. He motioned to all that were there to get gassed up, since the main pack would probably need gas when they got in, and then he directed them to pull off as far as they could so the pack would have room to pull in off the highway. The interstate was starting right there and from here to Washington was all interstate. No side roads.

Raunchy hadn't like that last stretch of road. He had over 8,000 bikes with him from all over the northwest and he knew that three had gone off the road. It wasn't a bad percentage, but still he didn't like it.

For five minutes before they were scheduled in the pack could be heard. As they pulled into view Raunchy looked for Treb. He found him right up in front.

As they started pulling in he walked over to Treb along with Wheels out of northern Utah, Shane Harley from Washington, and Chains, who was head of the Oregon group. They stood around talking for awhile as dick, Rom and Treb took turns walking to the nearby bushes to drain their lizards. It was starting to get hour out now and many of the bikers were using the rest time to take off their jackets and other heavy garb. Even though it was six in the evening it was still light and would be for three more hours. Treb looked up and gave thanks for daylight saving time and for the good weather too.

Soon there were on the road again. Now the snake was almost 40 miles from front to back and the latest news estimates were around 20,000 bikes. By now Treb and the rest of them were getting used to the sound and it wasn't even novel. They all knew what a sight it was when they pulled through a town, but what they didn't know was that Leroy Makelray had arranged for the local ABD affiliates to film the pack going through some of the larger towns and that night it would be shown all over the Midwest and East Coast. As Treb and his group slept just outside Rifle Colorado, thousands more bikers were introduced to what was going on.

By the time the bikers awoke in the first light of morning it was the most talked about event in the country. Even the politicians in Washington were starting to get worried.

The police departments along I-70 were already getting set for the onslaught. They planned on blocking the highways to cross traffic as the bikers went through. Event though the bikers were traveling at 60 miles an hour I still took a full hour for the pack to pass any given point. The snake was over sixty miles long by the time they passed through Denver. Snoopy and Oaf from the Sons of Silence had gotten over five thousand bikers to join there. And all the bikers from the rest of Colorado, led by Crazy Joe, and those who had come up from El

Paso, Tucson and Albuquerque were picked up just outside of town. No more big groups were expected to join now until Kansas City, but there were many small, one and two hundred bike groups waiting to join along the way.

After the Texas-New Mexico group joined in, the pack was estimated to be forty thousand strong and the snake, including the stragglers, stretched for over 100 miles.

Bikers from Houston and Fort Worth who had seen the protest on television were now heading for Kansas City along with all the bikers from North and South Dakota, Minnesota and Iowa. All the main arteries in the Midwest were jammed with motorcycles heading to Kansas City. A meeting point was set up for a night's rest just outside of Bonneville, Missouri, and plans were already underway for a big party that night sponsored by the Banditos and the Journeymen. This would be the last night on the road before Washington.

Bikers started arriving at the meeting place long before the pack was due in and by the time the sunset it was a full-fledged party, wall-to-wall.

Chapter 60

I was really beat. What kept the people going was beyond me. I was really starting to wish we had made it a three night run instead of trying to rush it like we had.

I glanced over a Dick and he looked tired too. Margo was leaning against his back asleep, just like I could feel Karen on mine. The only one who looked awake in the front of the pack was Rom. He had been taking some whites so he was roaring to go.

When we passed through Kansas City it was almost midnight. It had been a long day's ride from Colorado. I knew a lot of the bikers had stopped along the road to sleep, but they would catch us in the morning.

We rounded a corner and I saw a lot of bonfires.

At first I thought it was an army encampment or something that was there to stop us, but it wasn't. It was just Speedy from the Kansas group along with Indian and Big Eddie. They were with some 30,000 bikers who had come in to join the protest from Texas to North Dakota. It looked like something out of the Cecil B. DeMille movie.

I rode around the outer edge of the encampment and heard the pack behind me pulling in. Soon more fires were lit and lour music filled the air. It took hours for the bikes to pull in and more kept arriving all night long.

Karen and Margo walked around with John's old lady Ann until they found a place to throw down the sleeping bags. I knew Karen wanted to crash and I told her to go ahead. Rom gave me a couple of double crossed whites and I popped them into my mouth. I wouldn't sleep again until this was all over.

The group of us walked around checking out around the different bonfires to see what the general consensus of opinion was about the rally so far. It surprised me to find out how many of the bikers didn't even know about the protest until after it started and ABD News started pumping it. The other networks had gotten involved so they wouldn't look like they didn't know what was going on and soon al the TV and radio stations were banging away on it.

I made a note to thank Leroy one more time.

Those of us who were riding up in front, Dick, Rom, myself, John, Snoopy, Oaf and Raunchy all had the same feeling. We were doing too good. We sat over on a pile of old fencing and tried to figure out what the government might do to stop us. We knew they wouldn't try and arrest us all. They just couldn't handle it.

We talked for a couple of hours about it and nothing up. All the while bikes were pulling in. As the sun was coming up it really did look like something out of D.W. Griffith's epic silent film, Birth of a Nation. It looked like a movie west. It couldn't have been real.

But it was. A helicopter flew overhead and photographed it for CBS News. They counted the people in one section of the picture and multiplied it by the size of the encampment.

Later we heard on a radio that there were over 100,000 bikes involved in the protest so far. The word was also out that the streets and highways all up and down the East Coast were jammed with bikes heading for Washington. Most of them would join the pack along the way.

We all stood around in a state of shock. One hundred thousand bikers. Right here, right now. It was a bigger success than we thought possible. They couldn't stop us now.

Or so we thought.

A biker came over to where we were sitting and asked who was the leader of this protest. When I told him I was he started talking.

He had come west to join us, down Interstate 70. While he was coming through Illinois he tried to stop for gas, but none of the stations were open he finally fond one in Effingham that was open, but the owner told him he was supposed to shut down while the bikers were in the area. The police had told him to.

So that was it. I knew something would be tried, but I never even thought about the fuel supply. It was just like that old war movie I saw where Rommel's troops were stopped in Africa by blowing up the fuel depots. Only here all they had to do was shut them down.

It was four in the morning and the encampment would be getting up in an hour. We didn't have a lot of time. Fortunately most of the bikes had already filled their tanks and it was still at least a hundred miles to the place where the biker had said the stations were closed.

We say there for a few minutes trying to figure a way to get around it when Snoopy came up with the idea. After talking about it Snoopy and I left on our bikes. We had to get to a phone booth fast. There was a lot to do.

When we got back the camp was wide awake. It was a little after five and move out time was set for 5:30. That would be the first bikes out, anyway. The last bikes probably wouldn't be pulling out until well after seven or seven-thirty. It takes a long time for 100,000 bikes to maneuver into a two-lane riding position.

We couldn't see it from the ground, but the pack stretched for over 200 miles now and all of the side roads had bikes waiting to get into the pack. Some were joining for the first time and others were just trying to get back in after gas stops or food stops. Every gas station and restaurant along the way was full of bikers. It was our day for sure.

When we were through St. Louis and well into Illinois I saw that the gas stations were closed. It started at about Greenville, some forty miles from the state line. Pretty soon bikes started pulling over to the side of the road out of gas.

I was praying that soon our plan would show some promise. As I passed the Hamburg offramp, some twenty mile after the fuel stoppage was in effect, I saw the first truck. It had worked. There were three Outlaws waving at us from the top of the gasoline truck. I reached for my DB and told them where the first station was closed. Now we could see five or six more trucks coming behind the first one. Each was assigned an offramp and soon every exit from the interstate had a gas truck pumping gas. The price was lower than the stations had been charging. It was all set up in a very short time with just one phone call to the Outlaws in Chicago. As soon as I told them what the cops had done, they said it was no problem. They went out and hired every gas truck in Chicago and the surrounding vicinity. Soon the one hundred miles from Greenville to Terre Haute, Indiana, had more has than normal. Every station had a gas truck parked in it and they were pumping has and Harley oil like crazy Arabs.

As Mike Jones led the thirty thousand bikers from Wisconsin and Illinois onto the interstate he couldn't figure out what was going on. But as soon as he jumped in front with us and I told him what we were doing, he couldn't stop laughing.

The only ones not laughing were the police. They just sat in their cars on the side of the highway watching. It was out of their control now, no doubt about it.

After we skirted around Pittsburgh we headed out

onto the Pennsylvania Turnpike. When I saw the toll booths I just smiled. This was going to be fun. As I passed through the gate I reached into my pocket and threw a dime into the receptacle. I wouldn't want to be called a crook for not paying the toll.

By now we were 200,000 strong, since most of the riders from the northeast had joined us outside of Pennsylvania. And we were getting bigger all the time. As we cut off the Turnpike onto I-70 again heading south to Washington I knew nothing could stop us. We were on our way in.

When we hit the 81 junction at Hagerstown, Gizmo and his folks from New York joined us along with Playboy and all the bikers out of Connecticut. Here were about 50,000 of them. It was impossible for the new arrivals to pull into the back of the pack because it just went back for hundreds of miles. All the cars were pulling off the road and only bikes could get on. Gizmo and Playboy led their pack onto the highway and now we were filling all four lanes.

The news services had stopped trying to estimate the crowds. At my last gas stop I heard one reporter say we were over a quarter of a million strong, but there was no way to know for sure. They had one shot on television, according to this one gas station attendant I talked to, that was taken from a high altitude and it showed bikes on every road in every description for over 500 miles around Washington, and they were all heading in.

Wino Willie, Shady and Dingy Dave were leading the group in from the south and they had secured an area for camping and for the final gathering point before the ride tomorrow. I had told them to expect maybe 75,000 but none of us expected this. It was just too much to imagine. Leroy had said that television would make a difference, but I never realized how much. The states that were close enough to Washington, like Maryland, Delaware, Virginia and even New Jersey and New York sent all their bikers down just for the weekend. It was a short putt and it made them a part of the group.

The original spot that they had planned for camping was the Fairbank Highway Research Station, which was wide open and had a lot of room, but they didn't expect this many people. As I led the group closer to Washington I started to worry a little.

What if the place wouldn't hold all the bikes? I had to keep this protest together or it was all for nothing. Finally, at the 495 interchange, I pulled to a stop. The bikers had the whole street anyway so we might as well figure it out right here before going any farther.

I swung by kickstand down and got off my bike, then I motioned for all the leaders to come with me and we walked to the middle of the road.

I spread a map out on the street and we sat there looking at it in the headlight of my chopper. We had to decide where to lead this multitude. After a few minutes discussion a cop car came up the freeway, going the wrong way, and pulled up next to us.

"What's the problem?" he asked as he got out of his car and walked over.

I explained about where we were going to camp and how we didn't think it would hold all the people. He looked at the map for a moment and then he walked over to his car.

After a few minutes on the radio he came back.

"How about this? We will close off Highway 50 here," and he pointed at the map to a highway that circled Arlington National Cemetery, "to here. It will be all yours. There is a lot of grass there for camping and in the morning you can get to the capitol with no road problems at all. How about it?"

I thanked him and told him we would discuss it and get back to him. The place he was pointing to was just about perfect as far as location, but would it be big enough?

After we talked for about five minutes we agreed. We might as well try it since we didn't have any alternatives. Besides it was almost midnight and folks were getting tired. I motioned to the cop that we would camp there and he turned his car around.

For the next twenty miles we had a police escort with flashing red lights and everything just like visiting dignitaries. The cop radioed to the other police where we were going and they led the other bikers to the same area. We were there.

Chapter 61

The view from the 27th story of the Mayflower Hotel was breathtaking. From here Leroy could see nothing but bikes in every direction for as far as he could see. It made him feel powerful knowing that he had helped bring this about. He stood like a king looking down over his subjects.

He knew Treb and Rom were busy somewhere down below making plans for tomorrow's protest and that Mike Jones and all the other state leaders were busy too. This was a big day in their lives.

"Hell," he said out loud, "it's a big day for all of America."

This was one of the few times in 200 years that people who decided they had had enough got off their butts and did something about it. And it had to be the bikers who did it.

The more Leroy thought about it the more sense that made. The bikers were the last vestige of freedom's pride in themselves as a group. It stood to reason that when the government signaled them out as the target of the first mandatory self-protection law, they fought it.

Of course the government had tried to introduce mandatory seat belts next, but since car drivers are a majority in Congress they just said no and the idea was dropped. Since bikers are a friendless minority the government figured it would be no problem at all starting the self-protection laws with them.

They were wrong. All the money that the insurance lobbies and the helmet manufacturers had spent, it had all gone for this.

Who would have guessed it?

Finally Leroy turned from his window and walked to the bedroom. He untied the belt to his robe and dropped it onto the chair next to the bed. Sandy looked up at him and smiled. She had asked when he was in Daytona with her if there was any way she could see this thing to the end and as soon as he was sure he could do it he had called her and set it up It only cost a couple hundred to fly her to Washington and it was already worth it. He really liked her, even if she was a hooker. She was more honest than most of the women he met in the TV business.

He pulled back the covers and crawled into the bed with her. It felt good as she snuggled up close to him. He was thinking about making love to her, but that was all it was, just a thought, because before he knew it he was asleep.

Sandy looked at him and then she smiled. She liked him and wished that they weren't just together on a business relationship. Even though he was a lot older than she was she still got along with him better than any other guy she'd known.

Finally she rolled over and went to sleep.

While Leroy slept the network continued to gather data on the rally. Now there were almost 300,000 bikers in the Washington area and at least 50,000 more on the roads heading in.

Every state in the country was represented. The Alaska Motorcycle Club and Street Bikers United out of Hawaii sent their emissaries. This protest was as well attended as any network person had seen, including the civil rights and antiwar rallies.

At five in the morning Jim and Jack, Leroy's camera and sound men, loaded the truck and headed out to film what they could. They didn't get far, though. Since the national cemetery had filled up the bikers had just stopped their bikes in the traffic jam, pulled out their sleeping bags and proceeded to sleep and party right in the middle of the streets. No vehicles could get in or out of Washington.

Chapter 62

The sun was slowly rising over the Washington Monument. Treb and Dick were sitting on the steps of the Lincoln Memorial talking with Rom and Raunchy and a couple of the others who had been friends through this whole ordeal. The girls were out trying to scrounge up some food for them. They weren't very hungry because of the whites they were taking, which was actually diet style methedrine cut to a 15 % powder with lactose and pressed into pill form. Food was the farthest thing from their mind, but it was a good way to get the women out of their way while they made final preparations.

The plan was to lead the protest up the road to the Theodore Roosevelt Bridge then over to Constitution Avenue. They would follow it to 17th Street where they would make a left past the District of Columbia War Memorial and then they would pass between the reflecting pond and the Washington Monument.

Treb gazed out from where they were sitting and he could see the street they were talking about. All the plans had been like a dream, but not they were starting to come true. He looked down 17th Street to where they would turn, up by Pennsylvania Avenue. After one turn they would be right in front of the White House. There were no plans to stop there, however. This was just a dodge to get the police and National Guard to set up their defenses, whatever they might be, in front of the White House. Actually the plan was to pass right by there as the gathered troops looked on in relief and to parade right down Pennsylvania Avenue another mile to the capitol. There would be so many bikes on the road clogging up the throughways that the Guard wouldn't be able to relocate. They would be stuck, and then the bikers could hold their protest on the steps of the capitol which was what they wanted in the first place.

In fighting oppression like the helmet law the President can't really do much good. It's the House and the Senate that make or break the efforts so the capitol was the natural target.

Because of his previous experience dealing with the bike gangs the head of the Omega Squad was put in charge of the joint effort in the capitol. Charlie Bainbridge of the Omega Squad knew his job. He remembered when he had captured Treb back in Daytona and he was still after him even though the law had not yet been broken. He vowed to bust him and make a charge stick.

He had the National Guard setting up at seven a.m. all around the White House. He wasn't about to let those damn bikers get into the grounds, even. This was his chance to show the big shots what he could do. He could salvage his whole career right here today and he knew it.

Departure was set for 10 a.m. and the word was spreading like wildfire through the crowd. By now the networks were estimating the crowd at over 400,000 people, calling it the largest gathering that had ever taken lace in Washington, D.C.

Bikers were wheel to wheel for miles all around the city, but they stayed on the Arlington side of the river. No bikes went over to Washington. That was being saved for 10 a.m. when Treb and all the bikers who had worked so hard to repeal the helmet law would lead the parade.

At 9:30 Leroy had his camera set up on the Virginia side of the bridge and he was chatting with Treb in the news van. Leroy had film coverage of what went on before the protest started so he didn't want to start the live network feed until a couple of minutes before ten.

Treb looked like he didn't have a care in the world. He thanked Leroy for everything and vowed to pay him back the money he owed him as soon as possible.

Leroy just smiled. Because of Treb and what he had done Leroy was now a nationally famous newscaster. He would never work for a small station like KABD again and he would never work for those wages either. Now he was making over $100,000 per year, five times his previous salary.

He gazed grinningly at Treb. It was men like that who made life a kick. "Treb, you and I and Rom are all even. In fact I owe you more than I can ever repay you," he held out his hand.

"And besides that, friends never discuss money matters."

Treb didn't know what to say so he didn't say anything. They just sat there for a few minutes.

Then it was time.

When Treb emerged from the van a roar went up from the crowd. Their leader was there.

Rumors had been traveling through the crowd about Treb. The story of how he was hurt was changed into a heroic charge against the Omega Squad. He was a hero to this crowd of bikers.

As the cameras started and the network in New York stood by, Treb turned to Leroy. Then he explained to the camera what the protest was all about. It was near, simple and to the point.

When he was through he just stood there. Shouts were coming from the crowd. He walked over to his bike and swung his leg over it. Karen stood aside waiting for him to start it.

He didn't use the self starter. Somehow it just didn't seem right. He swung the kickstarter down and even though his leg hurt it started. As soon as the sound of Treb's engine was heard all the other bikers started up their machines. For miles and miles all that could be heard were bikes. The sound was threatening like thunder.

But it was beautiful too and Treb could sit and listen and hear the beauty.

He turned back to Karen. She leaned forward and

kissed him. His weariness fell away. He felt better than he had ever felt in his life.

Rom was sitting on his bike just looking at Treb, as were Dick and all his other friends.

All of a sudden Treb laid his bike over on the kickstand, got off the machine, leaving it idling. He walked over to Rom and embraced him, kissing him full on the lips in a biker's kiss. Then he went to Dick and did the same thing.

Then he was ready. He got back on his bike and aimed it across the bridge. He was ready for whatever happened.

Chapter 63

The National Guard was ready as the bikers came across the bridge. So were the police and the Army Reserve. Charlie Bainbridge had called them all out and still they were vastly outnumbered. The Army estimated that there were just under a half million bikers in the city. From the helicopter survey he had taken an hour earlier he couldn't tell. All he could see were bikes in every direction.

From his vantage point he could see down 17th Avenue to Constitution where the bikers would be entering. The walkie-talkie told him that they had just started across the bridge. He looked down the street.

Sure enough there they were and that damned Treb Lincoln was right in front. Why hadn't he wasted him in Florida?

The pack field past him and his troops and aimed toward the far end of the White House parking area. Charlie wasn't too worried because he knew that only about 10,000 bikes could get across the bridge without jamming up from the White House.

Then excited reports started coming over the walkie-talkie. There were bikers coming across the Arlington memorial Bridge being led by Dingy Dave and his group. Also they were coming across the Key Bridge being led by Mike Jones.

Just as he was about to say something into the walkie-talkie another message came through. They weren't stopping at the White House. They were still moving right down Pennsylvania Avenue.

All of a sudden it came clear to Bainbridge. They had outfoxed him. They were riding on the capitol.

The radio messages were coming fast now. Wino Willie was bringing in a group over the bridge riding north on the capital while another, led by Indian, was coming north up Pennsylvania.

Every bridge and every street into Washington was choked with motorcycles. Event he police on their scooters couldn't get through.

Charlie stifled an urge to panic. He knew he couldn't move any of his equipment and the bikers were as well equipped with communications as they were since CB radios were so plentiful in the crowd.

He called for his communications man and told him to find out what channel on the CB the bikers were using.

He got down off the truck and started walking

toward the capitol. It was the only way he could get there with all the bikes in the street.

By then 200,000 bikes were in Washington and more were still pouring in. On the steps of the capitol, a mile away, Treb had set up a loud speaker system that was carried in on bikes. There were just the usual guards on duty there so there was no problem. As soon as the speakers were set up Treb started to address the assembling crowd.

He had told the networks where they were going only moments before he led the pack in, giving them just enough time to set up by the capitol. They were all ready with their cameras as Treb started his talk.

Charlie Bainbridge started to run. He could hear the speeches up ahead and he knew he had been made a fool of. He was having a hard time weaving through the multitude and every time he would run into a bike he thought it was on purpose. He was getting really mad.

Chapter 64

John Trumbull held on to Ann's hand as he walked through the crowd gathered before the Capitol. It was more than he had ever imagined. Thousands of bikers, all like brothers, getting together to be a part of this historical moment.

Up on the steps was Treb. John thought back on that night when he and Dick had shown up on his doorstep back in Utah. If it hadn't been for that he would probably still be back there being bored by the life in St. George. He was glad how things had changed.

John looked over the crowd. He remembered what Dick had said at the meeting earlier in the morning. While Treb was in the ABD van talking to Leroy Makelray, Dick got together with a lot of Treb's friends. They talked about what had happened at the Los Angeles protest when the undercover cops had tried to break up the meeting. Dick and Rom were both worried about Treb so they asked John and Raunchy to be on the lookout for troublemakers.

The speeches were starting now and John could hear Treb telling the bikers about the helmet law. He looked at the crowd a little more closely now. He saw Leroy Makelray about fifty feet away, but there were so many people around that he couldn't even get close to him. Movement was almost impossible.

All of a sudden he saw a guy in a business suit trying to push his way to the front. He had a walkie-talkie in one hand and was screaming into it. He was about ten feet away and really looked angry. He just kept pushing his way forward.

A few feet behind him was an army guy in his fatigues and he had a pack on his back. It looked like a portable radio or something.

When the suit was just a few feet away, he put the walkie-talkie to his mouth. John could hear him then because he was almost screaming into the thing.

He was telling whoever was on the other end to have the men load and lock their rifles.

All of a sudden the guy in the suit fumbled in his coat. John couldn't believe what he was seeing. A gun was pulled out. With both hands he aimed it.

John didn't even think. It was more like a reaction. As the gun cleared the tops of the people's heads, John jumped for it and when he had it in his hand he held on with all his strength.

Captain Bainbridge was enraged when John grabbed his gun. He struggled with the grubby looking biker. Soon he and John were wrestling on the ground.

Leroy saw the scuffle when the people crowded back to give them room to fight. He pushed his way toward the opening in the crowd.

By the time Leroy was near enough to see what was going on it was all over. The bikers had taken the gun from Bainbridge and he was being held down by five or six big guys. One of the guys holding him down was John, whom Leroy had seen with Treb a couple of times. Leroy asked him what was going on.

After it was explained and Bainbridge had claimed down a little, Leroy took him by the arm and started to walk with him.

He calmly explained that ABD News knew what had gone on and if anything got out of hand, like any fighting or gunfire, they would know who started it. He pointed out the van parked a hundred feet away and told Charlie that the crew had shot the whole incident as it just happened, so they would have taped evidence that Bainbridge had been the instigator.

Bainbridge was almost calm by the time Leroy finished. The fight was drained out of him. All he could do was nod like a man in shock.

For years he had wondered what it was like to be in the limelight, but now that his chance had come he had blown it. The bikers had won this round and he knew it.

As he walked back to his post by the White House he would hear the speeches. The radio man followed dutifully along behind him.

Chapter 65

I looked into the eyes of one of the bikers who was standing a few yards in front of me. I had already explained all the problems involved in getting the helmet law dropped and now I was ready to introduce Senator Holbrook, who had agreed to sponsor a repeal bill.

"It is up to you," I said pointing right at the biker I had singled out of the crowd. "Are you ready?"

The crowd shouted they were. I raised my arms and tried to quiet them.

"Now I want to introduce Senator Mark Holbrook from Connecticut, who has agreed," I paused for a second to get them to quiet down a little bit more, "has agreed to introduce a bill that will stop the federal blackmail." The bikers all went wild. This was the beginning of the end of the lid law and they all knew it.

Senator Holbrook walked up to the mike. I shook his hand and then turned and walked off the platform. I could hear the suave voice of a trained politician taking over.

"What you people have done today is to prove that the people of America still have a way to voice their discontent with unjust laws. I am with you all the way."

As the bikers cheered I walked down off the stage. It was done. Holbrook had told me that the bill was as good as passed. The bureaucrat who had started the whole thing, some little guy in the Department of Transportation, had been transferred out and the opposition was already overwhelmed by the sheer number of people who turned out. The helmet law was as good as gone.

I wrapped my arm around Karen and walked into the crowd. Dick and Rom were standing near the reflecting pool and I slowly worked my way over there through the crowds. The Senator was getting a lot of cheering now and I could see the crowd was happy with what was going on.

When I got to Rom he just smiled and held out his hand. I took it and we embraced. He knew the battle was over too, as did Dick who smiled and pulled Margo a little closer to him.

We started back toward the District Court Building where we had left our bikes parked. As we walked through the crowd Raunchy joined us and by the time we reached our bikes Indian and Big Eddie had come over too. A joint was produced and we sat on the bikes and took a couple of deep hits. There was no way we could get our bikes out of this mess until some of the crowd dissipated so all we had to do was sit and wait.

John and Ann soon joined us and then some of the state coordinators. We all went over to a patch of grass and sat down. Nobody talked. We just listened to the crowd and tried to hear what the speakers were saying. It was pretty hard with all the yelling.

I looked around at my friends and I knew where I wanted to be. Right here with people that care. All I wanted to do for the next few months was ride and party.

Pretty soon the speeches ended and the crowd started to break up. We all just sat there on the lawn feeling the effects of the smooth weed reaching into our minds.

I don't know where the time went, but it was already two in the afternoon. As the bikes pulled out we all sat there and listened to the sounds we liked so much. The thumping of a big twin echoed hundreds of thousands of times.

For two hours we sat there smoking one number after another waiting for the area to clear enough to get our bikes out.

Finally we could see the capitol steps from where we were sitting. The first one to speak was Indian.

"Hey, you guys want to come down to New Orleans for a while? We got a run planned for next week that should be a good one. A whole pig to barbecue and plenty of cold beer..."

I didn't hear the rest of it. I just laid back on the

grass and dropped my head on Karen's lap. She smiled down at me.

"Hey Rom, why don't you and Dick go down there?" I glanced up at them for a second. "I think I want to a take a solo putt down through Georgia and Mississippi and just kill a couple of weeks."

I knew that hey couldn't pass up a party and wasn't a bit surprised when they agreed.

The next few minutes were spent saying goodbye to old friends and then I hit the starter button on my bike and pulled into the pack of bikes leaving the city. I didn't know where I was going and really didn't care.

All I knew was the feel of my bike and the feeling of a good woman behind me was al I needed. What more could a man want?

Chapter 66

The lights were bright in Leroy's eyes but he was used to it. What seemed a little strange was the set that he was on. He had become used to doing his broadcasts in the open. It seemed too formal in the network studios of New York.

The big feature for tonight's national broadcast was Leroy's story and he had it all rehearsed. Earlier he had been called to the 33rd floor where he sat down with the general manager and vice president in charge of news and community involvement. It was there that they gave him the word. Leroy Makelray was the newest anchorman in the New York network offices.

He had made it.

Chapter 67

The television screen was the only light in the dime bar. It laid a bluish cast over the three people in the room. Treb and Karen sat on stools near the set sipping beer and the bartender was buys rewashing a glass that he had already washed at least three times.

The screen was filled with the ABD News logo. Treb stood and turned the sound up so he could hear it. The bartender just glanced up and went back to wiping his glass.

"From New York it's the ABD News with Aaron Donaldson, Shari Reding, and tonight Leroy Makelray with our feature story."

Treb stared at the set as the familiar face of Aaron Donaldson filled the screen.

"Motorcyclists jammed the streets in the nation's capitol today. Here from Washington is Leroy Makelray with the story."

The screen filled with a view of hundreds of bikes passing beneath an overpass. Leroy was standing with his back to the camera. Treb recognized it as the Los Angeles protest.

Slowly Leroy turned and faced the camera.

"Today thousands of bikers have gathered to fight a law they feel is wrong." He stared into the camera.

All of a sudden the scene changed to the New York studio. Leroy sitting at a desk in the newsroom. He gazed solemnly into the camera.

"That was almost a year ago. Today half a million bikers rode to the nation's capitol to finish that protest. They won." He looked right into the camera.

"Here is the story of how a bunch of unorganized bikers changed the law of the land…"

Treb chugged his beer down and turned to Karen.

"Come on," he said. "Let's go do some riding."

....

XXX

About The Author

Robert "Bob Bitchin" Lipkin was born in Los Angeles, California in 1944. He spent 28 years riding motorcycles around the United States and Europe, writing of his experiences in all of the major motorcycles magazines of the '70s and '80s.

In the early '70s he acted as roustabout and bodyguard for famous motorcycle daredevil Evil Knievel, and later produced "CycleExpo," one of the largest motorcycle shows on the West Coast. During most of those years he lived aboard various sailboats that he would buy in rundown condition and restore to sell.

He went on to create *BIKER NEWS, BIKER Magazine and TATTOO Magazine* and was instrumental in forming *ABATE*, a legislative biker organization. In the mid '80s he sold his magazines and retired.

He spent several years sailing the Pacific, first on his Formosa 51' ketch *Lost Soul*, and then on an aft-cockpit Formosa 51 named *Predator*. In 1991 he purchased a derelict 68' ketch, which he renamed *Lost Soul*. A year later, after extensive repairs, he departed with his ladyfriend Jody on a voyage that would take them to the four corners of the World.

When they returned he founded *LATITUDES & ATTITUDES Magazine*, which has gone on to become the largest magazine in its field. He also created the weekly TV show *Latitudes & Attitudes* with his friend Darren O'Brien. He now spends his time between Redondo Beach, sailing, and his home in the Sierra Nevada mountains, in Berry Creek, California.

Other books of interest From Bob Bitchin

BIKER

A collection of true stories showing just what kind of fun and games a man can get into when he rides the highways of America. These are true stories that will keep you asking yourself: "Now who the hell would done something like that?!"

Emerald Bay

A Treb Lincoln Adventure

This novel follows Treb Lincoln as he tries to learn what caused the death of his young wife in a boating explosion in peacful Emerald Bay. The trail leads to places you would least expect. Fast paced.

King Harbor

A Treb Lincoln Adventure

When Treb Lincoln returns from a boating adventure, he is thrust into a mystery that will take him to the far reaches of the earth in search of a way to help a friend. Quick and spirited, this is a real adventure!

Letters from the Lost Soul

The true story of a five year voyage all over the world. Travel with Bob Bitchin and his wife Jody aboard the 60' ketch *Lost Soul* from the sun drenched beaches of Bora Bora to the Islands of Greece and the beautiful Caribbean.

The Sailing Life

A collection of insights into the world of cruising, as seen by the founder and publisher of Latitudes & Attitudes Magazine and the television show of the same name. See what makes people love the cruising lifestyle.

All these titles are available at:

www.seafaring.com 888-8-WE-SAIL

Table of Contents

Creepy Crawlers 115

The Birds 151

Beware! 187

From the Rivers to the Sea 211

Suggested Reading 243

Index 244

Introduction

Southern Oregon and Northern California, the region sometimes called the State of Jefferson, boasts one of the most diverse environments on the planet. Without too much difficulty, you can visit alpine meadows, hot, dry chaparral, coastal tide pools — even urban sprawl — within the span of a single day.

For over thirty years, Dr. Frank Lang, Professor Emeritus of Biology at Southern Oregon University in Ashland, Oregon, has roamed this complex and fascinating bioregion, learning its plants, animals and soils, and encountering the challenges we all face in keeping its biological diversity intact. Whether giant redwoods or microscopic water bears, Dr. Lang knows the non-human residents of the State of Jefferson as do few others.

The volume you hold in your hand represents over a decade of Dr. Lang's popular weekly commentaries, *Nature Notes,* aired on the region's public radio service, Jefferson Public Radio (JPR). Over the years, JPR listeners have delighted in Dr. Lang's commentaries on the natural world, and it is their many requests that have led to this book.

Dr. Lang first suggested this series to Jefferson Public Radio in 1988, hoping it would be an extension of his teaching, a way of spreading his love of the natural world beyond the confines of the university classroom. We responded that we loved the idea, and when could Dr. Lang begin writing and recording weekly commentaries? "Weekly?" Dr. Lang said, rather shocked. But he rose to the challenge of the care and feeding of a radio series. Soon, JPR listeners began to look forward to his wealth of knowledge about the region's environment, and his dry, sometimes mischievous sense of humor (which pops up in these pages as well).

While we do not intend *A Nature Notes Sampler* as a complete guide to the natural history of the region, we do hope that it will accompany your outings in the State of Jefferson. Through this book you can discover new places, and rediscover those you've visited many times. It is our hope that you'll marvel at the diverse life of the region, and develop a deeper understanding of the natural world and our place in it.

John Baxter
Director of New Media,
Jefferson Public Radio
October, 2000

I

Travelogue

Habitats

We hear much about habitat these days. Loss of habitat endangers natural salmon runs in the Columbia River. Many acres of ancient forest are set aside as habitat for the remaining populations of spotted owls and for 100 other vertebrates and 1,500 invertebrates found in the same habitat.

Besides commercially important forest trees, there are other plants and fungi that depend on old growth forest habitat. Nitrogen-fixing epiphytes and mycorrhizal fungi depend on old growth, and old growth depend on them.

After 50 years and more of competing with humans in the Pacific northwest, nature is the big loser. The loss of habitat is clearly evident and makes daily news. This precious habitat is the immediate environment in which an organism lives and includes shelter, food, water and breeding sites. Water is the critical substance and most strongly influences the survival and distribution of organisms. Nourishment also must be available in the habitat on a sustainable basis. If water or nourishment change, so does the habitat and so go the organisms. They leave if they can, die if they can't. Loss of enough critical habitat may lead to loss of the entire species. The loss is forever, and forever is a long time.

Besides water and nourishment, a suitable breeding environment that allows courting and mating activities is essential. The habitat must support the young to adulthood. Loss of this habitat feature is troubling salmon and the spotted owl.

Humans reduce natural habitats directly by logging, water diversion, plowing for agriculture, and building and maintaining our artificial habitats. We also reduce natural habitats indirectly by polluting land, air and water. Even if there is space available, it may be uninhabitable.

We worry mostly about wildlife habitat. For most that means game animals. Game managers want to maintain

enough proper habitat to keep high numbers of game fish, birds and mammals for sportsmen, often at the expense of other natural values. A case in point is the destruction of native vegetation and vernal pool habitat on the Agate Desert by the Oregon State Department of Fish and Wildlife. They plow and plant annual cereals to feed their flightless pheasants.

Wildlife means all the wild things, including dickey birds and plants. A primary reason for the establishment of the Lower Table Rock and Agate Desert Preserves by The Nature Conservancy is to protect sensitive plant habitats. Animals that use the habitat are protected as well.

We now realize that more than space is necessary to maintain a stable population. Mere survival is inadequate. Organisms must survive and reproduce. Offspring are the future. They are the parents of the next generation, they may serve as food for other organisms, they may die of natural causes. Heat and cold, rain and drought, flood and fire, disease and famine all take their toll. To survive, the habitat must provide more than space. Long-term survival depends on intact functioning ecosystems, not an acre here or there. It must provide all these elements to avoid catastrophe.

The hard question is, who has the rights or prior rights to the so-called spaces of nature that serve as habitat? Humans, or the creatures present at our creation?

Marshes

Are small marshy areas in fields, along roads, around edges of ponds, or along streams of any value? Places where cattails grow and redwing blackbirds sing? Whether you said yes or no, you answered another question: Does wildlife have value?

We often think of wildlife as game animals we hunt and fish. There is a broader definition. Any non-domesticated (that is native) plant or animal may be considered wildlife. Many wildlife species use marshes, inundated wetlands with herbaceous plants adapted to constantly wet soils. We tend to think that marshes are large, like the north end of Klamath Lake, with an abundance of fish and waterfowl. Marshes can be small, just a few feet in diameter, and though small, play host to many plants and animals that prefer this habitat. In our area, typical marsh plants include cattails, rushes and sedges. Occasionally willows may appear along the margin. If trees and shrubs dominate the wet area, we have a swamp.

Do humans value the small marshy areas in their fields and along their roads? Generally not. We usually consider them a nuisance. We like to plow all our land, or groom it with more familiar vegetation. We drain it, dry it up, make it suitable for human needs and desires. Another nesting pair of waterbirds, a food-seeking shorebird, or a water-seeking, nest-building bird won't make much difference in our lives. We won't miss them, or the insects produced by the marsh, consumed by insect-eating birds. The birds will miss them though, and as the insects become less abundant so will the birds. We wouldn't miss the occasional small mammal whose hearth and home is in the marsh. Would we miss the creepy-crawlies, seen and unseen, heard and unheard? We probably would miss the frogs. What about the plants? Most don't know what they are, so what? Roadside ditches are great for carrying

away runoff. About the time they become interesting biologically, along comes the machine and strips them back to mineral soil. Who needs a flash of black and red wing to remind us that spring has sprung?

I do!

A marsh, no matter how tiny, gives us a slightly different aspect of nature to enjoy. It gives us a spot of green in the yellow parch of summer. It gives us a little moisture in the hot dry air. For curious, adventurous youngsters, a marsh is fascinating place to visit and explore, to discover nature.

Does nature in all its varied ways have a right to exist on its own merits? Must we reclaim all wild lands and convert them for our purposes? Why does a piece of land we can't use for our own purposes, fulfilling its rightful destiny, irritate us so? Ignorance, or worse? Maybe we need to cultivate an individual appreciation for nature to be expressed as a marsh. Take time to understand and enjoy these vignettes of our natural heritage, unique survivors of one of our earthly origins.

Unfortunately, marshes don't even count by modern-day values, unless we wisely decide that nature, as a marsh, deserves to exist. To learn to appreciate marshes and their unique beauty, read Sally Carrighar's *One Day at Teton Marsh* and join a small, but serious band of marsh-watchers. Huge marshes and small damp places are disappearing from the earth and with their disappearance, a sense of well-being disappears as well.

Bigelow Lakes

I go to Bigelow Lakes near Oregon Caves National Monument to look for wildflowers and grapeferns. The last time I was there, with a group of Forest Service people, we were treated to a close look at an animal that makes your overactive mutant Ninja teenager look like a slowly melting ice cube. We had a close encounter with a water shrew.

We located a substantial population of grapeferns, which was no small feat. They are only a few inches high, and are not conspicuous in any way, save for their clusters of tiny grape-like sporangia.

We walked down to the edge of the upper lake where we were startled by a small cylinder of gray fur rushing toward shore, under water, from the water lilies. Its churning legs left a trail of bubbles that turned into spray as the tiny beast made landfall and sped across a small grassy area to the creek that feeds the lake. We drove the poor creature up and down a short section of the creek while trying to get a closer look. I loudly announced that it was a water shrew, *Neurotrichus gibbsii.* Right on the common name, wrong on the scientific name. *Neurotrichus* is the shrew mole, an equally fascinating animal, that is really a mole and not a shrew.

The water shrew we saw could have been *Sorex palustris* the American water shrew or *S. bendirii,* the Pacific water shrew. It didn't sit still long enough for us to see if it was light below (American water shrew), or dark below, (Pacific water shrew). In any event it was at home in the water.

Water shrews can run across the water's surface supported by a fringe of stiff hairs on the outer and inner margins of their front and back feet, hairs that aid in swimming. When they dive they don't remain submerged long. The silvery layer of hair surrounding their bodies soon causes the shrew to pop to the surface like a fishing

bobber. Their fur often begins to wet and they must return to shore to dry out by rapidly grooming with their hind feet. As we discovered, water shrews are extremely agile on land.

Water shrews are the largest shrews in North America. Like all shrews they have a high metabolic rate and an appetite to match, maintained by a diet of insects, aquatic or otherwise, snails, slugs, leeches, small fish, and I suppose puppy dog tails if the opportunity arose. Captive water shrews store or use almost all their body weight in food per day.

We finally left the poor animal alone when someone suggested permanent burn-out might result from its encounter with *Homo sapiens.*

Bigelow Lakes is worth visiting for more than grapeferns and water shrews. In late spring or early summer when the snow is gone you will see a profusion of wildflowers in the meadows and the rocky cliffs above the lakes. According to Art Bernstein's *90 Best Day-Hikes in Southwestern Oregon and Far Northern California,* the Forest Service lists 14 sensitive plant species for the Bigelow Lakes area. He also warns of grazing cows.

Check with the Illinois Valley Visitor Center in Cave Junction for more precise directions to Bigelow Lakes, a Siskiyou National Forest botanical area and water shrew preserve.

Crater Lake

Crater Lake is one of planet Earth's great scenic wonders. 7,700 years ago, or so, a former mountain of considerable height had an accident. It blew up, then down. In the process it scattered ash, pumice and hot rocks all over, then collapsed in upon itself. Mount Mazama, 12,000 feet or so tall, became a caldera, a basin-shaped volcanic depression that eventually filled with water to become Crater Lake. Today, a 1,932-foot deep lake of indescribable blue occupies the six-mile diameter caldera.

Crater Lake National Park was created almost 100 years ago, so that people like you and me could enjoy its considerable natural beauty. When I think of Crater Lake I think of certain animals and plants: the golden-mantled ground squirrel, Clark's nutcracker, and the pumice moonwort. There are others, but for me they are Crater Lake.

At first glimpse, many people think golden-mantled ground squirrels are chipmunks. Although both have stripes along their sides, golden-mantled ground squirrels have a pronounced eye-ring instead of stripes along their heads as chipmunks do. Most park visitors encounter these little beggars along the rim. They are fat, as they should be to make it through the winter when tens of feet of snow cover their nests in average years. Their normal varied diet includes insects and green vegetation besides seeds, fruits and nuts. Rim rodents eat like park visitors, however. Their diet consists of junk food fed to them by visitors — popcorn, Cheez-Its, and balloon bread, in spite of the objections of the Park Service.

Clark's nutcrackers are noisy, black and white and gray crow-sized birds. They fly about the rim in and out of mountain hemlock, fir and whitebark pine. They are an alpine species thought by many to be a major agent in the migration of alpine tree species. Clark's nutcrackers are

hoarders and cachers of conifer seeds. They hide away as many as 30,000 seeds in late summer and fall in the soil of warmer, south-facing slopes. They can carry up to 95 pine seeds per trip. To survive they must recover at least 1,000 caches a year. Amazingly, nutcrackers do this by means of a prodigious spatial memory, as ornithologists have shown. The birds remember where they hid the seeds. They disperse and bury two to three times as many seeds as they eat in a season. They don't get or need them all. Rodents sometimes benefit instead, and certainly the tree species involved, as well.

The inches-tall pumice moonwort produces spores in sporangia arranged in tiny grape-like clusters. For many years the plants were known only from the pumice flats on top of Lloa Rock at Crater Rim. The species is now known from Newberry Crater and the Three Sisters area, always in pumice-rich soils. Fifteen thousand individuals are known, all in Oregon, a real native.

When you visit Crater Lake be sure to stop by the Crater Lake Natural History Association sales area at the headquarters building on the way to the rim or at their shop at the rim. At this point they don't know if they will be in a trailer at the rim or in their usual spot in the small Kaiser building near the rim viewpoint because of construction plans. Like all National Park Cooperating Associations they sell books and other items selected to help the visitor learn more about the park and the natural world. No rubber tomahawks and colored turkey feathers here. Besides that, all the profits go directly back to the park to aid in their interpretive programs or for park research projects.

Emigrant Reservoir

Early autumn is a good time to visit Emigrant Reservoir, near Ashland, Oregon. You will find some interesting plants in the drawdown area, the intertidal zone, if you will. As you walk down the bank from high to low pool levels, you will discover that the plants, mostly beggar ticks and cockleburs, are in all stages of their life-cycles. The plants are in full fruit at the upper levels where the soil has been exposed since early summer. At lower levels, where the soil has just been exposed, the plants are seedlings. Beggar ticks and cocklebur are admirably suited for getting about. Their fruits and associated tissues are armed with stout spines that become entangled in the hair or clothing of passing animals and thus move on to new locations. The plants also get around the reservoir because the fruits and enclosed seeds float.

As you walk toward the water's edge, you may find plants that look as though they were covered by masses of orange spaghetti, or maybe vermicelli. The strands aren't very thick. The orange tangled mass is dodder, a parasitic flowering plant that gets all of its nutrition from its host, usually the cocklebur or beggar tick. The plant has specialized root-like extensions called haustoria that penetrate the living, nutrient and water-rich tissues of the host.

Dodder may be one of the few flowering plants that actually moves from one place to another, on its own, without the help of wind or water or animals. When the seeds are shed and germinate, no root forms to anchor the seedling. The elongated seedling grows at one end and shrivels at the other and thus moves forward for a chance encounter with a host.

Dodder and beggar ticks were a source of considerable taxonomic confusion for me one fall sometime ago. I was at Emigrant Lake in the draw down area looking at the flora when I happened upon a plant in flower that I

did not recognize. It looked like a sunflower plant but had totally different flowers. I tried to key it out. Got nowhere. Tried a different book, tried another different book. No luck. Decided to look closer. It was then that I noticed that the flowers were growing out of the stem in strange places. I realized that I had not one, but two plants. It was dodder, in full flower, parasitizing an immature cocklebur. I had one of those rare flushes of pleasure and excitement that you get when you have finally figured out a puzzle or a problem. A kind of academic high that makes you want to come back for more.

Occasionally you will see a plant or group of plants that towers a meter or more above the lower vegetation. A closer look reveals white trumpet-shaped flowers to ten centimeters long and large oval spiny fruits. It is *Datura* in the Family *Solanaceae,* the tobacco, potato, tomato, nightshade family, famous for its poisonous alkaloids. *Datura,* or Jimson weed or thornapple, to choose among a score or so of English common names, is no exception. Thornapple (named for its fruit) is very poisonous and has the dubious distinction of causing more cases of human than animal poisoning. It got its other common name, Jamestown or Jimson weed, because of a celebrated case of mass poisoning of soldiers sent to quell the Bacon rebellion at Jamestown, Virginia in 1676.

If you are looking forward to a boring evening with nothing to do, wear wool socks and bring your long-haired dog along for fun when you visit Emigrant Reservoir. You will spend the evening discovering how some plants get from place to place.

Granite Quarry

Mount Ashland formed during the late Jurassic, at least 150 million years ago, as an underground mass of granitic rock. Subsequent uplift and erosion has exposed a mountain that rises 7,530 feet above sea level. While most of the granite of the Siskiyous is light colored, coarse textured and easily weathered, there are a few areas where granite of a different kind was deposited. Just west of Interstate 5 near Ashland, Oregon, where Neil Creek moves out of the Siskiyous into the Bear Creek Valley, granite of a different sort is found. Erosion by Neil Creek and its nearby tributary, Quartz Creek, exposed granite layers that had been protected from weathering since the age of dinosaurs. Here a beautiful fine grained, smooth textured granite evenly flecked with light and dark minerals was formed that was relatively free of cracks and seams. Ideal building stone.

At the turn of the century, 1900 to be exact, this high-quality deposit was discovered by a hunter, Mr. Frank Fish, who by chance had previously worked in the famous granite at Barre, Vermont. Fish soon spread the word and it was not long before a quarry was established for monuments, a polite way of saying tombstones. The Ashland Marble Works placed an advertisement in the April 4th, 1901 *Ashland Daily Tidings* that read... "Bottom bases of either fine blue sandstone or of the Ashland grey granite."

Over the years, several operators removed both monument and building stone. In 1916 Walter Blair began developing the site as a major quarry operation. His sales amounted to between $20,000 and $30,000 per year from 1921 to 1927. In 1937 the property was taken over by Ashland Granite Quarries, Inc. who opened an upper quarry for building stone, while continuing to use the lower quarry for tombstones. The Reconstruction Finance Corporation took possession of the quarry in 1940, and it has been more or less idle ever since.

Where was the stone used? In local cemeteries for one. Look for the Haskins family headstone in Mountain View Cemetery on the corner of Normal Avenue and Highway 66; the large granite Lithia water drinking fountain at the Ashland Plaza and in local buildings, parts of the old bank that is now the Shakespeare building, the base course and steps of the Jackson County Courthouse, the outside part of the old Copco building in Medford. Farther afield, the granite was used for base courses for state office buildings in Roseburg, Salem, Eugene, Portland, and the floor of the capital building in Salem. There are three family mausoleums in Portland with each roof of three 14-foot-long blocks of Ashland granite.

The quarries are on private land, don't try to visit them. Perhaps, sometime in the not too distant future, we will need to return to brick and stone for building material and the quarries of Neil Creek will be back in operation.

Kalmiopsis

One summer I spent two sweltering days of backpacking in the Kalmiopsis Wilderness west of Grants Pass with five US Forest Service employees. *Kalmiopsis leachiana,* a rare member of the rhododendron family that grows in the wildlands west of the Illinois Valley in Josephine County, Oregon gives the 180,000 acre wilderness its name. The small pink flowers of this low evergreen shrub resemble the flowers of the better known and more widely distributed *Kalmia.* Another, as yet undescribed species, grows on rocky outcrops above the North Umpqua River in Douglas County, Oregon.

Kalmiopsis is Oregon's very own, native no place else on planet Earth. You will only find it in identification books that cover the flora of southwest Oregon, books like Morton Peck's *Manual of the Higher Plants of Oregon* (long out of print) or Abrams' four volume *Flora of the Pacific States,* still available from Stanford University Press.

The species was unknown until Lila Leach and her husband John, from Portland, discovered the plant growing at Gold Basin, June 14, 1930. Eminent botanists of the day, Louis Henderson at the University of Oregon and Alfred Rehder at Harvard University's Arnold Arboretum, established its present name, after considerable botanical musings, to honor the Leaches and note its resemblance to *Kalmia.*

The species has not been extensively studied. In the late 1960s and early 70s several of my students looked at various aspects of the plants. Dick Stehil, now Dr. Richard Stehil, compared vegetative specimens from the wilderness and the North Umpqua. Nancy Woodworth, now Dr. Nancy Woodworth Callan, horticulturalist for Montana State University, looked at the cytological development of the egg cell. In 1977 Robert Marquis, a graduate student at Oregon State University, studied the species distribution

and ecology. Robert Meinke and Thomas Kaye propose the Umpqua populations a new species. In spite of these studies, *Kalmiopsis*' relationship to other members of the Rhododendron Family is still not clear. New techniques that study proteins and DNA have not been applied to *Kalmiopsis*. Don't be surprised if we consider a new name for the wilderness as an outcome of such a study.

What brought a Southern Oregon University botanist and five Forest Service people in to the heart of one of the least visited wilderness areas in the United States? Rene Casteran, a New Yorker, recent Southern Oregon University graduate and seven years the Forest Service Kalmiopsis Wilderness Guard, discovered patches of dead and dying plants on the rocky slopes above the Chetco River upstream from Taggert's Bar.

Jerry Beatty from the Forest Service's Forest Pest Management Program in Portland was with us to determine the cause of death. Until cultures can be established and analyzed we don't know what the problem is, or what the hazard might be to the species. Is it part of a natural cycle, or an indication of other, greater problems? Time, if there is any left, will tell.

I commend the Forest Service for investing time and energy toward other resources, beside timber and the spotted owl. The loss of *Kalmiopsis* to disease, especially if human caused, would be sad indeed.

Visit Limpy Rock or Dry Creek on the North Umpqua in late April or early May, an easy way to see *Kalmiopsis* in bloom. For greater adventure, walk the Illinois River Trail to York Creek in May or drive to Babyfoot Lake in the Illinois Valley in early June. If you want a wilderness adventure, walk from Chetco Pass to the river in May and hope you can ford the river . . . and don't count on Taggert's Bar for refreshments.

Klamath River

Last Sunday my friend Rick Preuz lured me to the Klamath River to check out the spring flora. We botanized the Klamath from Tree of Heaven Campground, west of Interstate 5 along the Klamath River Highway, to the Klamathon Road east of the I-5 rest area. The weather was great and the flowers performing.

We pulled off the freeway and drove toward Tree of Heaven. I noticed flashes of purple as we passed the first rocky road cuts. Brewer's rockcress, *Arabis breweri*, a member of the mustard family, was in full bloom. Brewer, some of you will recall, was the botanist with JD Whitney on the California Geological Survey for whom Brewer or weeping spruce was named. His rockcress bloomed on almost every rocky outcrop.

When we reached Tree of Heaven Campground, we parked at the top of the long steep grade down to the campground and the river. We ambled out along the sharp rocky ridge that forces the Klamath River to jog sharply south then north again on its westward journey to the sea. Here we saw more Brewer's rockcress up close and at zero miles per hour instead of forty. Fremont's silktassel bush was in bloom as well. Silktassel bushes, of separate sexes, are five to six feet tall with shiny green opposite leaves, and long pendulous silky inflorescences. The limp male tassels produce copious amounts of pollen; the stiffer female tassels with receptive stigmas flashing await wind-borne pollen.

While walking along the ridge looking at the ground, as botanists are wont to do, I noticed movement out of the corner of my eye. A quick glance revealed a mature golden eagle sweeping down the canyon, at eye level, within a stone's throw from the ridge. What a surprise, what a thrill! The eagle was surprised as well, but probably not very thrilled. It immediately started back upstream, then

gained elevation, spiraling upward until it was a tiny speck in the sky.

On our way back we stopped near the Ash Creek bridge and clambered up the steep slope on the north side of the river. Here we found several rock ferns and phlox just beginning to bloom.

Our final stop was another huff and puff up the ridge just across the interstate east of the rest area along the old Klamathon Road. There we spotted two more golden eagles, an immature and an adult. Botany was good. There were many yellow bells, *Fritillaria pudica,* in bloom. A tiny bright blue annual, veronica, a European weed, naturalized and living in the Yreka area, covered the dry, rocky open ground in places. A rare member of the buttercup family, *Isopyron stipitata,* was in full bloom beneath the oaks.

Besides the two eagles, the big animal event here was the discovery of several dozen steely metallic-blue flea-beetles congregating on a gooseberry branch for the expressed purpose of committing unseemly acts. Acts unseemly, I suppose, only in the view of a voyeur like myself. Flea-beetles get their name from the quick hopping motion they make when disturbed, no matter what they are doing.

Pilot Rock

Pilot Rock has stood as a beacon for travelers crossing the Siskiyou summit since Native Americans first reached southern Oregon. Hudson's Bay Company explorer Peter Skene Ogden and his crew probably noticed the rock on their trip over the Siskiyous in February 1827. Today, travelers on Interstate 5 know they are approaching the pass when they see the 5,910 foot promontory silhouetted on the sky east of the highway.

Pilot Rock is the neck or plug of an ancient volcano formed during the Oligocene some 37 to 25 million years ago. In the millennia since its formation the volcano has eroded away leaving the harder lava of its core. Post-like columnar joints formed as the lava cooled. To the south of the rock, volcanic breccia, remains of cinder beds that accumulated around the volcanic vent, form spires or hoodoos, as they are sometimes called.

There are wonderful wildflower sights to see in the vicinity of the Rock starting in the spring and continuing through July, and there are spectacular views of Mount Shasta and the surrounding mountains any time of year. The rock can be reached via the Bureau of Land Management's Pilot Rock Road just south of the summit of old US 99. Stay on the Pilot Rock Road and don't turn left, even if the road seems better. Stay on the main road and park at the graveled area where the Pacific Crest national scenic trail crosses the road at the divide between the Rogue and Klamath Rivers. The road south is blocked to motorized traffic, but is open to other means of transportation.

Be careful if you try the non-technical scramble to the summit. The rock is a killer that attracts climbers who sometime slip and fall. The rock has lured at least one plane into its south face. I am told the view is worth the climb.

A gentle hike east of the rock along the Pacific Crest Trail will bring you to some beautiful natural rock gardens

as you pass in and out of conifer forests. In the deep shade of the firs, look for pinkish coralroot and pure white phantom orchids. We now call them mycotrophs — plants without chlorophyll that use fungi to steal energy from nearby green plants. We used to call them saprophytes — plants that do not undergo photosynthesis but use fungi to break down dead and decaying organic matter in the soil for energy, but that is now way *passé.*

When the wild buckwheats are in full bloom, they color open rocky areas cream and yellow depending on the species. One meadow is blue with Frasera, a member of the gentian family. Old-man-in-the-ground, with its huge underground tuber, forms dark green tangled masses in the middle of the rocky areas. Occasional flashes of red indian paint brush and scarlet gilia may be visible.

Scarlet gilia, sometimes called desert trumpet, is frequented by hummingbirds. How many of you have rested in mountain meadows only to be startled out of your reverie by what at first sounded like the world's largest bumblebee? It was, of course, a hummingbird attracted to whatever article of bright red clothing you might have been wearing, but surely not your scent.

At the parking lot, walk south along the closed road to the wet meadow, then up to the west along the wide rock garden for more nice wildflowers in season and spectacular late afternoon and early evening views of Pilot Rock any time of year. Continue walking up the rock garden to the west and around the knoll west of Pilot Rock. You will reach the Pacific Crest national scenic trail. Walk east and you will soon reach the parking lot where you started out.

Pilot Rock is an important part of the new (Year 2000) Cascade-Siskiyou National Monument. If you are not pleased with its designation and its restrictions on consumptive work and play (timber, mining, motorized recreation) now, believe me your descendants will be in 20 years or so when relatively undisturbed, undeveloped natural areas become scarce.

Rainie Falls

Had my first outing of the season last Saturday. Took the Grants Pass Audubon Society down the Rogue River from Graves Creek to Rainie Falls along the south bank trail to look at ferns. We found thirteen species, 11 ferns and two fern allies, a scouring rush and a spikemoss. Amazing what you can find if you know what you are looking for and take the time to look.

There were not many plants in flower, except a couple of early bloomers, always a hopeful indication that winter is leaving and sweet spring is on its way. On the damp shady vertical rock bluffs, Howell's saxifrage was starting to bloom. A cluster of small, white-petaled flowers rose on a single stalk from a rosette of small, spatula-shaped leaves with saw-toothed margins. Thomas Jefferson Howell, pioneer Oregon botanist, first collected this plant in the 1890s on the Coquille River. The species was described and named in honor of Howell by Edward Lee Greene, defrocked Episcopal priest and first professor of botany at the University of California, Berkeley.

Another harbinger of spring was what I learned as grouse-flower, that others call snow-queen. Botanists the world over call this plant, *Syntheris reniformis,* a member of the snapdragon family. Its low growing reniform leaves, the shape of kidneys, renal artery, reniform, kidney-shaped, get it? Anyway, its low-growing leaves and small lavender flowers with a pair of purple stamens brighten lowland conifer forests sometimes as early as mid-January. A welcome sight indeed.

We also saw another early spring landscape brightener, *Crocidium multicaule,* known as spring gold. Along the trail we saw just one or two in bloom. On the way home, just past Indian Mary Campground, across the river, on one of my favorite bare serpentine hillsides, I saw a bijillion of them, like someone spilled gallons of yellow

paint across their landscape painting. Spring gold is a sunflower just several inches high, with yellow rayed flowered heads. I am always amazed how the sum of the total is greater than the sum of its parts.

We also saw and heard some birds. A couple of people saw an immature bald eagle just above Rainie Falls. We heard what was either a prairie or a peregrine falcon. Other birds included a great blue heron flapping its way majestically upstream. On the water we saw a group of merganser or fish ducks as they are sometimes called. I couldn't tell with certainty if they were common or red-breasted mergansers. Because of the male's white sides, I suspect they were common mergansers.

They use their narrow, hook-tipped, saw-toothed bills to catch swimming prey, aquatic insects, tadpoles, and, alas, small fish. This latter preference gives them an unsavory reputation among the ignorant in the human fishing community. The main prey likely isn't game fish, but a multitude of smaller fish, minnows, shiners and the like. In any event, they have coexisted for millennia with our native trout and salmon and cannot be blamed for their decline. That is largely due to the activities of bipedal primates.

One other thing. I got home to discover a deer tick burrowed in high up on my abdomen. Poor thing likely thought it hit a toxic waste-dump.

Mount Eddy & John Jeffrey

When snow leaves the high country, consider an outing to one of my favorite places, Mount Eddy and the Deadfall Lakes in northern California. Drive south on I-5 from Oregon and the Klamath River and stop at the viewpoint that looks out across the Shasta Valley. To the south you will see Mount Shasta to the left, and Mount Eddy to the right, with Black Butte a pimple in between. If you can't see all this, consider coming back another day in better weather.

Turn off I-5 just south of the Weed airport and drive west on the Parks Creek/Stewart Springs Road, past the springs, then south and up and up to the crossing of Road 17 and the Pacific Crest national scenic trail. Take an easy walk two and a half miles south along the trail past open meadows, fir woods and California pitcher plant fens. If you are feeling a little wimpish or have wimps along, make the Dead Fall Lakes your destination. If you are feeling strong, hike the steep ascent to the summit of Mount Eddy. The trail is not dangerous, just steep. Danger could come, however, in the form of inclement weather, so be prepared. The summit is 9,025 feet above the sea.

The view from Eddy's summit is panoramic, to say the least. On a clear day you can see distant Mount McLoughlin and nearer Mount Ashland and Pilot Rock to the north. To the west are the Marble Mountains and further south the Trinity Alps, with snowy Thompson Peak on the horizon. To the south, look down on Castle Crags, the site of one of my great adventures, a 12-hour bushwack down the Crags' spine from Castle Lake to Castle Dome, a trip I do not recommend for wimps or sissies. Lassen Peak, at the southern end of the Cascade Range, is to the southeast. To the east, there is Mount

Shasta, all 10,000 feet of her 14,161 foot magnificence rising above the surrounding plain.

Because of my interest in John Jeffrey, of Jeffrey pine fame, the stand of foxtail pines, *Pinus balfouriana,* growing along the ridge to the south of Deadfall Lakes particularly pleased me. Foxtail pines have a mysterious disjunct distribution; scattered stands in the Klamath Mountains and then no sign of them until they reappear in relative abundance in the southern Sierra Nevada.

Jeffrey's story is an odd and incomplete one. In 1850, the Oregon Association, a group of wealthy British horticulturalists, sent Jeffrey to North America to follow in the footsteps of fellow Scots Archibald Menzies, who was the naturalist on the Vancouver expedition to western North America in the 1790s and David Douglas, who botanized the west in 1826. Curiously, all three men were natives of County Perth, Scotland, born just a few miles apart in distance, miles apart in terms of time.

Jeffrey arrived at York Factory August 12, 1850. He did not reach the west coast until the 15th of July, 1851. That winter and spring he collected in western Canada. In May he started south. September 27, 1852, he was at Mount Shasta. On the 29th he discovered the trees that were to become *P. balfouriana* on a mountain range between Shasta and Scott valley. Although the species also occurs on Scott Mountain a few miles to the east, I would prefer to think that the place Jeffrey found it first was the stand on Mount Eddy.

He discovered other trees before returning north: Jeffrey pine in the Shasta Valley and what was to become the lodgepole pine subspecies of *P. contorta* in the Siskiyou Mountains. He returned to Fort Vancouver for the winter, then headed south in April 1853 arriving in San Francisco. In the spring of 1854 he left to explore the deserts of the America southwest. He was never heard from again.

While you stand among Mount Eddy's foxtail pine, think of Jeffrey and how lucky you are to be at such a wonderful place with such great objects of creation.

Mount St. Helens

May 18, 1980, Mount St. Helens, the sweetest of the Cascade volcanos, blew her top after a month or so of warning and turned into a hag. In October, 1792 George Vancouver named the symmetrical cone for a friend recently dubbed Lord St. Helens. The Klickitats called the mountain Tah-one-lat-clan — "Fire Mountain," a far more accurate name.

The mountain's eruptive history is short in geological terms, and violent. The volcano was last active in 1857 after a period of activity dating from the 1840s. Before that, the last major period of volcanic activity ended about 1647 A.D. when the mountain reached its maximum height and pre-1980 form.

That Sunday morning in May, I was at Silver Falls State Park east of Salem attending the annual meeting of the Native Plant Society of Oregon. Didn't hear a thing at Silver Falls, although the blast was heard as far away as British Columbia. Didn't know what had happened until hearing about it on the radio late that morning on our route home to Ashland.

What a catastrophic event it was. Two hundred and thirty square miles of forest laid flat, fast. The front of the moving ash cloud may have exceeded the speed of sound. The blast displaced Spirit Lake, sending a flood 600 feet up denuded mountainsides, washing back thousands of trunks of downed timber. Fifty seven or so people died; fried, bludgeoned or suffocated by the cyclonic force, 680° of heat and ash.

One fall, a little over ten years after the eruption, I had a chance to visit the blast site. To view the crater you must approach the mountain from the east. There are two routes to drive to see the mountain; from the south via the towns of Battle Ground and Cougar, or from Randle, Washington. We took the White Pass Highway from

Interstate 5 to Randle then turned south to the National Volcanic Monument. We chose to follow the narrow paved road to Ryan Lake. As we approached the lake the living forest took on the appearance of being burned in a forest fire. A look at the skyline revealed the silvery standing skeletons of dead trees, all pointing to the northeast. All trees were down along the ten miles from Ryan Lake to the mountain. At Ryan Lake two people and two horses died. Another person died later from ash inhalation. The devastation was unbelievable.

Devastation is also apparent from the air. When in an airplane I love to watch the ground. Not long ago I flew from Seattle to Medford, Oregon. I watched the ground. I was astounded by the logging, clear-cut after clear-cut. The worse the devastation, the more upset I became. Then I looked ahead. Oops, my anger was somewhat misdirected. We were flying over the St. Helens blast zone. Mother Nature was to blame and not greedy timber barons. There was little sign of recovery from 20,000 feet in the air. However, recovery on the ground is more apparent, in fact, amazing.

Fireweed, pearly everlasting, huckleberries, mountain ash, rushes, grasses and sedges, young Pacific silver firs, are common, especially away from the mountain. Some areas are taking longer than others to recover, especially directly in front of the mountain where the devastation was the greatest. Left alone and given enough time, natural events will heal the scars. Ecological succession will continue and everything will return to normal, at least in human terms. Until, that is, Tah-one-lat-clan has another case of colic.

Table Rocks

Early spring is the time to think about a hike to the top of either Upper or Lower Table Rock to view the wildflowers. The two flat-topped mesas are located north of Medford in the Rogue River Valley. Stop by the Bureau of Land Management office on Biddle Road in Medford for information on the Rocks and how to reach the trail heads. Public access to the top is by trail only. Although the distance is not great, the trail is moderately steep in places and can be slick and muddy if wet.

On the way up you will see many wildflowers in bloom. In the oak woodlands look for the rose colored Henderson's shooting star with its reflexed petals, bright lilac Henderson's fawn lilies, deep blue larkspurs, and yellow buttercups. Look at the back of the buttercup's petals. If the back is brownish, you are looking at the Rogue Valley's very own *Ranunculus austro-oreganus,* the southern Oregon buttercup. One striking member of the lily family that you will see on the way up is red bells, a tall plant with whorled leaves and scarlet petals.

Once on top you will discover a vast treeless plain, with mounds of soil scattered between dry rocky areas or wet vernal seeps. Each area has its own distinctive set of plants. The mounds are blue and white with lupines, popcorn flowers, and blue-eyed Marys. The dry rocky flats are covered with yellow goldfields and white California sandworts. In the wet areas we find the dwarf meadow-foam, a subspecies found only on the top of the two Table Rocks.

If you are early enough, purple-eyed grass, a member of the iris family, will be in full bloom. The plant has purple blossoms on slender, grass-like stems. Occasionally, you will find an albino individual, a mutant, who lost a gene that made an enzyme that played a role in forming the purple pigment of the flower. No gene, no color. Another early bloomer is Piper's lomatium, a member of

the carrot family, that grows in mossy areas between the mounds. Its cluster of small white flowers with purple stamens grows right at ground level. Its small, round, starch-filled corms were an important source of carbohydrates for Native Americans in earlier days.

On a clear day you can get a beautiful view of the Rogue River Valley and the surrounding mountains. The Siskiyou Crest from Mount Ashland to Dutchman Peak, the Cascades from Grizzly Peak, Aspen Peak, Brown Mountain, Mount McLoughlin, the Sky Lakes Wilderness, to the Crater Rim and the Rogue Umpqua Divide.

On your hike take water to drink and be warned that there are no toilet facilities on the top. Watch out for poison oak, ticks, and rattlesnakes. Don't pick the wildflowers, don't take short cuts on the trail, but do have fun and enjoy nature's beauties.

II

Flora

Soils

Soil is that layer of mineral particles, pore space, moisture, and living organisms that covers most of the surface of terrestrial earth. Without soil, life as we know it would not exist. Dirt, on the other hand, is what is you find under your fingernails or what you sweep under the rug.

The erosive action of mechanical and chemical agents reduces bedrock, known in the soil trade as parent material, to soil particles of various sizes. Mechanical agents include freezing and thawing, heating and cooling, and the forces of wind and water. Chemical agents include the mixture of carbon dioxide from the atmosphere and water that forms weak carbonic acid or organic acids produced by lichens growing on rock surfaces that may hasten the breakdown of some rocks.

Erosion not only forms soil particles but transports them as well. Water transports alluvial soils. Their particles are characteristically smooth, and rounded by the constant bumping and grinding action of the water. For example, the presence of smooth rounded pebbles is evidence that water once flowed across the surface of Upper and Lower Table Rocks in Jackson County, Oregon.

There are many different kinds of soils with different characteristics caused by a complex interaction of different parent materials, climates, and living organisms. As precipitation falls on the soil's surface, the water moves down through the soil profile dissolving and redepositing mineral components as it goes. In dry climates the water may evaporate before reaching the water table, leaving behind a hardpan layer of calcium carbonate.

The resulting layers, called horizons, have different characteristics, different colors, different textures. Horizons, particularly the "O" or organic horizon, have a host of tiny and not so tiny arthropod inhabitants. Some have incredible adaptation to their soil homes. One such

beast is the ant lion, the larval stage of the lace wing. Adults bear a general resemblance to dragonflies with short-knobbed antennae.

Ant lions make pits in sandy soil about the diameter of a silver dollar where the O horizon is missing. Perhaps you have seen them in your yard. Mine are underneath the strawberry tree on the south side of the house. Ant lions lie with fearsome pinchers just showing in the sandy bottom of the pit waiting patiently for an ant to stumble in. Ant lions are sensitive to vibrations and make quick work of foolish ants. Ants are grasped by the pinchers, immobilized by a secretion, predigested, then sucked dry. In case you are worried about your child or pet, ant lions are measured in millimeters.

Not only is parent material eroded to form soil, but wind and water erode soil. Unfortunately, soil is disappearing faster than it is being formed. The loss of top soil is an ecological and economic disaster of major proportions. Long forgotten are the lessons of the 1930s Dust Bowl of the American midwest, too much money to be made.

Try the *Atlas on the Biology of Soil Arthropods* by Eisenbeis and Wichard at the Southern Oregon University library for more information and great SEMicrographs. If you want to learn more about soil erosion try Worldwatch Paper 60, available from the Worldwatch Institute.

And don't let me ever hear you say dirt when you mean soil.

Temperate Rain Forests

Tropical rain forests are the focus of great attention these days. We constantly hear about their importance in the ecosphere, their high species diversity and their appalling rate of loss. Our lack of knowledge about tropical rain forest ecosystems impresses us. Are there unknown medicinal plants that could save the human race from its own foolishness? Will the loss of rain forests alter global climate? How will the loss effect the human race that lives in the warm, moist tropics?

What we do know impresses us as well. Three square miles of tropical rain forest can have 2,600 species of vascular plants, four acres can have 98 different tree species. Floristically rich, we like to say. There is a host of animal species as well. On the face of it, the mighty, mysterious tropical rain forest makes other terrestrial ecosystems puny by comparison.

There are other ecosystems that are as impressive in their own way. Where can we find earth's greatest living creatures, the largest living individual organisms? Where can we find 200 to 250 species of invertebrates per square meter of soil? Where can we find as many as 75 species and up to 200,000 individual oribatid mites per square meter? Where can we find a promising cure for ovarian cancer? We can find these things in our own back yard, in the coniferous forests of the western United States.

I'll bet you thought the world's largest living organism was a blue whale in the ocean or some giant tropical rain forest tree. Wrong! The great cone bearing trees of western North America are the champions. Redwoods are among the tallest living things. California big trees are the heaviest — 2,756 tons. The largest blue whale weighs a measly 209 tons.

We can find enormous numbers of arthropods in undisturbed coniferous forests. Scientists like Andy

Moldenke at Oregon State University are just beginning to understand the role these tiny creepy-crawlies play in the life of the big trees. They provide a critical link in the nutrient-cycling process. The arthropods, with soil fungi and bacteria, break down litter, wood, and carcasses, releasing important nutrients to be recycled back into the ecosystem. Invertebrates help the process by encouraging microbial growth, mixing soil layers, aerating the soil, and transporting bacteria and fungi about.

One important arthropod you may have seen is that marvelous black and yellow cyanide-producing millipede, *Harpaphe haydeniana,* so common in northwest conifer forests. *Harpaphe* is the first link in releasing nutrients tied up in conifer needles. The millipede eats fallen needles and in the process mixes the remains with bacteria in its gut. Fungi invade its fecal pellets and are eaten by, wouldn't you just know it, mites. The mites introduce new enzymes and gut bacteria and manufacture smaller pellets. Baby millipedes may eat the smaller pellets and, in turn, mix them with mineral soil. With the help of mycorrhizal fungi, conifers may take up the nutrients again to make new needles.

That's one mite's role. What about the other 74 species? In spite of years of study, there is much we do not know about our own back yard. Our temperate rain forests are as fascinating in their own way as tropical and subtropical rain forests. Why is it easier to get excited about environmental problems away from home than it is to get excited about environmental problems in our own back yard?

Fens

I was botanizing in the Illinois Valley on a research project with colleagues. We were interested in the relationship between the purple and white-flowered form of the large-flowered bog lily. We collected leaves for chemical analysis, and buds and individual flowers for pollen to try to determine if the forms are really different species. These rare Illinois Valley endemics are known only from the California pitcher plant fens and streamsides on the west side of the valley from Deer Creek north of Eight Dollar Mountain, in the Josephine Creek drainage, south to Rough-and-Ready Creek.

We used to call the fens, bogs. Not anymore, except when accidentally slipping back into old, bad habits. These wetlands are fens by most definitions because the water's pH is nearly neutral; that is, not very acid nor very basic. Bogs are acid. Fens are dominated by rushes, sedges and grasses. Bogs are dominated by sphagnum moss. Water flows year round through fens. Water stands in bogs.

These fens are a wonder, filled with fabulous plants, rare plants, unusual plants. There is always something interesting to see any time of year. In spring, the azaleas bloom in profusion around the fens' edges, filling the senses with color and scent. The pitcher plants bloom with hanging maroon and chartreuse flowers, which later turn upright as fruits form.

Pitcher plants form new bright green insect-trapping leaves after flowering, perhaps to avoid catching their own pollinators. About late July or August, the fens turn mostly yellow, with yellow bog asphodel, a lily family member, and the California cone flower, surely a *Saturday Night Live* favorite. Another interesting lily is western tolfieldia. Its densely glandular, sticky stem rises from a fan-like cluster of grass-like leaves. Perhaps the sticky hairs

deter pollen-stealing insects from sneaking up the flowering stalks. Perhaps the sticky hairs just amuse botanists.

Later in the summer watch for the brilliant blue flowers of the Waldo gentian. This rare plant is found mostly in Illinois Valley fens and wet places and one place in California. The new *Jepson Manual*, the newest California flora, calls this species the Mendocino gentian. It occurs one place, Red Mountain, Mendocino County, California, and all over the Illinois Valley in Oregon. I like Waldo gentian best.

Stop by the fens along Eight Dollar Road south of Selma for a real natural treat. These fens, these natural treasures, are a sustainable resource if you just look or photograph. Please don't try to take plants for your garden.

Our *Hastingsia* investigations have not been without their hazards, both natural and human. There was the single button rattlesnake that didn't rattle nor bite and the rattle-less tick that bit. I just know there are good people in the Illinois Valley. However, we have had distributors stolen, cars vandalized, and have been inadvertently shot at by nervous neighbors warning off another interloper on public land. David Douglas had to put up with natural hazards and irate Native Americans, we, with boobs, ninnies, yahoos and adle-brained nincompoops. What won't we do in the name of science?

Tall Trees

What is the tallest planted tree in the Rogue Valley? It isn't native here but grows nearby. It's a conifer, producing seeds from cones, not flowers. Its evergreen needles fall off the tree as branchlets, not as individual needles. Although it seems to thrive in the hot, dry summers and colder winters of the valley, its native habitat is mild, cool and foggy. What is the Rogue Valley's tallest tree? My guess is the coast redwood, *Sequoia sempervirens*. The tree is tall wherever it grows. In its native habitat it is earth's tallest living thing.

Our enthusiasm for the world's biggest this or tallest that is a long-standing human passion. John Muir was interested in such things. In a letter dated July 17, 1904 he wrote:

> Dear Scholars four, . . . I was far away in Australia [searching for giant trees] throughout Asia and Australia beneath the Southern Cross when your kind good letters to me were written & when I got home & read them. None of the big pile on my desk pleased me more. It was very kind of you to write these letters, & I thank you & your teachers & others for the honors you report, especially the dedication of your Arbor Day Redwood.
>
> The Redwood grows taller than any other tree in the world. One that I measured was 340 feet high & some may be 50 or 60 feet higher, while the tallest Australian Eucalyptus, as far as known does not exceed 300 feet in height. Many, in many of the stories about them, are much taller.

This letter, to four young students, goes on to describe his trip and his harsh Scots schooldays. "Our teachers said that thrashing and irritating the skin excited the memory, & I supposed it did for by the time we were ten or eleven

we had committed whole books to memory." And we wonder how Muir could face the rigors of nature the way he did.

The passion for tall trees continues to this day. Arcata, California resident Ron Hildebrant recently measured the National Geographic tree located in the Redwood Creek area of Redwood National Park south of Orick, California. He found it to be about 375 feet tall, five feet taller than the Harry Cole tree. It may be the world's tallest tree.

Measuring tall trees is no easy proposition. You need a clear view of tree's top. Next time you are in the redwoods, crane your neck and see if you can decide which group of needles represents the top. Angles must be determined, distances measured, and trigonometry applied. Subtle things like the trunk's tilt must be factored into the equation for accuracy. It takes hours to make an accurate measurement, and that must be confirmed independently.

What goes up must come down, as the saying goes. For giant redwoods the come-down is hard. On March 24, 1991 the Dyerville Giant, the fourth tallest redwood, was blown over with a little help from its friends. Redwoods have shallow root systems for such tall trees. That makes them prone to wind-throw. They rely on each other as wind breaks for general support. This works fine for a long time but eventually one falls and frequently carries several of its fellows down as well. Don't be too sad to see a tree such as the Dyerville Giant go down. Remember, such events repeat, over and over, for millennia. It's nature's way to keep the ecosystem dynamic and functioning in a constant cycle of death and rebirth. Oh, by the way, check out the planted trees in your neighborhood. Redwoods are the tallest, right?

Redwoods

A favorite field trip of mine is to Stout Grove in the redwoods. The grove is located on the south side of the Smith River in Jedediah Smith Redwoods State Park in Del Norte County, California.

Turn south off Highway 199 and cross both forks of the Smith heading west along the south bank. After passing the last few houses, the road moves away from the river to the higher, flat redwood covered benches. The road is narrow, slow, and sometimes bumpy. Don't try it in a recreational vehicle or if you are towing a trailer. It just isn't safe. If you stay on the road, you will end up in Crescent City, which is what I like to do if I have the time. Closer to Crescent City several trails lead off into fine stands of redwoods.

Turn off at Stout Grove, park in the lot above the grove and walk down the road to the grove below. On the way down notice the ferns growing on the bank beside the road. You will see maidenhair or five-finger fern, deer fern, sword fern, lady fern, and licorice fern. The maidenhair and lady ferns are deciduous, and may not be very obvious early in the season. The deer fern is dimorphic, that is, has leaves of two kinds, a flat rosette of sterile vegetative leaves with upright fertile reproductive leaves rising from the center.

Once you reach the grove you will discover a magnificent sight — huge, sky-high redwoods with a solid green carpet of redwood sorrel between the trees. Scattered about are dark green fountains of sword ferns and various understory trees and shrubs. Except for the occasional call of a bird, it is quiet, really quiet, a hushed quiet.

Redwoods have been around a long time. Known from the fossil record of the Cretaceous Era some 100 million years ago, redwoods were widely distributed in the northern hemisphere. Except for a greatly restricted distribu-

tion, redwoods then and now are much the same. They are now found in a narrow strip along the Pacific coast from California north to southern Oregon. Redwoods do best where their huge crowns and finely-divided, needle-like foliage can absorb water from coastal fog during summer months. Fog condenses on the foliage then drips to the ground in prodigious quantities.

If you choose to drive out to Crescent City, stop and walk the trail to the Boy Scout Tree. If you make this hike in May, you are sure to see the red Clintonia, a member of the lily family. The plants may be half a meter or more tall with large green leaves and terminal clusters of deep rose-purple flowers. If you are too late to see this handsome plant in flower you are still in for a treat. Its fruits are a cluster of deep metallic blue berries. Pick up a copy of Rudy Becking's *Pocket Flora of the Redwood Forest* before you visit the redwoods. The nice illustrations and keys help with identification.

If you are feeling down and need some woodland solace, some time in the redwoods contemplating the wonders of creation might just be the place for you.

Port Orford Cedar

Port Orford Cedar, *Chamaecyparis lawsoniana,* CHLA, or POC, is one of our region's very own, an endemic species, native here and nowhere else on planet Earth. Although unknown to science until 1854, the tree was used for timber in 1852 at an Oregon town on the Pacific coast. The town was Port Orford. The tree is Port Orford cedar, *C. lawsoniana.* The collector's brother named the tree for Peter Lawson, the Scots nurseryman who purchased the collection at a "liberal price." In 1854, William Murray discovered the species near Mount Shasta at the most eastern and southerly portion of its range. This was not its first collection. Botanists of the Wilkes US exploring expedition collected the tree in 1840 but never properly named it.

Port Orford cedar's many horticultural varieties grace temperate gardens worldwide. The native tree grows straight and tall. It may be a tree 100 feet in height or a shrub as low as three feet in a variety of colors; blue-green, silvery blue, dark green or golden yellow and blue-gray. Twenty years after its introduction in 1855 some 27 horticultural varieties were available to British gardeners. The third edition of the *Sunset Western Garden Book* lists eleven.

Its aromatic, weather-resistant wood has many fine qualities: straight-grained, strong dimensional stability and excellent machining qualities. For years it was highly sought after for domestic use. It was used in ship building, as electric storage battery separators, in the manufacture of Venetian blinds, and in building airplane fuselages. Today its major domestic use is for arrow shafts and an occasional boat.

The species is at risk for two reasons. In 1923, a killer root disease of unknown origin appeared on ornamentals near Seattle. It slowly spread south until it reached the cedar's native range in the mid 1950s. There is no cure for

the disease. The fungus invades the tree's rootlets. Fine roots disintegrate. The fungus slowly attacks the growing regions of the inner bark of roots and stems. Foliage wilts and dies at once due to root death.

We know the major spread is through earth movement in construction, public road use, and logging operations. Soil tracked about by cattle and rarely by native species like deer and elk, contribute to fungus spread along with Vibram soles and tennis shoes. Spread also depends on free-flowing water, along seeps and streams. Dry season logging, washing vehicles, entering and leaving infected areas, and removal of infected roadside trees help control the disease. A never-ending search for resistant individuals continues.

The species is not only under attack from disease. It and Alaska yellow cedar are the only tree species that can be exported overseas from federal lands as whole logs. Why? Because of our timber export laws. The law allows a species to be exported if it can be proved to the US Secretary of Agriculture that domestic use of the timber is absent or minimal. Special-interest groups have made the case for our two cedars, allowing raw log export to foreign lands.

The Japanese value Port Orford cedar wood because it resembles hinoki, *C. obtusa,* a rare oriental species important in home and temple construction. A Port Orford cedar log may be worth $10,000. Why don't we mill the logs ourselves to their specification? Maybe for the same reasons we won't make a car the Japanese will buy.

The main hope for Port Orford cedar is how the local national forests treat the species. Local silviculturalists can exclude the species from timber sales and look after the trees' best interest. They have a mandate to perpetuate Port Orford cedar as a functioning part of its natural ecosystem. Encourage them at every turn. The Japanese protect their cedars, shouldn't we?

Subalpine Fir

I spent one Saturday with Dr. Charles Welden, Southern Oregon University's community ecologist and Gene Parker, the local expert on true firs, on the summit of Mount Ashland taking a close look at the subalpine firs that grow there. Gene was checking out the firs for the Rogue River National Forest.

I always point out the clump of subalpine fir to students and field trippers when I am with them on the mountain. I tell them that its nearest neighbors are miles away in the Cascade Mountains and that it is a relict from the Ice Age. Maybe it's a relict, maybe it's a recent arrival. The jury is out on that one. To tell the truth, I had never really looked closely at the stand before this particular Saturday.

The stand appears low and scrubby with taller trees emerging above the knee to waist-deep foliage. The stand is some 300 feet around. The tallest trees are 18 or so feet high. The year I visited, the taller trees had purple, pitchy cones. Noble fir and white fir, the other true fir species on the mountain, also had a good cone year.

Subalpine fir, *Abies lasiocarpa,* is the most widespread of the true firs. It is found from the Yukon south through the Rocky Mountains to New Mexico and west along the Cascades and coast mountains to southern Oregon, with several scattered populations in northern California. Subalpine fir is most abundant near timberline. It can be the perfect picture of a true fir, tall and straight, conical, with short, stiff branches arranged in perfect whorls that extend to the ground. They are the perfect picture, unless they are krummholz. Krummholz — the trees look like the name sounds, low and gnarly. Krummholz, a German word that translates "crooked wood," refers to dwarfed trees caused by harsh environmental conditions at the upper limit of tree growth.

Subalpine fir sometimes adapts to its harsh environment by layering. When its low, sweeping branches contact the moist organic accumulation of duff around the base of a tree, the branches root. Often, the tree whose branches have layered dies and rots away. The layered shrubby branches then form timber atolls. Timber, like coral atolls, have an open center with a circular fringe of shrubs or trees, instead of coral reefs.

Close examination of Mount Ashland's subalpine firs yielded a surprise for me. Individual trees were indistinguishable. Elongated, horizontal branches covered the ground like giant serpents. The upright portions, including the taller trees, were not much more than upturned branches. There was no clear sign of individual trees.

The living trees on Mount Ashland are less than 80 years old. That is not to say the stand isn't old. In the interior of the stand I found four distinct layers of branches from live ones on the surface to well rotted branches deeper in the soil. My impression was of an active stand of trees dealing with its precarious site by constant growth and renewal. At the edge of the bowl, the fir probably spends a good part of the year protected by a cornice of snow. Its greatest danger will come if human activity changes the snow accumulation pattern and exposes the stand to the howling winds of winter.

Brewer's Spruce

What was the last major tree species to be discovered in the United States? It was our very own weeping, or Brewer's, spruce, *Picea breweriana.* A rare tree worldwide, Brewer's spruce is found only in the high mountains of southwest Oregon and northern California. Brewer's spruce tolerates infertile soils, cold temperatures, low light and snow pressure. On better sites it can't compete with other conifers. But on difficult sites, rocky ridges with poor soil, steep north slopes with lots of snow, places other conifers don't like, it holds its own. Although its present range is restricted, the tree is known as a fossil from 15 million-year-old Miocene deposits in northeastern Oregon.

Weeping spruce refers to its pendulous, hanging branchlets, similar to the hanging branchlets of its distant cousin the Norway spruce, cultivated in Ashland's Lithia Park.

There is an interesting story behind the weeping spruce's specific epithet "breweriana" and its other common name. Sereno Watson at Harvard University described the tree based on specimens collected on rocky ground along the trail from Happy Camp, California, to Waldo, Oregon, by the venerable Thomas Jefferson Howell in June of 1884. Howell, a self-taught Oregon botanist, made several very fruitful plant-collecting trips to Waldo in the Illinois Valley of southwest Oregon in 1884, '86 and '88. He sent many specimens that were new to science to Harvard University where they were named after him by the Harvard botanists Sereno Watson and Asa Gray. But Watson named the spruce *P. breweriana* not *P. howellii.* Why, you ask? Because Howell already had too many plants named after him? No, it was because JD Whitney, Chief of the Geological Survey of California, had given William Brewer, botanist on the survey, specimens of a spruce from the Castle Crags area in California. However,

there was not enough material to name. Brewer had a young assistant by the name of Sereno Watson. Are you starting to get the picture? When Howell sent his specimen with cones to Watson, Watson recognized the plant as being the same as Whitney's scrap, and proceeded to commemorate his old boss, Brewer. Maybe it should have been *P. whitneyi,* but then Whitney has a mighty tall mountain named after him.

After the snow has gone, plan a trip to look for weeping spruce. Try the vicinity of Babyfoot Lake west of the Illinois Valley, or the rocky ridge northwest of Miller Lake in the Applegate, or in the headwaters of Indian Creek on the old road from Waldo, Oregon to Happy Camp, California, where Howell probably first collected his specimens. Look for a small to medium sized spruce (the needles are on tiny wooden pedestals) with a narrow cone-shaped crown, numerous short, spreading branches and long, thin, hanging brachlets.

If you go to Miller Lake, there is a real treat in store for you. It is where the largest known Brewer spruce on planet Earth is found. Thirteen feet, eight inches in circumference, 170 feet tall. Check with the Star Ranger Station along the Applegate River south of Ruch for precise directions. Be prepared for a moderately difficult mountain trail.

No matter where you go, when you find the trees, feel privileged. Some people travel halfway around the world to see the trees.

Sisyrinchium

Your favorite genus might be Carl Sagan or Albert Einstein. A favorite genus of mine is *Sisyrinchium*, better known to many of you as grass widows or, depending on the color of the flowers, purple, blue, or yellow-eyed grass. They aren't grasses at all, but brightly, sprightly, members of the Iridaceae or iris family. Although they have grass-like foliage, a close look at their brightly colored flowers reveals characteristics of the iris family; an inferior ovary (the ovary beneath the other floral parts) and just three stamens. Like iris, this slender tufted perennial has two-ranked leaves, though often very narrow.

The narrow leaves account for part of its common name, grass widow. What about the widow? In my first wildflower book, *Wild Flowers of the Pacific Coast*, author Leslie Haskins supposes that the name may originate because each stem bears but a single flower at a time. In Haskins' words — "a flower widow, alone but not dejected— a widow who enjoys her single state, since it gives her the privilege of dancing, and smiling, and winking at every passer by." I would remind readers that Mr. Haskins wrote those words in 1934. On blustery spring days the brightly colored blossoms do nod and bob about on the end of slender stems.

Largest and most handsome of the widows is the purple-eyed grass, *S. douglasii,* first collected by our friend David Douglas at Celilo in the Columbia River Gorge in 1826. He probably collected his specimens in March when he was on his way to Walla Walla, Spokane and Kettle Falls. Celilo Falls, once a famous Native American salmon fishing spot, is no more, sunk beneath the back waters of the Dalles Dam.

In March, the species will be in full bloom brightening our landscape with its purple flowers. Look for it in dry, well-drained meadows or rocky hilltops, like the knoll

at the south end of the dam at the entrance of the county park at Emigrant Lake near Ashland, or the top of the Table Rocks, north of Medford. The rocky areas on the summit of both Rocks have colorful displays, well worth the trip, in spite of the slick and muddy trail. If you miss them there, travel up to the Cascades to see them blooming later at places like the Irene Hollenbeck Environmental Study Area at the junction of Conde Creek Access Road and Dead Indian Memorial Road in eastern Jackson County.

When you find a population of purple-eyed grass, look for occasional plants with white flowers. The gene that creates the enzyme that normally makes the purple flower pigment mutates to a form that prevents pigment formation, so the flowers are white.

White-flowered plants occur in other species as well. Look for pink and white-flowered blue-eyed Marys. Genetic studies show that two genes form the final blue pigment. Color mutants occur in camas, sea blush, and red flowering currant, among others. If you are interested in wildflower genetics, try the paperback of the same name by Griffiths and Ganders published by Flight Press of Vancouver, British Columbia.

In late spring and summer look for blue-eyed grass in wet areas in the Illinois Valley and elsewhere, and yellow-eyed grass in bogs along the coast. Though not as brazen as the purple-eyed grass, these widows are equally attractive in their own quiet way.

Blackberries

August is usually blackberry month. I am not sure how good the blackberry crop was this year. The ones I know were not very plump, and ended up dry and wizened on the vine. And, like the blackberry seeds scattered about by birds, seeds of autumn were found everywhere in August. The sun dropped a bit further south, some ash leaves began to fall, most summer flowers finished blooming.

Most years the blackberry vine gushes forth in all its glory in August —and it couldn't be missed. We see people parked along roadsides, coffee cans in hand, taking their share. Blackberries turn up in pies, on ice cream or corn flakes, in jams, all sorts of delicious places.

To some people our common blackberry, *Rubus discolor* (now known as *R. armeniaeus*), the Himalayan blackberry, is just a nuisance, a weed, originally from Eurasia. No one knows when or where it first arrived, but when it did the Himalayan blackberry sure made itself at home. When looking at the wild tangles along local streams, one wonders what native species were displaced by this alien being.

Our native trailing blackberry or dewberry, *R. ursinus,* is a humble bramble by comparison. Its low scrambly vines often cover the ground in cut-over, burned or otherwise disturbed moist places. Although it doesn't seem as vigorous as *R. discolor,* its smaller, tart fruits make pies to die for, so tasty and delicious. Blackberry snobs like me prefer them every time. Trailing blackberry pickers often complain of blighted berries. Not so. The flowers are unisexual, and the blighted berries are male, staminate flowers that will never form fruits. Our trailing blackberry is one of the ancestors, with *R. idaeus,* of the loganberry and its cultivar the boysenberry.

The vigor, quantity and accessibility of the Himalayan blackberry make it a favorite of the *hoi polloi.* Its vigor is

what can make it a pest, in spite of large quantities of insipid fruits. It grows and grows and grows, almost impossible to control.

Its tough, fibrous roots defy digging — one gets the feeling there is someone large in Australia holding on to the other end. A landscaper, once asked about the best way to get rid of Himalaya blackberry said, “you can't, there is one massive blackberry root under all of Oregon.” Once you got 'em, you got 'em, though people try everything from goats to chemical weapons of mass destruction to eradicate them.

If that isn't enough, birds spread blackberries' aggregate fruits far and wide. Tips of canes can root wherever they touch the ground, effectively enabling your blackberry patch to march across your property. It has consumed whole pastures and uncounted acres of roadside and riparian habitat. Guess what else? Himalayan blackberries are favored food and shelter for rats, or so says the *Jepson Manual.*

Blackberries are really very democratic plants. They grow most anywhere, for example, under and through the pavement of your driveway. They grace backyards of rich and poor alike — they treat everyone the same. And, as with democracy, they require some sacrifice to be achieved: one must do battle with an army of thorny vines in order to obtain the sweet fruit that is ultimately available to all.

Cucurbits

Its Hallowe'en, what better topic for *Nature Notes* than a discussion of . . . the *Cucurbitaceae*. "What?", you say. "I thought you'd pick something creepy, like bats, or spiders, or snakes, or politicians." Sorry to disappoint, pumpkin head, but we are going to talk squash. My inspiration came this morning while I carved away on the family Jack O' Lantern. The *Cucurbitaceae* is the squash, gourd, melon, pumpkin family. The family is mostly tropical and subtropical, with few temperate species.

One summer, I had occasion to examine Oregon's only native cucurbit, *Marah oregana,* also known as old-man-in-the-ground, in some detail. The spiny fruit is extremely bitter and not at all palatable. Its common name is supposedly derived from a huge underground tuber-like structure. While botanizing the Pilot Rock area, with some Japanese guests, we came upon a marah plant on a road cut. After telling them about the plant, we got out our digging implements to look for the old man. It didn't take long to discover he was there, a large underground structure with thick, ropy-looking limbs and three-foot body. We didn't dig it all up, and we filled in the hole as good botanists do. What we got were very heavy chunks, saturated with water, which gets our native gourd through long, hot, dry summers.

We eat, as fruits and vegetables, many members of this family: melons, watermelons, cantaloupe, muskmelons, honeydew, casaba, and cucumbers and squashes, winter squash, summer squash, spaghetti squash, vegetable marrow, and zucchini, but not zucchini squash. Zucchini squash is redundant — zucchini is Italian for squash. Surprise, surprise, technically all these are fruits. Just because they are not sweet doesn't make them vegetables. Any plant organ produced from the ovary of a flower, as these are, is a fruit.

Even that strange pear-shaped chayote with the large single seed is a fruit, though the taste and texture are somewhere near cucumber, and zucchini, with a splash of kohlrabi. Its mild flavor can stand some jacking up with spices. The entire plant is edible including its yam-like 20-pound root.

Not all are edible. The calabash or bottle gourd is one of our earliest cultivated plants. As pointed out in Heywood's *Flowering Plants of the World*, it is the only species with an archaeologically documented pre-history in both hemispheres of planet Earth. The loofa sponge, that strange looking cylindrical object of the bath, is the bleached vascular skeleton of the fruit of *Luffa*, a genus in the *Cucurbitaceae*. Some cucurbits are used as a vermifuge (*vermis* = a worm, *fugare* = to put to flight) to clear human bowels of intestinal worms.

During Hallowe'en our pumpkin Jack O' Lantern cast its spell and lured several dozen ghosts and goblins from the darkness to our door. Maybe it's the curmudgeon in me (or the glutton) but I much prefer my pumpkins in a pie.

Darlingtonia

One of our endemic plant marvels is the insectivorous *Darlingtonia californica.* The California pitcher plant, or hooded cobra lily, is found in sphagnum bogs along the Oregon coast near Florence, inland to southwestern Oregon, and northern California to the Sierra Nevada and the Trinity Alps. Inland, the plants are usually found along streams or in seepages on steep slopes in areas with serpentine soils.

This strange, exotic native plant was discovered by Charles Breckenridge, botanist with the US Exploring Expedition in 1841. The party was on its way to San Francisco. They were not having much fun, what with rascally Rogue Indians and ague, as malaria was then known. The Shasta Valley wasn't any kinder to them. "Weather very warm. No water for 15 miles. Miserable Country, the Shaste valley —" wrote Charles. That was on October 1st. On October 5th, along the Sacramento River the party of explorers bolted at an alarm from Indians. Breckenridge saw a strange-looking plant, grabbed a clump and brought it back to camp. It was, perhaps, his most interesting discovery. Hope it gave the dour Scot some pleasure. The species was not described for 12 years when the New York botanist John Torrey commemorated his "highly esteemed friend" William Darlington.

Darlingtonia traps insects, attracted by sight and smell, in their upright tubular leaves. There are small nectar glands on the pitcher-like leaf, especially the "mustache" that hangs down in front of the mouth and around the thickened "lips"of the opening. Once inside, flying insects are attracted to light entering the hood through transparent ceiling "windows." After buzzing around inside the hood, insects land on the smooth waxy interior surface where they slide toward the pool of fluid at the slender base of the pitcher. On the way down, they pass over stiff

downward-pointing hairs that prevent their upward escape. At the bottom of the tube insects drown in bacterial soup. Insect carcasses are broken down by bacterial activity. According to traditional wisdom, *Darlingtonia* obtains nitrogen from decaying insect parts as the plant absorbs released nutrients.

Attractive down-turned flowers with large yellow-green sepals and smaller maroon petals are produced in the late spring, a single flower per stalk. After pollination, the flower turns upright as the fruit matures. Occasionally, last year's upright capsules can be seen scattered among this spring's new blossoms.

Years ago, one of our students, Frank Cook, studied the floral biology of *Darlingtonia* by placing mesh bags over some flowers and not others. He discovered that bagged flowers do not set seed as readily as unbagged flowers. More recently, another of our Southern Oregon University students, Susan Nyoka, studied pollinators in *Darlingtonia*. Spiders seem to be implicated. Frank is teaching high school in outback Alaska. Susan hopes to go on to graduate school. You never know where peering down the maws of *Darlingtonia* will take you.

There is an hypothesis that the insects and pitcher plants have a mutualistic relationship; that is, both partners benefit. How? Not all insects may fall prey to the pitcher, and more might benefit from nectar than die in the soup. The pitcher plant profits from the supply of nitrogen.

To find pitcher plants visit the Darlingtonia Wayside near Florence on the coast or go to the Illinois Valley. There are nice bogs along the Eight Dollar Mountain Road west of Highway 199 near Selma and where the old Oregon Mountain Road crosses Whiskey Creek southwest of O'Brien. Please leave these wonderful creations in the wild where they belong. Their growth requirements are difficult to duplicate, and cultivation almost always fails.

Helliborine Orchid

Orchids are always exciting to find. My discovery of the Helliborine orchid in Jackson County was no exception. The beauty of its flower was not that exciting, although it is a step above the tway-blade and rattlesnake plantain. I didn't recognize it; that is what made it interesting. Not to recognize species of sedges or willows is one thing, not to recognize an orchid is something else.

The plants were not in bloom when first discovered. I mentioned to my companion I thought the leaves looked like the chatterbox orchid, *Epipactus gigantea.* We left without collecting specimens intending to return when the plants were flowering. The next day I checked specimens in the Southern Oregon University herbarium and did a little reading. The plants didn't seem quite right for the chatterbox. I had to wait for flowers.

When I finally saw the plant in bloom, it was apparent it wasn't the chatterbox. I identified the plant using Donovan Correll's book, *Native Orchids of North America.* The plant was the Helliborine orchid, *Epipactus helliborine,* not a native plant. My first guess wasn't too far off the mark. It turns out this plant is our only weedy orchid, an Eurasian native, and has a fairly well-documented history of invasion across North America from east to west.

Mrs. MO Rust of the Syracuse Botanical Club first collected the plant in North America, August 1879, at Syracuse, New York. In 1890, it was reported from Lamberton Mills near Toronto, Canada. In subsequent years, it spread rapidly throughout eastern North America. By 1950 it was known from Quebec, Ontario, New Hampshire, Vermont, Connecticut, New York, New Jersey, Pennsylvania, Maryland, Michigan, Indiana, Missouri, Montana (where it was probably a cultivated plant) and Eurasia, its native home. In the 1960s, it was reported from gardens in Victoria, British Columbia and from

counties around San Francisco Bay. In 1985, I found the Jackson County population of several hundred plants growing under Douglas fir, big-leaf maple, Oregon ash, and white alder on an old river terrace between Dodge Bridge and Shady Cove on the Rogue River.

How did the Helliborine orchid get to Jackson County, Oregon? Perhaps the species is widespread, as Lewis Clark maintains in his book, *Wildflowers of the Pacific Northwest.* Perhaps it is widespread, but unrecognized, and there are nearby, undiscovered populations. Not likely with all the knowledgeable botanists around these days.

Perhaps it was introduced in a nearby garden where it grows unnoticed. What gardener wouldn't notice an unexpected orchid in the roses?

Orchid seeds are among the smallest known, often just a tiny collection of cells weighing micrograms. Wind can carry seeds this small for considerable distances. But here the nearest known populations are hundreds of miles away and the prevailing winds aren't quite right. Not likely.

The Jackson County population grows in a woodlot where cattle have been run for the past 25 years. The land owner thinks some of the cattle were imported from Montana or California. Could cows have carried seeds in hooves or hair? A long shot at best.

We probably will never know how the Jackson County population became established. Look for this distinguished weed, though. Perhaps you'll find some botanical excitement of your own and help solve another one of nature's mysteries.

Fall Leaves

"Dull November brings the blast, Then the leaves are whirling fast."

If we beat the blast, we still might have good fall color this year. Why? Because we haven't had a heavy frost. Contrary to common belief, early frosts dim autumn's brilliance by killing or severely injuring the leaves before their bright pigments reach maximum intensity. Photoperiodic change starts things off. Longer nights and shorter days stop chlorophyll production in leaves. Green chlorophyll pigments break down to reveal yellow carotenes and xanthophylls. Sometimes a rise in sugars accompanies the breakdown of chloroplasts in leaves, which enhances the production of water-soluble red and purple anthocyanin pigments. The result is one reason why I like fall so much.

One fall, several years ago, I was treated to a fantastic sight. The deciduous trees had turned color and were about to drop their leaves. The morning after our first hard freeze I remember walking along the frosty street on my way to an eight o'clock class. Glancing up I noticed, through the mist, the yellow leaves and dark branches of a black walnut. Beyond, I could see a patch of milk blue sky that promised warmer temperatures as morning progressed. For some reason, I returned home, probably to get something I had forgotten, about the time of promised warmer temperatures. A beam of sunlight illuminated the black walnut. A leaf fell, no big deal, that's what's supposed to happen this time of year. Then two leaves fell, then four, then eight. I stopped and looked up and down the street. Leaves were beginning to fall off all the black walnuts as sunlight bathed the trees. Suddenly the leaves began to fall at once. Within ten minutes the trees were bare with knee-deep piles beneath them. No weeks of raking up black walnut leaves that year, they were on the ground in moments. Amazing. Here is what I think happened.

Deciduous trees go through a typical fall ritual. Auxin, a plant hormone, maintains an intact zone of cells at the base of the leaf stalk called the abscission layer. With adequate auxin levels, leaves stay on the tree. Aging leaves, and the longer nights, shorter days and cooler temperatures of fall cause a drop in auxin levels. With low auxin levels the cells of the abscission layer separate and leaves fall off the tree, usually a few at a time, not all at once.

The black walnut leaves had a fairly well-developed abscission layer. When the leaves froze, ice crystals formed in the abscission layer and ruptured the cells. The layer remained intact until the warm sun lit the trees, melted the ice and all the leaves fell off at once. If you have black walnuts, a word to the wise. The leaves make terrible compost. They contain a substance that inhibits the growth of other plants.

If this year's dull November blasts don't send your leaves whirling fast, the trees might be in trouble. If not watered, some deciduous cultivated trees and shrubs may succumb to our long dry summers. Keep them watered till it starts to rain.

I had help with this *Nature Note* from Mother Nature and Mother Goose.

Pumpkins

The *Cucurbitaceae* figure greatly in the world's food basket. It is the plant family that includes squashes, melons, cucumbers and the like. This time of year the pumpkin figures greatly in our diet as pies and in our folkways.

Jack'O Lanterns made of pumpkins are probably an invention of North American Christians, since pumpkins originate in the western hemisphere. Celts, who celebrated the festival of Samhain (Saw win) and early European Christians, who celebrated All Saint's Day on or about October 31, used turnips or, perhaps, gourds to fashion grotesque masks. But the pumpkin shell is best, easily carved and lighted from within to form a most hideous and frightening visage — a visage hideous and frightening enough to scare away the evil spirits of that night.

Cucurbits are native to both the old and new worlds: squashes and pumpkins from the western hemisphere, melons and cucumbers from the eastern hemisphere. Most all cucurbits are annual vines that like warmth. Domesticated species are monecious; that is, have male and female flowers on the same plant. The hard-rinded fruits, flower stalk at one end, flower scar at the other, are called pepos.

Most of us, those who have gotten over gagging on squash, eat the flesh, but pass up the seeds, high in important sulfur-containing amino acids. Next time you do your Hallowe'en pumpkin, save the seeds, salt them, toast them in the oven, hand them out for tricks. Better yet, save them for yourself for treats.

We commonly eat and/or utilize three *Cucurbita* species. *Cucurbita pepo* includes summer squash, zucchini, yellow crookneck, those weird little ornamental gourds and our Hallowe'en pumpkin. *Cucurbita moschata* gives us many of our winter squashes such as the butternut. *Cucurbita maxima* produces buttercup, turban and hubbard squash.

Cucumis is the melon genus that gives us everything from watermelons to cucumbers. Cucumbers were carried throughout the arid Middle East as living canteens that filled you up and quenched your thirst because of their high water content. If you want a different cucumber treat, soak slices in diluted rice wine vinegar left in the fridge. You might better understand why cucumbers are often eaten with sugar in their native southern Asia.

In the fall, on the open rock slopes of the Klamath Ridges River Ecoregion, we often see a mass of tangled yellowed vines. It's our perennial native gourd, called old-man-in-the-ground or manroot after its human-sized underground parts, which weigh 100 pounds or more. Like its annual cousins it dies back at first frost, but then the following spring leaps forth with a jungle of climbing, twining vines. Its small, oval, prickly fruit is bitter as sin, virtually inedible, although small herbivorous mammals seem to relish the endosperm-rich seeds. Its generic name, Marah, is one of the few Hebrew scientific names. It means bitter.

Have an unsightly compost heap? Plant a few pumpkin seeds on top. Your pumpkin vines, with awe-inspiring speed, will soon cover up your warm pile of rotting vegetation with a mound of large green leaves. Later, if you are lucky, there will be enough big orange pumpkins to scare away a host of goons and goblins.

Yams

There is a good chance you had sweet potatoes or yams with your last Thanksgiving feast. Chances are very good that if you thought you were eating yams, you weren't. You were probably eating a variety of sweet potato with orange flesh. There is a lot of confusion about yams and sweet potatoes; a confusion frequently created by common names. Let me explain.

Ipomoea is the sweet potato genus in the *Convolvulaceae*, a dicot plant family that includes morning glories, bindweeds and other herbaceous climbers that always twine to the right. Some are lianas, woody vines, to 30 meters long, others herbs, shrubs and at least one tree. Besides the sweet potato, some *Ipomoea* are eaten as a leafy vegetable, others are sources of hallucinogenic drugs, others high-order, effective, drastic purgatives.

Ipomoea batatas produces the edible underground tuber-like root that we call the sweet potato. According to Elizabeth Schneider's *Uncommon Fruits and Vegetables, a Common Sense Guide,* a very sweet, orange fleshed sweet potato was introduced in the 1930s as a Louisiana yam. This marketing ploy served to distinguish it from our white or yellow-fleshed, drier (source of the gag factor in small children), less sweet, sweet potato. Because of this, what most of us call a yam, the rest of the world does not. To them a yam is quite different.

What the rest of the world calls a yam comes from the genus *Dioscorea* in the *Dioscoreaceae*, a monocot family. Several different species are eaten around the world in prodigious amounts: 25 million tons, one of the world's greatest food crops. Not only are amounts prodigious, so are individual yams. According to Ms. Schneider, on some Pacific Islands, yams are described as two-man, four- or six-man, depending on the number of men, not women, it takes to lift the tuber. In many societies yams are held in

such high esteem that only men are allowed to cultivate them. One tuber was reported to be six feet long and weigh 600 pounds.

Real yams don't often appear in local markets. They kind of look like sweet potatoes but tend to be more log shaped, not tapered at each end, and have a brown to blackish shaggy-coated covering. By most accounts, the edible underground portion of a yam is a tuber, a modified stem, similar to our white potato. Some species may store food products in roots, however.

Some *Dioscorea* yam species produce a chemical that is used as a starting point for the production of cortisone and hydrocortisone, and progesterone used in birth control pills.

When you buy sweet potatoes, store them at room temperature. A quick and easy way to cook them, with what seems to me to be a lowered gag factor, is to nuke 'em in the microwave: fast, easy and delicious. Lots of butter also lowers the gag factor, not too healthy maybe, but it beats death by gagging. Try Ms. Schneider's book *Uncommon Fruits and Vegetables* for other recipes for yams and sweet potatoes, and get ready for Christmas dinner.

Foxtails

Several years ago I visited the most northerly known population of foxtails on Lake Mountain, a 6,900 foot promontory south of Seiad Valley and the Klamath River. From the summit there are panoramic views in all directions: the high Siskiyous from Preston Peak to Mount Ashland; the Marbles, from mountain tops to valley bottoms.

This trip was particularly interesting because Ron Mastrogiuseppe was along. Ron and his wife Joy intensively studied the Lake Mountain foxtails a decade or so ago. They studied them so intensely that they named many of the trees, The Twins, The Puma Tree, The Four Guardsmen, Ron's Tree. Ron was excited to see his trees again.

John Jeffrey, as we have mentioned before (page 23), was the first European to discover foxtail pines on the ridges between Shasta and Scott Valley, probably on Mount Eddy, September 29, 1852. Foxtails have an unusual distribution: one group in the Klamath Mountains, another in the southern Sierra Nevada, 300 miles away. Ron and Joy discovered that the northern trees have larger cones, down-swept branches, and gray bark. Their southern counterparts have smaller cones, upswept branches, and cinnamon bark. Foxtail pines have five needles, a characteristic shared with whitebark pine, a tree of high elevations and harsh habitats. Whitebark pines have a close relationship with that large gray, black, and white crow-like bird, Clark's nutcracker.

These timberline foxtails have straight trunks to 50 feet, unusual considering their windswept, harsh environment. They share this mountain top with the oldest and only operating forest lookout remaining in California. The trees are old, not just lookout old, but Methuselah old, that antediluvian patriarch of 969 years. One stump from a tree near the helipad at the lookout was just less than

1,000 years old. Many, still-living trees at Lake Mountain have trunks as large.

Sadly, I say, still living. Thirteen, including Ron's Tree, were killed by the 1987 forest fires. Most were in the stand below the lookout to the northwest. Snags or downed logs set nearby living trees afire. Others fell victim because their descending branches reached near the ground where surface fires in the grass and manzanita set them ablaze. Art's tree, named for a long-time Lake Mountain lookout, survived the flames of '87, but nearly perished several years ago when a Forest Service communications truck burned up beneath its now singed needles. Life, it seems, is dangerous.

Age seems to run in the family. Its nearest relatives are the Rocky Mountain and Great Basin bristlecone pines. Great Basin bristlecones can exceed 4,000 years in age, making them among the oldest living trees on planet Earth.

You don't need to travel to Lake Mountain to see the lookout or the trees. Ramona Hammerly beautifully illustrated both in Stephen Arno's book *Timberline: Mountain and Arctic Forest Frontiers* published by the Mountaineers, Seattle. The lookout with the Twins just below it is on page 131. The Puma Tree, in all its glory, is on page 133. Puma, thankfully, survived the fire. It looks today much as Ramona illustrated it. With any luck at all, Puma's seeds will provide a new crop of recruits for the next millennium.

Grapeferns

I expended a certain amount of energy one summer looking for grapeferns, also known as moonworts. Most readers have never heard of moonworts and those who have, may have never seen a live one. What an interesting group of plants. They are vascular plants with special tissues to conduct fluids from root to shoot and back again. They reproduce by spores produced in tiny round sporangia, a millimeter or less in diameter, which, altogether, look like clusters of grapes. Their generic name *Botrychium* is from the Greek *botrys*, a bunch of grapes.

Oregon is home to a dozen different species. Most of them are tiny and none of them common. Most grow in rich, moist, organic soil in mountain meadows which adds to the pleasure of looking for them. The Wallowa Mountains have the greatest concentration of grapefern species of any place on planet Earth. David Wagner, curator of the University of Oregon herbarium and our local grapefern expert, found a Wallowa meadow with seven different grapefern species growing in it.

Want to look for grapeferns? Here is what to do. Anytime from late July till September drive to a high elevation meadow, like the damp meadow on the north or east side of Mount Ashland or Elk Wallow on the Galice Access Road to Agness. Walk around the meadow, head down, and look for dark rich soil that is not soaking wet. Search first for the largest and most common *Botrychium* in Oregon, the leather-leaf grapefern. It grows in sun or shade from sea level to mountain meadows. Its single leaf divides into a vegetative portion with a thick, leathery evergreen leafy portion and a much different looking fertile part that bears the grape-like clusters of sporangia. Once you find a leather-leaf grapefern, the fun begins. You now get down on your hands and knees and comb carefully through surrounding vegetation looking for other,

much smaller species. They are a sociable lot. The leather-leaf grapefern can be a robust six to eight inches tall or taller. The others? A slender inch or two or less. Our Mount Ashland meadow has two other species, the least moonwort, *B. simplex,* and *B. crenulatum,* the crenulate moonwort. You find them with your nose at soil level.

One of my favorites is the pumice grapefern, though I have never seen it. It is southern and central Oregon's own, found nowhere else on earth. For a hundred years it was known only from Lloa Rock on the rim of Crater Lake. In the past few years, diligent botanists discovered it growing in raw pumice or pumice soil in the Three Sisters area, near the Newberry Caldera, and in lodgepole pine south and east of there.

One Oregon species is the widely distributed, *B. lunaria,* or common moonwort. In Europe its unusual appearance has led to many folktales. In pastures it can undo shackles and locks on livestock and remove horses' shoes if stepped upon, or change mercury into silver. Not only that, fairy-sized people use the fairy-sized leaflets as fairy-sized saddles on fairy-sized horses. Its key-like appearance led to the myth that it could unlock locks.

Dr. David Wagner's 1991 Willamette Valley nature calendar featured original illustrations and some fabulous facts about Oregon's dozen species. If you are interested in a current calendar check with Dave Wagner at Box 30064, Eugene, Oregon 97403.

Holly

Humans have decked their halls with boughs of holly for a long time. The present custom of holly at Christmas seems to make sense, what with blood-red fruits and thorny leaves. However, the custom goes back before the birth of Christ to Celtic Druids, who thought that holly symbolized the sun and so brought sprays of holly into their homes in dismal winter months, and back to ancient Rome when Romans, slave and citizen, celebrated Saturnus' grand festival in December. Gifts were given, parties held, holly used for decoration and "*io Saturnilia,*" not "Merry Christmas" was the order of the day. Today we still use holly as a decoration in December.

Hollies, all 400 or so species in the genus *Ilex*, are found worldwide except western North America and southern Australia. We know one at Christmas time, the European Holly, *Ilex aquifolium.* Growers cultivate holly in the Willamette Valley and Portland area as a Christmas green. Holly growers have had a terrible time with another European native who has done well in North America, the starling. Starlings descend in enormous numbers to strip holly trees bare in moments. Cannons, scarecrows, traps, nothing seems to work. One large flock of startled starling took off *en masse* and destroyed the trap in the process.

If you have a holly tree that isn't bearing fruits, there could be several causes. Holly is dioecious, of two households. One household consist of trees with only male or staminate flowers. The other household consists of trees with only female or pistillate flowers. If your tree is staminate or male, no bright red fruits can form because only pistillate flowers can form fruits. If your tree has female flowers, but no fruits, there are probably no male trees around to pollinate it. It takes pollen and bees for fruit formation.

Most, if not all, hollies are poisonous. Many species of birds beside starlings eat the berries with impunity. Humans, on the other hand, find holly a terrific purgative. That effect is clearly shown by the scientific name for yaupon, a native holly of the southeastern United States, *I. vomitoria.* Certain Native American tribes used yaupon's emetic qualities in their Black Drink ceremonies. An infusion made from the leaves of *I. paraguensis* yields a tea known as mate.

American holly wood is white, light, and lacks patterns, no matter which way the wood is cut, and comes as close to ivory color as any American wood. The wood is used for inlay, small musical instruments, and as piano and organ keys.

So, good people of all religious persuasions or none at all, deck your halls with boughs of holly, be jolly, don your gay apparel, troll the ancient Yuletide carol and enjoy the Christmas season, heedless of the wind and weather.

Mistletoe

The loss of leaves this time of year uncovers hidden surprises on many species of deciduous trees, but particularly on our Garry or Oregon white oak, *Quercus garryana.* Suddenly gray branches, shaggy with lichens appear, and in some trees, dark green clusters become more obvious. Close inspection reveals that these are clearly not a part of the oak, but another plant with only stem and leaves showing.

This parasitic plant, the mistletoe, *Phorodendron villosum,* grows directly from the branches of its host. Highly modified root-like structures called haustoria penetrate the tissues of the branch to rob the tree of water and minerals. Because the mistletoe is green and photosynthetic, this partial parasite can manufacture most of its own food. But if the green aerial portions break off, the mistletoe's haustoria can obtain all nutrients from its unwilling host and stay alive in the infected branch for years.

Mistletoe is spread by birds like robins, bluebirds, thrushes and cedar waxwings who feed on its berries. The small white to pinkish fruits contain a single seed surrounded by a viscid pulp. Birds eat the fruits, digest the pulp, and poop the still living seeds about, often on branches of susceptible trees. The sticky droppings give the germinating seeds a chance to penetrate the host tissues. Others think the sticky seeds attach to the beaks of birds and then adhere to the bark of the host when the birds wipe off the seeds. Opinion seems to be divided.

Some pathologists think that mistletoe concentrates in some trees and not others, because once an infection starts, the birds are attracted to one fruit-laden parasite and hang about eating and pooping or wiping their beaks in the same tree; so more mistletoes become established, *ad infinitum.*

Heavily infected trees can be weakened and sometimes killed. During drought, weakened trees are predis-

posed to insect attack and can die. And infected branches are more likely to be broken off in winds.

Our *Phorodendron* is found from the northern Willamette Valley south to Baja California. Here, Oregon white oak is the principle host, though it may be found occasionally on California black oak, manzanita, alder, and further south on California buckeye.

The mistletoe is held in high esteem at Christmas as a decoration and for the pleasant custom of kissing under the mistletoe, which can add to the enjoyment of the season. Be careful, though, especially with children. The leaves and stems are toxic, and at least one death has been attributed to eating the plant and berries.

Christmas Trees

O Christmas tree! O Christmas tree!
Your leaves are faithful ever!
Not only green when summer glows,
but in the winter when it snows,
O Christmas tree! O Christmas tree!
Your leaves are faithful ever.

When I was a child growing up in Olympia, Washington, I knew Christmas was upon us when the family, aunts and uncles, cousins, mother, father, sisters, the whole family, as I recall it said, packed up on a cold and wet Saturday and proceeded to Hawks Prairie to cut each family's Christmas tree. What an adventure! What a place!

In the late 40s Hawks Prairie was still a prairie: open grassland, surrounded by a forest of Douglas fir. Around the margin were many smaller trees — Christmas tree-sized trees.

The family arrived in force, got out of the cars, and then began what I swear was the beginning of the world's greatest annual slowdown ever, the countdown till Christmas morning. Christmas eve, of course, was when time stood still, perhaps moved backward. As you might suspect, we opened presents at our house Christmas morning, after Santa Claus had come and gone. I still look askance at families who open presents before Santa has officially arrived. I think they are depriving themselves of one of our culture's greatest anticipatory events.

On the prairie, in the wind and rain, we walked around looking at countless candidates, looking for the perfect tree. More often than not, we cut one of the first trees we scrutinized.

Prairies in the middle of the Puget Sound lowland? How could it be? I didn't find out till years later when I studied the vegetation dynamics of the gravelly prairies of

western Washington for my Master's thesis. The prairies formed on the draughty soils of the outwash at the terminus of the last great Pleistocene glacier. Constant burning by natural fires set by lightning or Native Americans maintained the prairies. Once the Europeans established fire protection, seedling firs could get established, an event that is playing out with the disappearance of the open grasslands. Today, Hawks Prairie is gone and in its place is a Douglas fir forest that has trees that might do for the White House, but not my house.

As you might suspect, the Christmas tree tradition continues here in southern Oregon. For years the families of friends and colleagues have gotten together to venture forth on an annual Christmas tree expedition to the local high country. It's a mixture of popcorn balls, mulled wine and adrenaline, for me. How much snow? Will we get stuck? Will we get the elusive silver-tip or have to settle for a white fir, or god forbid a Douglas fir? I still love 'em, Douglas firs. Someone else is spoiled. The silver-tip is the noble fir, called by many in southern Oregon, the Shasta fir. It makes a beautiful Christmas tree. I don't feel too badly about cutting Christmas trees. It cuts down on competition for the others. I suppose I should be ashamed. Sorry, I am not.

There are two odors that bring back a flood of pleasant memories: the heady smell of Douglas fir in the house first thing in the morning when you get up, and the distinctive smell of the Sears Roebuck Christmas catalog. What memories.

O Christmas tree! O Christmas tree!
Your faithful leaves will teach me
That hope and love and constancy
Give hope and peace eternally.
O Christmas tree! O Christmas tree!
Your faithful leaves will teach me.

Piper's Desert Parsley

In February, *Lomatium piperi,* or Piper's desert parsley, is in full bloom on the top of Lower Table Rock. It is quite a sight, if you can find it. Look down this time, not up. The plant grows in the shallow soil of moss mats in the rocky areas away from the vernal pools and soil mounds. You have to get right down on the ground to see the small mass of white flowers and blue stamens. Unlike most desert parsleys, the underground parts are small, round corms filled with carbohydrates.

The plants are more common east of the Cascades. There, Native Americans collected the corms in quantity. After peeling off the outer layers, they ground the corms into flour to make into cakes or biscuits for later use. Near Klamath Falls "Kouse," as the Klamaths called it, blooms in the nearby hills about March 10th. The Klamaths also collected Epa and Yampa, other, larger, plants with elongated tapered corms in the genus *Perideridia* for food. Corms were dug about the first of May and eaten raw when they were soft and milky or more often dried and saved for later use.

Kouse, yampa and epa are members of the *Umbelliferae* or *Apiaceae* if you want to use the modern name. Many familiar and edible plants are members of this family: celery, carrots, parsnips (barely edible, in my opinion) and, of course, kouse and epa. Parsley, dill, caraway, anise, fennel, chervil, lovage, and angelica are condiments or seasonings.

Other members of the family, common and widespread, are somewhat less than edible, in fact, downright poisonous, deadly poisonous, as Socrates discovered. Socrates, or so the story goes, died from drinking a concoction of poison hemlock, *Conium maculatum.* This naturalized European weed is often found along roadsides, the edges of drying waterways, and in waste places in

southern Oregon. Poison hemlock's tall green stems, splotched with purple, finely divided foliage, and distinctive chemical odor are easy to recognize. Children and adults may occasionally eat the plant because of ignorance or mistaking the plant for parsley or anise. The seeds and roots are especially toxic.

Western water hemlock, *Cicuta douglasii,* is also very poisonous. A piece the size of a walnut can kill a cow. Water hemlocks have thickened, chambered, underground stems or tubers and exude a yellow parsnip-smelling fluid that gradually turns to reddish brown on exposure to air when cut. Water hemlock grows in marshes, along freshwater streams and ditches rooted in soil under water or in mud. In Oregon, river-rafter types have died after mistaking water hemlock for wild parsnips.

Parents, do yourselves a favor, teach your children not to browse and graze the landscape indiscriminately. Children should not eat or chew on any plant not served to them on a plate.

Moenchia Erecta

The story begins on a warm spring day in May 1984 on a visit to what was to become the Bureau of Land Management's Round Top Research Natural Area, in Jackson County, near Obenchain Mountain east of Medford, Oregon. I was with two Conservancy people on a botanical reconnaissance of the area. We walked in about two miles from the vehicles to the base of Round Top. We crawled under a barbed-wire fence onto a very wet flat below Round Top that was covered with what appeared to be a small white annual, *Arenaria* or sandwort. We collected a few specimens and then began to try to identify them using the keys in the first edition of Peck (1941) (crucial to the outcome of this story), and in the 1973 edition of Munz's *California Flora.*

When we looked closely at our "*Arenaria,*" we found that it was four-merous (had four sepals and petals) and wouldn't key out in Munz or Peck. Excitement mounted — a new genus or at least a new species! Plans were laid for publication. What would be a suitable name? How would we deal with the Latin descriptions? Many eggs were laid before the hatching, or is it many chickens counted?

After searching the area, we discovered that the plant was widely distributed in wet seeps. We walked past the plant along the road on the way in. When we returned home, I immediately headed for the university library. After some sober thought, I figured that the plant was probably not a new genus, or even a new species, but was probably a new weed. Because many of our weeds came from Europe, I tried to identify the plant using *Flora Europa.* It keyed out with little difficulty to *Moenchia erecta.* After searching the floras of North America in our library without success, I broadened my horizons by looking in *The Flora of the Australian Capital Territory.* There

it was, with an illustration that matched our specimens, and the statement that it was of European origin, widely naturalized and common in seepage areas in ACT. We had our identification.

A new weed is almost as exciting as a new species, if not a new genus; but even that was not to be. I called Ken Chambers at Oregon State. "Ken, are you familiar with Moan-key-a?" "What?" he asked, sounding somewhat puzzled. "It's a small, four-merous member of the *Caryophyllaceae* that looks a lot like *Arenaria,*" said I. "Oh, you must mean Moan-chee-a. It's in the second edition of Peck (1961), and has been collected on gravelly flats in central Jackson County" he said. I didn't say what I was thinking. What I said was, "Oh, yes, that's the plant. Well, we found it up by Round Top," and changed the subject.

What a disappointment. No new genus, no new species, no new weed, no nothing except a hard lesson. To add insult to injury, I went to the Southern Oregon University herbarium and discovered that a former student of mine had collected the species in the spring of 1967. After a glance at the second edition of Peck (1961), I knew that if we had that manual in the field, we would have identified *Moenchia* in an instant, with only a momentary flush of excitement, instead of giant ups and downs.

Since we first reported this story we have discovered that *Moenchia*, masquerading as sandwort, is much more widespread than just Jackson County. It has even made it to one place in California, if the new *Jepson Flora* is to be believed.

Morels

Spring brings the best of the edible mushrooms, the morels, popping up out of the ground at various locations in southern Oregon and northern California. If you ask people where to look for morels, they will be evasive, worse than fishermen. Early in the season look for morels at lower elevations growing under shrubs, including poison oak, in areas that have burned in the not too distant past. Later move to higher elevations in the Cascades and follow the receding snow line.

Morels are members of the group of fungi mycologists call Ascomycetes, the sac fungi, because their reproductive spores are produced in tiny sacs. Most of our other mushrooms are Basidiomycetes, the club fungi, with spores produced on microscopic structures called basidia. The morels are among the safest of all fungi. Their distinctive hollow fruiting body and cap honeycombed with raised ridges and deep pits or chambers on the surface make them easy to identify. They look like sponges poking up through the duff. At first they are difficult to find. You look and look and find nothing. Once you find one and establish a search pattern, you may see them everywhere.

A mushroom that you might confuse with the morel is the brain mushroom or false morel in the genus *Gyromitra*. Its species, also Ascomycetes, have contorted, lobed or wrinkled brain-like caps that lack the hollow caps and sharp ridged pits of the morels. Brain mushrooms are very poisonous. They contain monomethylhydrazine, MMH, the exact same chemical as rocket fuel. Believe me, if you consume MMH, you too will end up in outer space. In Europe, it is the second greatest cause of fatal mushroom poisoning after *Amanita*. MMH is volatile and can be boiled off in cooking. Breathe the vapors and you are in trouble, leave on the lid and the vapors stay in the pot. My advice to you is stay away from *Gyromitra* species.

If you are still interested in the true morel try looking in the woods of the Dead Indian plateau or in the vicinity of Lake of the Woods. My spring systematic botany class often returned from our field trip to the Dead Indian Plateau with bags bulging with plump morels. I am ashamed to say that I am often able to convince my students that teacher should be the recipient of such treasures. Who wants apples when morels are around?

If there is a moral to this story, I haven't found it yet.

Shaggy Manes

I recently saw a sight that makes the hearts of mycophiles everywhere go pitter-pat. I saw some shaggy manes. In the fall amateur and professional mushroom lovers start to pray for rain. If we are lucky, when it rains and when it freezes will be well placed in time, and mushrooms will appear in woods, and pastures, even gravel roadsides, in great variety and number.

Among the easily identifiable edible mushrooms are the shaggy manes, which pop up through the gravel along our local logging roads, some years, in great abundance. They stand, sometimes in clusters, like British soldiers in white shaggy busby hats with a touch of brown on top. Mycologists, those of us who study fungi, and mycophagists, those of us who eat fungi, call the shaggy mane by its scientific name *Coprinus comatus. Coprinus,* from the Greek, meaning dung, for many of its smaller coprophilous, dung-loving relatives, and *comatus* from the latin meaning long-haired, as in a shaggy mane. For you mycophagists who might worry about such things, the shaggy mane gets its nutrition from other sources in the soil.

As it ages, strange things happen to the shaggy mane. Its gills and cap deliquesce; that is, they self-digest and turn into a black fluid, as does its relative the inky cap, *C. atramentarius.* It is said the black fluid can be diluted with water and used as ink.

But the shaggy mane is better eaten. Picked when young, the mushroom is edible and choice, though somewhat watery and delicate of flavor when compared with other mushrooms. Flavor can be intensified by boiling off the water during cooking. Denis Benjamin, in his excellent book *Mushrooms: Poisons and Panaceas* suggests shaggy manes should be treated like corn . . . the butter should be melted in the pan before you pick them. He is

joking, of course, but the speed with which they mature to deliquescence makes fast action necessary.

Although among the safest mushrooms, the shaggy mane may, very rarely, react with your physiology like the inky cap usually does with everyone when consumed with alcoholic beverages. Ears and nose turn red, and strange metallic tastes, lightheadedness, rapid heartbeat, and sometimes nausea or even worse are experienced. As some of you may know, these are the same symptoms of Antabuse or Disulfiram, the drug sometimes given to alcoholics to make consumption of booze an unpleasant experience. The toxins coprine and antabuse both interfere with alcohol metabolism causing acetaldehyde to accumulate in the blood. Fortunately for alcoholics and unwary mycophagists, recovery is normally spontaneous and complete.

Start looking for shaggy manes soon after the first rains. They pop up as if by magic. Eat them quickly for soon they turn to ink. Don't worry about coprine poisoning from shaggy manes; it is very rare and seldom fatal, just unpleasant. If you are really concerned, don't drink alcoholic beverages and dine on shaggy manes.

Mosquito Fern

Have you ever noticed that small ponds, the edges of slow streams and backwaters in southern Oregon sometimes turn brick red? Its enough to make a pharaoh faint.

The cause is not an act of retribution, but a tiny, floating fern, *Azolla*, also known as the mosquito fern, that forms red anthocyanin pigments when under stress or too much sunlight. We think the red pigment protects the photosynthetic apparatus from solar overload.

Mosquito fern shares the same habitat as the equally small flowering plant, duckweed. The chartreuse duckweeds have small oval leaves attached to tiny stems. Roots may or may not be present depending on the genus. The flowers of the duckweed are appropriately small, with tiny stamens and a tiny pistil, as individual flowers, on a single plant. No sepals or petals, just the reproductive parts.

The mosquito fern does other amazing things besides turn red. The lower surface of the upper leaf has pouch-like cavities which contain a blue-green alga. These two organisms have a symbiotic relationship where both partners benefit. The alga changes atmospheric nitrogen to a form that can be used by other plants, especially mosquito ferns. In return, *Azolla* supplies the alga with some nutrients and a protected cavity at the surface of the water in the sunlight.

Enough nitrogen is produced to share, however. The water fern can be used as a green manure in cultivating rice — a far less expensive nitrogen fertilizer than the usual energy-intensive sources.

The mosquito fern, six species world-wide, has tiny overlapping leaves along a slightly elongated stem with small roots that hang below the water's surface. Its dangling roots and those of rooted duckweeds make the plants popular with those of us who raise live-bearing tropical fish like guppies. The dangling roots make places for

young fish to hide from hungry parents, uncles, aunts and cousins.

We think the mosquito fern gets its common name because the plants can grow so densely on the water's surface that mosquitos cannot penetrate the mass of fronds to lay their eggs nor can their larvae reach the air to breath.

To find water ferns in the Rogue Valley try Railroad Slough north of Tolo just before you reach Gold Ray Dam, or the farm pond just before you reach Crowson Road as you head south of Ashland on Old US 99.

Nodding Brome

A number of years ago two of my colleagues and I hiked the Pine Forest Mountains just south of Denio, near the Nevada-Oregon border. On the first Friday the thirteenth after the summer solstice we watched a full moon rise over the Santa Rosa Range from Bare Pass in the Pine Forest Range. We swore at the time we would visit that not too distant mountain range. It was a magic moment.

Although it took us nearly a decade to do it, the wait was worth it: great scenery, beautiful wildflowers, good company. The first day we hiked up the southwest flank of Santa Rosa Peak and spent the night under the stars. As we made our way along I became increasingly aware of a certain itchiness around the top of my boots. I realized they were filling up with fruits of one of the west's most noxious weeds, nodding brome, an alien grass. I had turned into a disseminating mechanism, although I was carrying coal to Newcastle. We were walking into populations of nodding brome numbering in the millions. Counts of as many as 10,000 plants per square meter are known from demographic studies.

What I call nodding brome you may know as cheatgrass, downy brome, downy chess, bronco grass, Mormon oats, six-weeks grass, or June grass. Botanists call it *Bromus tectorum*. I like nodding brome, it describes the shy way its spikelets hang down. The grass is seldom very tall, not much higher than your knees, usually mid-calf or lower. Its shy look and diminutive stature belie its truly nasty nature, something I notice from time to time in higher primates. Nodding brome is in the same genus as the ripgut brome, that scourge of outdoor pets and livestock. Although not as bad as ripgut, it still can cause lumpy jaw and blindness in livestock.

This Mediterranean invader infests millions of acres of the intermountain west and elsewhere. For me it is still

an indicator of poorly managed rangeland, in spite of what some ranchers and range managers tell me. According to Robert Devine in the May '93 Issue of *Atlantic Magazine,* nodding brome is a major contributor to the decline of western rangelands. Nodding brome and livestock grazing, let's not forget the cows.

Like all weeds, nodding brome thrives on disturbance. Before livestock grazing, before nodding brome, intermountain rangelands were sagebrush and native bunchgrasses tied together by a thin layer of mosses and lichens that made life difficult for weeds. Enter cattle, sheep and nodding brome and the ecosystem changed. Livestock broke down the moss and lichen layer making a lovely seedbed for nodding brome. Shy-appearing nodding brome is an aggressive annual that out-competes the natives and creates, by its sheer numbers, a tremendous fuel load. The natural sagebrush/bunchgrass ecosystem lacked the fuel for major devastating fires. Nodding brome ecosystems burn with increasing frequency and vigor. Thirty years ago central Idaho had 60 to 70 fires a year that burned 30,000 acres at most. In the 1980s an average of 115 fires burned 186,000 acres a year. Fires fueled by nodding brome.

It out-competes its bunchgrass rivals. It germinates and gets established before the bunchgrasses start growing. Its roots grow at temperatures that keep the natives asleep. It uses up available water before native plants get started. It is ruining our western ranges and there is not much that can be done about it.

Cattlemen are on the horns of a dilemma. For six to eight weeks in spring cattle relish nodding brome. Then it hardens off, lumps form, eyes go blind, ranges burn up. Maybe cheatgrass is the better common name.

Oak Galls

Those strange structures you have noticed on the leaves and branches of our native Garry oak, *Quercus garryana,* are plant galls formed by a parasitic interaction between the plant's tissues and a tiny stingless wasp.

The round, light-brown, speckled spheres attached to the leaves that you find littering the ground in the fall in almost any oak grove are oak apples. If you step on them you will discover why some people call them "pop balls." Oak apples start in April to June when a tiny Cynipid wasp, *Besbicus mirabilis* Kinsey lays its eggs in the tender tissues of the midrib of the oak leaf. The plant responds by forming the gall around the wasp's larvae. The larvae are enclosed in a small capsule suspended by silken hairs in the center of the thin, outer, speckled wall. The entomologist who named this little wasp in 1930 is the same Kinsey who later shifted his attention to the human sexual response.

The fist-sized bullet galls are formed on oak stems by another small Cynipid wasp. When mature, these spherical or kidney-shaped galls are hard to miss. Young galls start to form on two- to four-year-old stems in early May and reach maturity by mid-summer. They start out juicy and white and end up dry and brown, often spotted with a black mold that may live on sugary secretions of the gall. Break a mature gall open and you will see a hardened, many-chambered central lump, each chamber containing a single larva, surrounded by a stringy mass that supplied plant nutrients to the insect parasite. When you break open old galls, you may be surprised to find what biologists call inquilines, from the Latin word for tenant or lodger, animals that habitually live in the nest or abode of another species, like your unemployed brother-in-law. In this case the inquilines include mites, small spiders, rove beetles, and the like. When mixed with soluble iron salts,

extracts of oak galls have been used for centuries as a source of tannins to make writing ink.

Another wasp forms tiny oval galls about 1.5 mm long (or the thickness of a dime and a half) on the underside of the oak leaf. In July and August the galls fall to the ground. And there the galls begin to jump. Yes, jump. Inside the gall the larvae begin to flex suddenly, and when they do the gall moves.

Oak trees get nothing from this relationship. In fact the gall is what we call a nutrient sink. Nutrients the oak could use for bigger, better acorns are drained away to provide a wasp nursery. The gall provides the wasp with nutrients and protection from the elements. Next time you are in a Garry oak woodland look for galls. You will find these and the possibility of finding another thirty or so different kinds.

Osage Orange

An Ashland listener called me, puzzled by strange objects littering the ground beneath a tree in town. The big, round, chartreuse objects were finely wrinkled, reminiscent of the brain's surface.

They turned out to be the multiple fruits of the Osage orange, a medium-sized, thorny tree native to Arkansas, Missouri and Texas. The champion tree in Charlotte County, Virginia is 294 inches in circumference, 51 feet high with a spread of 93 feet. It is widely naturalized beyond its native range throughout the east and south because of its utility as a hedge plant. As a hedge it is, as Donald Culross Peattie says, "horse-high, bull-strong, and pig-tight."

Its tough, heavy wood is as remarkable as its fruits. Until trees of suitable size became too scarce, Osage orange was sought after for railroad ties, outlasting softer oak, chestnut and catalpa by 18 to 20 years. Osage orange, also known as bowdark, makes excellent bow wood. The highly valued bows spread throughout the Great Plains tribes by barter with the Osage Native Americans. Its red-stained heartwood and handsome grain make particularly attractive pieces. I wonder if archers still value bowdark bows in this day and age of high-tech fibers and pulleys?

Its common name, Osage orange, comes from Osages of Arkansas and Missouri who made such magnificent bows from its wood. Orange refers to its peculiar fruit. Thomas Nuttall named the plant *Maclura pomifera* for his geologist friend William Maclure. Nuttall, you may recall, was the featured naturalist, Old Curious, in Richard Henry Dana's classic sea adventure, *Two Years Before the Mast.*

Peattie reports that deer in Texas and fox squirrels in the Midwest, who carry the fruits up trees in order to smash them open by dropping them to the ground, eat the fruits and seeds. I don't think they are fit for human

consumption. According to Peattie, the odor of a single fruit in a room will drive away cockroaches.

The tree in Ashland is on the corner of Helman and Orange Street in the yard of the old Abel Helman home. Abel Helman, one of Ashland's earliest residents, planted the Osage orange in his yard in the 1870s. A photograph taken in 1887 of Abel and his son and granddaughters in front of the family home shows the faint silhouette of what must be the sapling tree for which Orange Street in Ashland is surely named.

Somewhere in the neighborhood there must be another, orangeless, Osage orange. The species has female trees that bear the oranges and male trees that provide the pollen.

My first memorable experience with Osage orange trees was in a picnic area at the Missouri Botanical Gardens. We were having a picnic. The wind came up, the oranges came down like cannon balls. Box lunches were flattened, soft drinks exploded. We beat a hasty retreat to safety. It is a good thing Newton wasn't under an Osage orange, he never would have known what hit him.

Persimmons

Walking down the hill toward school in Ashland I heard a terrible din, the sound of a tree muncher. I looked several blocks down the street to see a cherry picker in the midst of an interesting row of shade trees along the street. From my end, the first tree was a huge California valley oak, then some trees that included a shagbark hickory, black walnuts, and a tree that makes for some pretty fancy footwork certain times of the year, a persimmon. I wonder who put together such a nifty streetside arboretum?

From a distance, I tried to figure out which old tree had fallen to the woodsman's chainsaw. My guess had to do with messiness, either the persimmon or a black walnut. When I got close, I discovered the persimmon being ground to smithereens. A huge grinder reduced all but the trunk and largest branches to shreds as fine as Ollie North's reports. I suppose the tree was too messy for the new owners, dropping its small plum-like fruits all over the ground and street.

I can't be too critical. Several years ago, I cut down a black walnut in my yard because of messiness. It always was dropping or dripping something: male catkins in the spring, then icky-sticky honeydew from aphids in the summer, then the leaves, then the walnuts in their nasty, squashy, black, staining husks. If that wasn't bad enough, the leaves made lousy compost because of plant growth-inhibiting substances in their tissues.

Persimmons are not native to the northwest, but two are native to the United States, the Texas persimmon and the common persimmon of the southeast. The common persimmon is food for all kinds of animals: deer, raccoons, foxes, skunks, birds and small rodents. It is also food for humans. Persimmon fruits are eaten after the first frost when the flesh is mushy and the skin is wrinkled. Then it

is sweet flavored, before it is so bitter that its flavor will pucker you inside out. Really bad.

The large orange-sized persimmon of some yards and supermarkets is an Asian native, *Diospyros kaki,* named kaki after the Japanese name for the fruit. The fruit is well described in Elizabeth Schneider's *Uncommon Fruits and Vegetables: A Common Sense Guide,* which has persimmon recipes: freeze ripe persimmons for an instant sherbet, broil persimmon halves with brown sugar, nutted persimmons, spice rolls with persimmon and cream filling. Or you could just eat 'em ripe, but raw.

In the wild, common persimmon grows as a small to medium-sized tree to 100 feet, 20 to 30 inches in diameter. The fine-textured, tough, strong, fairly straight-grained sapwood has been used in making golf-club heads and weaving shuttles. The wood is so tough the shuttles last a thousand hours before wearing out.

Diospyros is also the ebony genus, an important commercial tropical timber species, no safer there than along the streets of Ashland.

Puncturevine

I once had the pleasure of a bike ride along the back roads of Scott Valley, in Siskiyou County, California. My companions and I started at Fort Jones, biked around Chaparral Hill to Orfino, then up Quartz Hill to the lookout, down the hill to Quartz Valley, then to Mugginsville, Greenville, and back to Fort Jones. Twenty-seven miles with pleasant companions in clear, brisk weather, in retrospect an altogether pleasant experience. An experience not without a certain level of excitement, however, caused by farm dogs and a dreadful Old World weed, the puncturevine.

Farm dogs. I never have really gotten over fears generated by childhood dog bites and paper routes. Before every bike ride, thoughts of huge, fast, slavering farm dogs flash through my mind. On this trip I realized and conquered my worst fears between the north end of Chaparral Hill and Orfino townsite. I spotted the dogs ahead of time, got going as fast as I could to blast through their territory as quickly as possible. I wasn't fast enough. The biggest dog soon approached my flashing legs. What to do? I did what I had read might work. I leaned down, looked the dog in the eye and shouted NO as loud as I could. It worked, the dog backed off fast. A victory for me, defeat for the dog.

When we reached Orfino, one of our party, on his first biking adventure with us on his new spotless mountain bike, had a flat tire, actually two. Inspection showed that small, sharp-pointed, tack-like objects had penetrated the wall of his new knobby bike tire and both walls of the inner tube. It was clearly the work of the dreaded puncturevine, *Tribulus terrestris,* a member of the *Zygophyllaceae* or caltrop family. Why the caltrop family? The fruit resembles that ancient Roman weapon of war, the caltrop, a sharp, pointed, four-pronged metal device that always has one point up when the other three are down. Romans

found caltrops effective against foot soldiers and cavalry. *Tribulus* finds the same design an effective way to spread its fruits and seeds about, in the hair and hooves of animals, for very short distances in the soles of barefooted humans, and, in recent times, for longer distances, in pneumatic tires.

If that is not enough, all parts of the plant are toxic with three kinds of sapogenins and toxic levels of potassium nitrate. Sapogenins lower the surface tension of aqueous solutions, alter the permeability of cell membranes and react with proteins to cause toxicity. The toxins cause a condition known as bighead in sheep. Do not confuse this with a different condition of the same name prevalent among certain humans.

Fuller and McClintock, in their book *Poisonous Plants of California,* mention a homicidal use of the puncturevine's spiny fruit. In a South African incident, the spiny fruits, smeared with the poisonous juice of a different plant, Bushman's Poison, were scattered along a path used by the intended barefoot victim.

Watch out for puncturevines. The plants are low and flat with reddish stems, opposite, pinnately compound leaves, and small yellow flowers that develop nutlets with two bony, sharp spines that look like goat horns. If you find them, eradicate them as quickly as you can. If you are biking in areas where puncture vines are present, stay off the shoulders of the roads, and carry lots of tire patches.

Trilliums

What do biology professors do on holidays like Presidents' Day? They take the University Biology Club on field trips to the coast to see the wonders of the redwoods and the beautiful Pacific, that's what. One Presidents' Day, a number of years ago, Professor Ron Nitsos, eight members of the biology club and I visited Redwood National Park south of Crescent City. We stopped for lunch on high bluffs at the south end of Crescent Beach to look for whales. Lunch was great. Gray whales were not to be seen, though there was perfect viewing weather; overcast skies meant no bright reflections, and a slight breeze meant no distracting whitecaps.

After lunch we drove south along Highway 101 to the Damnation Trail at Mile Marker 16. The 2.1 mile trail descends a thousand feet to the ocean. On our hike back out we discovered how the Damnation Trail probably got its name. You hike down a thousand feet, you hike back up a thousand feet.

Although the trail was steep in places, it was wide and well maintained, with lots to look at and enjoy. Huge old redwoods loomed above. Once out of hearing of the highway, only occasional bird sounds broke the silence. We heard the call of varied thrushes and, at one point, a series of high melodious trills right near the trail. After a brief search we discovered the source, a winter wren, a tiny mite of a bird for such a loud and joyful sound.

A little farther along the trail we could hear the sound of the surf, evidence we were getting closer to the bottom. As we walked along we noticed early wildflowers in bloom. Johnny-jump-ups, violets with bright yellow faces, appeared with increasing frequency as we dropped in elevation. Soon toothworts, so called because of their tooth-like underground corms, appeared along the trail. Then we found what was for me the highlight of the trip

— trilliums or wakerobins in bloom, a sign spring was on its way.

We saw not one, but two species growing side by side. One was the common trillium, *Trillium ovatum,* with its flower on a stalk above its three leaf-like bracts. The other was a different species with stalkless purple flowers inserted on the bracts. This species had special meaning for me. I am certain it was *T. kurabayashii,* named in 1975 for the late Dr. Masataka Kurabayashi, an outstanding Japanese cytologist and population geneticist, who devoted most of his career studying the genus *Trillium.*

In the spring of 1960 Dr. Kurabayashi visited the University of Washington on a quest for western North American wakerobins. I had the privilege of taking him on the longest automobile ride of his life, from Seattle to the Bald Hills of Thurston County, Washington. I was a 23-year-old graduate student. He was of undeterminable age, probably old, he died a year or so later. We returned from the collecting trip successful, with living plants for the good professor to examine. I was exhausted and hoarse. He seemed pleased, and I suspect, deafened. His English was halting, my Japanese nonexistent. My response was to talk as loudly as I could as though he would better understand my slang-filled English. If Americans really want to get along in the international scene, we would be far better off learning how to speak English to foreigners than to learn a foreign language. But I digress.

If you find trilliums in the woods, please don't pick them. They need those leaf-like bracts to manufacture food for the next year if they are to flower again. It is all they have for photosynthesis. Some say it takes seven years before the plants will bloom again. Too bad they make such attractive, long-lasting, cut flowers. Fight the temptation, be a conservationist.

III

Fauna

Raccoons

Years ago we entertained several members of the Stuttgart Symphony Orchestra who were in town for a concert. After dinner we were extolling the virtues of Ashland when the conversation got around to the local wildlife. Raccoons were mentioned. Seeing the Germans' puzzled look, I described a small mammal a little bigger than our dog, black-masked, full, bushy, ringed tail. "Ah, Waschbären," they said in unison. They knew our raccoon as the washing bear, an immigrant that has become a fixture of European fauna since 1945.

We don't know why raccoons wash their food before they eat. Perhaps they wash their food to clean away sand and grit. Others maintain that they are feelers. They find their underwater crayfish prey by grope and feel. In captivity they wet their food, perhaps to heighten their sense of touch. If there is no water, they rub and eat dry food. If there is no food, they rub their hands together, maybe in anticipation of another meal. Maybe it is just a nervous habit.

Ashland raccoons are natives, but not true urbanites. True urban dwellers live in attics, crawl spaces, and dormant chimneys. Urban raccoons use storm systems and sewers as freeways. Ashland raccoons are more suburban, entering town to work and dine, but spending much of their time sleeping in the wild.

Raccoons are omnivores with teeth to prove it. Sharp canines and incisors for crayfish and other small animals and flattened molars for berries, nuts, and seeds, or your sweet corn and cherries.

At the time, Ashland's bold, brassy raccoons were quite a nuisance. Noisy late-night interludes included "chirring" noises in the backyard lawn over big fat nightcrawlers, or maybe something, err ahh sexual. There were climbing and feasting in grape arbors and fruit trees. Ears of sweet corn with husks pulled back with just a dainty bite or two removed were on the ground. Piles of excretory offerings from your or neighbors' trees and garden resulted. There were confrontations with your cat or dog, or you. Big surprises on your side of the pet door, like 40 pounds of indignant raccoon who didn't like his meal interrupted by the help.

What to do or not? Trapping, live or the other way, won't work. Others will occupy their space. Decreasing the carrying capacity of their environment is the best solution. Quit feeding them, don't leave out Bowser's uneaten dinner, lock up the garbage can, prohibit public feeding. If they are using attics, crawl spaces and dormant chimneys, seal them over.

As far as I know rabies hasn't been reported in Oregon raccoons . . . yet. Rabid raccoons are not a direct threat to humans, though pets are at risk. Immunize Fido and the cat against rabies, and don't take on raccoons yourself. In the southeast, raccoons carry at least 13 pathogens known to cause disease in humans. Still want to feed raccoons on your deck?

The raccoon problem disappeared in Ashland when Mother Nature asserted her somewhat less than gentle self. Canine distemper caused the local raccoon population to crash. I have seen but one in the last five years. Friends tell me they are back in town and my tiny patch of watered lawn has little cavities dug out by raccoons hunting earthworms. I just haven't seen them.

I have read that raccoon meat is good (tasting somewhat like lamb), but all fat should be removed before roasting. Horace Kephart, source of our opossum recipe (page 106), suggests removing the scent glands under each front leg and on either side of the small of the back before parboiling with one or two changes of water depending on the animal's age. Horace says stuff it like a turkey, bake it to a delicate brown, and serve it with fried sweet potatoes. Be sure to cook it well. As with all omnivores, trichinosis is always a risk. Horace Kephart doesn't mention bourbon whiskey as an accompaniment this time, as he did for opossum. I do, for you.

Silver-Gray Squirrels

When I was out for my usual early morning walk with Inu (my dog) we saw one of his favorite animals, rating close, I think, to the neighborhood cats. It was a western gray or silver-gray squirrel, *Sciurus griseus,* a common, handsome west coast mammal. Dog and I both fume when our native silver-grays get into our bird feeder to help themselves to sunflower seeds. Our silver-gray encounter this morning inspired me to resurrect this *Nature Note.*

Our gray squirrels occur in mixed broad-leaved coniferous woodlands and spend their daylight hours out doing squirrel things. They groom, explore, feed, play, loaf, try to stay out of harm's way, and in January and February indulge in one of their few group social activities, mating. Mature gray squirrels seldom get together except for s-e-x. If you see a mid- to late-winter crowd, you may prefer to exercise viewer discretion and avert your eyes. The crowd consists of several amorous males and a willing and able female. After mating they go their separate ways. The female nests in a tree cavity to give birth and raise her two to four young. The males, like some humans, don't lift a finger. They don't gather nuts for the family. They don't repair the nest. They don't pay alimony or child support.

Mature squirrels nest alone in stick nests called drays high in trees. In winter they construct a protective leafy roof. In summer they air condition by roof removal. Gray squirrels are active year-round, but will stay in during truly rotten weather. They are out just after sunrise for about an hour. By noon many squirrels retreat to their individual nests until late afternoon, when they are out again for several hours. Gray squirrels are not night owls. Most return to their nests an hour before sunset to spend a safe and quiet night.

Gray squirrels are scatter-hoarders. They bury acorns and nuts, then attempt to find them later using their keen sense of smell. They are also fond of underground truffle-like fungi, which they eat fresh, in great abundance, in the spring. Squirrels in their mushroom searches dig many of the small holes we see in our oak woodlands. They may play an important role in woodland ecology by distributing mycorrhizal fungal spores as they poop around the woods.

All is not sweetness and light in squirreldom. Native predators include bobcats, coyotes, foxes, and the occasional red-tail hawk. Non-native predators include Fido (read Inu here, if he had half a chance), Kitty, Honda, Buick, and Chevrolet. Gray squirrels are also considered a game animal in Oregon and are hunted by humans.

Various parasites afflict gray squirrels: mange, ringworm, ticks, mites, roundworms, and seven kinds of fleas. Parasites may account for long-term fluctuations in squirrel populations.

Like many diurnal animals western gray squirrels are secretive and cautious. When squirrels perceive danger, they retreat to dense foliage in tree tops. There they remain motionless and nearly invisible until the danger has passed.

Thanks to Dr. Stephen Cross for the loan of his thesis and his efforts to understand the biology of our native gray squirrel.

Hibernation

Many warm-blooded animals spend much of their time in a state of greatly lowered metabolism called torpor. Hummingbirds, incredibly active during the day, can conserve energy when food is scarce by becoming incredibly inactive at night. A hummer's temperature may drop from an active high of 104°F to near the ambient temperature, perhaps 50°F. Its basal metabolism reduces by a third. This way, heating calories are not wasted.

Other animals, like mammals, enter a seasonal torpor to avoid unpleasantness. Mammals of hot arid climates may estivate, that is, sleep away the summer. Others may avoid the cold of winter by hibernation. In both cases the animals may slip off into a deep sleep. Breathing may drop to a breath per minute and the heartbeat to four to eight beats per minute. Body temperatures drop, sometimes to just above freezing. Energy conservation is the name of the game.

The game is not without its costs. Animals must add a lot of weight, mostly as brown fat and muscle tissue, to provide enough energy to make it through its seasonal torpor. Metabolism continues, albeit at a much reduced level, and toxic waste products accumulate that must be excreted or detoxified. Energy derived from fat breakdown uses water; dehydration can be a problem. Energy from muscle breakdown adds water. The deep sleep does not allow for urination. Urine formation may be suppressed by pituitary hormones. Special chemical reactions lessen the toxic effects of urea.

Many rodents estivate or hibernate. Some like marmots, our western equivalent of the woodchuck, do both. Marmots eat prodigiously of green stuff until they bulk up to half their body weight in fat. Then they slip away to dens where whole colonies sink into a seven-month slumber, from late September to early May in the mountains, or, east of the mountains, from mid-summer after forage dries up, till early spring.

Black bears, contrary to popular opinion, just sort of hibernate. They often find a den and sleep away the nastiest winter weather, but their sleep is shallow, and their temperature only a few degrees below normal. When disturbed they are quickly roused, and, I suspect, quite grumpy.

I frequently face torpor as certain students in my lectures slip away, not into the deep sleepy state of marmots, but the shallow sleep of bears. Their state must be like that of bears. Their behavior on arousal is much the same.

I frequently experience torpor most Friday afternoons at 3:00 P.M. No matter how dynamic the speaker or how interested I am in the topic, our Friday Afternoon Science Seminars at the University put me down. I have decided this is no reflection on the series' quality. If you want to attend the science seminars, call or write the School of Science at Southern Oregon University for a schedule of speakers. The public is invited to attend and the series is free. One thing though, don't rouse the torpid prof. He's worse than bears!

Mountain Beaver

In 1805, Chinook Indians showed Meriwether Lewis and William Clark a soft, brown fur robe made from the skins of a small mammal. Lewis noticed that none of the skins had tails and asked to see the animal. What he saw was a small, chunky, densely-furred mammal about the size and shape of a loaf of bread, blunt on both ends. The front? Equipped with long, stout whiskers, a pair of small, bright shiny eyes and small, round ears. The rear? A small, furred stump that passed for a tail and, in between, a muscular body with short legs and strongly clawed toes. Lewis and Clark called the animal "sewellel," their version of the Chinook word for cloak or robe, "she-wal-lal."

Later, early settlers called the animal mountain beaver. Other common names include boomer, whistler (it is said to have a quavering cry like the notes of a little owl), mountain rat, Chehalis, or North American short-tailed beaver. (It isn't a beaver in spite of its common name.) Lewis thought it was a squirrel, a group to which it is most closely related. Today we consider the mountain beaver, or *Aplodontia rufa* to use its scientific name, the only surviving member of the most primitive family of rodents with a fossil history dating from the Upper Eocene about 50 million years ago. *Aplodontia* is found nowhere in the world except the wet climate areas west of the Cascade Mountains from southern British Columbia to northwest California and the Sierra Nevada.

Mountain beaver live in shallow burrows that they dig in soft, moist soils of gulches and ravines. Burrows radiate out from nests and frequently water trickles down the runways. Mountain beaver cannot concentrate their urine and require a high daily water intake, which may explain their preference for wet burrows and vegetation of high water content. I'll bet they just love our so-called wintery spring this year.

A single mountain beaver occupies each nest. Home ranges overlap and runways are shared. Although they venture forth to forage mainly at night, you might get a glimpse of them in the early morning or at dusk. They do not hibernate.

Mountain beaver harvest vegetation which they bring back to burrow entrances to line their nests, or store to eat. They collect whatever plants are in their territory. Unfortunately, the little beasts include important timber species among their gatherings. The most frequent damage is to newly-planted seedlings in plantations. The timber industry wages a trapping war where mountain beaver damage is a problem.

In our area the mountain beaver lives at higher elevations. To find colonies drive up Tolman Creek Road south of Ashland to above 4,000 feet, and walk around in wet meadows or go to Bear Camp Pasture on the Galice to Agness Road west of Grants Pass and walk uphill near the outhouse. Look for piles of fresh cut vegetation or fresh soil tailings at burrow entrances for evidence of activity. If you aren't careful you might discover, as I often have, how they might have gotten the common name of mountain boomer. When you suddenly step through their shallow burrows on steep hillsides, you fall down and go boomer.

Opossums

The holidays are coming up. Tired of the same old offerings for Thanksgiving, Christmas, or New Year dinner celebrations?

In the past ten years or so, mammals that look like cat-sized rats appeared on highways of the west as DORs (that's biology talk for dead on road). They have long gray fur and long, round, scaly, rat-like tails. What are they? Not muskrats, brown and oval tail. Not nutria, brown with a round tail. Maybe you need more hints.

Its tail is prehensile and it sometimes carries nesting material, dry leaves, sticks and the like, in a bundle snugly secured by a loop of the tail. It has large, naked, black ears with pinkish tips. The famous turn of the century naturalist and illustrator, Ernest Thompson Seton, described it as a silly grinning idiot, a description that applies to only a few mammals besides humans.

The male has a forked penis. This feature accounts for the quaint, but totally false myth that mating occurs through the nose. The female does have a forked vagina, which accounts for the unusual male organ and the animal's generic name, *Didelphis*, based on Greek words for two or double (*di*) and womb (*delphys*). About 12–14 days after a proper mating, one to 14 tiny, bean-sized embryos are born that climb through the hair on the mother's belly into a pouch in her abdomen. Here some or all of the young attach to nipples where they remain for another two months. The animal is North America's very own native marsupial, the Virginia opossum.

The opossum ranged as far north as northern Ohio and northern West Virginia before the arrival of Europeans. They have subsequently become widespread with the help of humans. They now occupy much of eastern North America and the coastal portions of the Pacific coast from British Columbia to Mexico.

One establishment event in Oregon occurred in Umatilla County in the early part of this century. On several different occasions animals were either deliberately released or were escaped pets. They are now well established from this and other independent events.

The animals were hunted by dogs or trapped for their not very valuable fur or for their meat, considered a delicacy by some. Here is the Holiday Meal suggestion, roast opossum!

If you are interested in trying opossum and not the same old ham or turkey, a word or two of warning. As a good omnivore, like pigs, bears, and humans, the opossum is a creature of catholic tastes. It eats almost anything, especially whatever is most abundant. It could be garbage, mushrooms, earthworms, poisonous snakes, or carrion — opossum or otherwise. When you clean your opossum, be careful not to break or damage the GI tract and wash the carcass well before cooking, lest you run the risk of Salmonella poisoning. Your opossum should be cooked well done. *Trichina*, the parasitic worm that causes trichinosis, is known in opossum and other omnivores. For those of you who might want a slightly different holiday dinner, Horace Kephart, in his book *Camping and Woodcraft*, has a recipe for opossum. Before baking, surrounded by sweet potatoes in a Dutch oven, parboil your opossum in five gallons of water with two red peppers for an hour, then change to fresh water and boil another hour. Kephart says bourbon whiskey is the traditional accompaniment. A lot of bourbon whiskey I'd say. Happy Holidays and... Bon Appetit!

Pikas

A few summers ago I had a brief encounter with a favorite animal near the shore of Snow Lake at the base of Unicorn Peak in the Tatoosh Range in Mount Rainier National Park. The sky was as blue as it gets, that alpine blue, a sky unobscured by the scuz and crud of modern lowland skies. The air, ah the air, spicy with the high alpine perfume of conifers and wild flowers. As I walked around the south side of the lake along the base of the talus slope, a sharp "eenk" and then another split the air. I instantly recognized the call of the pika, a small mammal classified in the same order as the rabbits but in a different family.

Pikas are ventriloquists, they throw their voices. I knew from experience that I would have to look carefully to find one. Suddenly I noticed movement almost opposite where I thought I heard the pika. There it was. A small brown ball, a little smaller than a Guinea pig, all hunkered down on the flat top of a boulder. The name pika is our version of the northeastern Siberian Tunga people's name, peeka.

Our pika, *Ochotona princeps,* is distributed primarily in subalpine areas in the Cascade, Sierra and Rocky Mountains. They haven't made it across the Puget Sound lowland to the Olympic Mountains. Pikas are absent from the Klamath Mountains and Vancouver Island.

Ochotona is a Mongolian term. *Princeps* means a chief based on a Native American name for the animal that translates, "little chief hare," hare as in rabbit. Pikas often do look chief-like. They sit on their boulder in stoic silence, nose slightly tilted upward, small rounded ears back, bright little eyes surveying their rocky talus home.

Rugged individualists, pikas get together only to mate and maintain nearest neighbor male-female territories. This does not mean that the colony does not watch out for one another. They use their sharp call to announce territory and alarm. There are reports of pikas getting together to totally confuse their mortal enemy the weasel. If a weasel is pursuing one pika, other pikas start to run about distracting and tiring the predator. Is this altruism, a behavior where individuals are willing to lay down their lives for the good of the colony, or just plain foolishness caused by the excitement of the moment?

Pikas do not hibernate. They remain active all winter under snow in the spaces created by the jumble of rocks and boulders of the talus slopes. They subsist on several bushels of dried, cured hay, vegetation that individual pikas collect from surrounding meadows. Pikas spend the brief summer and autumn making hay. Pikas make quick trips from their protective rocks to collect mouthfuls of fresh plants. They select species that are high in nutrients and avoid some abundant species that may contain toxins. Back in the talus they pile up the plant material in little haystacks, on, or often under, rocky overhangs. Later, pikas move the hay to dry spots within the rocky talus for winter-time consumption.

Many of us should take a lesson from the pika. When it comes to preparing for hard times the pika is no piker.

Pronghorns

One summer some visiting Japanese botany colleagues wanted to collect arid land species to analyze for exotic chemicals. I took them to Harney County: land of the Stinking Water and Pueblo Mountains, the Alvord Desert and Steens Mountain, one of North America's great natural wonders. It was a land more arid than usual, although aridity was placed in perspective when I noticed the bison skull in the Buchanan Store collected from the bottom of Malheur Lake when it dried up in 1932.

Dave Kennedy, the expedition's *majordomo*, and I excitedly pointed out wildlife when we saw it. Like the coyote who tried unsuccessfully to nail a sandhill crane in a field outside Diamond, Oregon, or deer herds, or antelope. David and I were taken by the pronghorns; our guests were not. How could anyone not be excited about pronghorns, North America's own special ruminant, neither sheep nor goat? How could one not get excited about seeing a doe and fawn slowly meandering across a flat near the head of gorgeous Big Indian Gorge?

But pronghorns are fascinating. They are fast, clocked at a maximum 57 miles per hour for nine miles. Normal running speed is about 24 miles per hour. Wiley coyote has a problem. Pronghorns can adapt quickly to new conditions, the urban fringe, traffic noise, and gardens. They signal one another with their flashy white rump patches. They are curious, something that doesn't always work to their advantage. They are short-lived, nine years at most. They shed their black, short, forked horns each year like a Bowie knife's leather sheath. The smooth, skin-covered "knife" remains attached to produce new horns of agglutinated hair for next year's frolics.

Nature has decreed death to all but two of the four to six embryos that implant in the uterus in pregnant pronghorns. Sharpened membranes of a pair of embryos puncture vital membranes of their womb mates. The damaged embryos die of no nutrition and are reabsorbed by mother. The remaining pair survive for birth.

Had my Japanese friends visited the Rogue Valley in 1841, not 1992, we would not have had to travel all the way to Steens to see pronghorns.

The Rogue Valley, September 1841:

> An antelope was killed, which was one of four that the hunters had seen; it was of a dun and white color, and its hair was remarkably soft. The Indians take this animal by exciting its curiosity: for this purpose they conceal themselves in a bush near its feeding grounds, and making a rustling noise soon attracting its attention, when it is led to advance towards the place of concealment until the arrow pierces it. If there are others in company, they frequently remain with the wounded until they are all in like manner destroyed. This species of antelope, according to the hunters, only inhabits the prairie, being seldom seen even in the open country. The flavor of the meat was thought to be superior to that of deer.
>
> From the narrative of the US Exploring Expedition,
> Lt. Charles Wilkes, Commander.

Wow, pronghorns on the Agate Desert, and large herds on the Klamath, towards Mount Shasta, according to the narrative. Pronghorns extirpated from their former range. Extirpated, a term we use more and more, as we intentionally or inadvertently elbow our fellow creatures from the path of progress.

Spotted Skunk

We are all familiar with the striped skunk. Bambi's friend Flower and Pepe Le Pew were striped skunks. In southern Oregon we have another, less commonly seen skunk; *Spilogale putorius,* the spotted skunk, civet, or polecat. *Spilogale* is the Greek word for spotted polecat: *putorius* is Latin for stench. Some mammalogists consider our more slender western version, *S. gracilis,* a separate species. Gracilis means slender.

As North America's smallest skunk, these nocturnal mammals weigh two pounds or less and are under 20 inches long. The weasel-like spotted skunk differs from other skunks by its extremely silky fur and an arrangement of irregular elongated white patches the length of its body. Spotty's tail is tipped in white.

Active, agile, spotted skunks have no trouble climbing bushes, trees, and the rafters and beams of barns, chicken coops and other farm buildings. When threatened, spotted skunks stamp the ground repeatedly with their front feet, then do a handstand. The handstand is a deceptively powerful defense. With its hind legs high in the air, the skunk spreads the long white hairs of its tail to form a conspicuous target between the attacker and its body. When the attacker tries to bite the obvious white target, it gets a very rude surprise. The skunk unloads a powerful spray of a most obnoxious fluid from its anal scent glands. The attacker, with its mouth, nose and eyes saturated, quickly loses interest. The malodorous secretion can accurately hit a target 12 feet away and cause severe burning or temporary blindness if it gets into the eyes.

Spotted skunks have little fear of humans and often occupy any suitable space in or under buildings, porches, mobile homes, or abandoned vehicles. Almost any secure darkened cavity lined with dry vegetation can be used as a den. Several individuals may share a den with more than one litter present at a time.

They eat insects, rodents, mice, frogs, crayfish, small birds, and eggs. They will raid garbage cans, eat table scraps and commercial cat food if given an opportunity. They will enter hen houses for eggs. They will uproot crops in gardens while hunting insects. They will uproot hops (the beer flavoring) because they like to eat the roots. Some evidence suggests that spotted skunks resist rattlesnake venom and will eat the snakes. Few animals eat spotted skunks except great horned owls and a host of tiny parasites.

Some people kill spotted skunks because they think they are a nuisance or they trap them for their low-priced pelts. Consider keeping them: they are excellent natural mouse and rat traps. If your dog is so dumb that it just can't leave the skunk and its white target alone, don't kill it. The skunk, that is. Drive pesky skunks away by sealing up entrances to potential dens. If they have already taken up residence they can be discouraged by training flood lights in the den area. If that doesn't work, try one teaspoonful of neutroleum alpha in a gallon of water as an effective deodorizing bath. Save the tomato juice for vodka when it's over.

Woodrats

The flat bench just below the final pitch to the summit of the Lower Table Rock trail in Jackson County, Oregon, is forested with a dense stand of stump-sprouted madrone trees. I often stop here on my way to the top of the rock to catch my breath and look at large piles of sticks and branches scattered in the undergrowth that are the homes of dusky-footed woodrats.

Dusky-footed woodrats build homes of wood with multiple entrances and chambers. Like their real packrat cousin, the bushy-tailed woodrat, they add various items to their homes beside sticks and twigs. Woodrat houses are also home for many inquilines, animals occupying the home or nest of another. Spiders, springtails, centipedes, beetles of various kinds, sometimes frogs, salamanders, fence lizards, and other small mammals occupy woodrat homes.

Not only do dusky-footed woodrats share their homes with others, but they share their bodies as well. Dusky-footed woodrats are hosts to a horrific number of external and internal parasites. Some of them are enough to make the Marquis de Sade wince. Take warbles, for example: large, oozy, open, lumps that contain fly larvae. Larvae that may be 26 mm long, 12 mm in diameter and weigh nearly two grams. Larvae that slowly work their way out — ugh!

There is something else you or the Marquis won't want to hear, either. Other parasites include fleas, mites, lice and ticks. Among the ticks are two that belong to genus *Ixodes*, the Lyme disease vector. One tick, *I. neotomae,* sticks to woodrats and other small rodents. The other, *I. pacificus,* has more catholic tastes and bites other hosts, including humans. Among woodrats' internal parasites are various roundworms, tapeworms, protozoans, and a spirochete, *Borrelia burgdorferi,* the cause of Lyme disease.

Discovery of the spirochete helps explain some features of Lyme disease in the western United States, or at least in California. In the eastern United States 25% to 50% of the ticks are infected. In the west only 1% to 3% are infected, although there is some evidence this has been underestimated. We didn't know why. Deer mice carry the parasite in the east. We didn't know what the natural animal reservoir might be in the west. In California and likely Oregon, it turns out to be the poor dusky-footed woodrats, who infect each other via woodrat ticks. Only occasionally will *I. pacificus* ticks pick up the disease from woodrats and pass it on to humans: just often enough to transmit the disease to humans, but far too often for those who get the disease and let it go too long without proper treatment.

Another sink down whose drain Lyme disease goes are *I. pacificus* ticks that attach to reptiles like our western fence lizard and our alligator lizards. Ticks attached to them, not us. This means we don't get the parasite because some factor in lizard blood kills the Lyme disease bacteria.

If bitten by a tick, carefully pull it straight out, by the head and not the abdomen, as soon as you discover it. Save the tick. If flu-like aches and pains soon follow and/or a strange round rash occurs, get to a physician with your dried-out tick. Treated early, antibiotics kill the Lyme disease parasite. Left too long Lyme disease is very difficult to treat and may lead to a human life of painful misery.

Don't go out killing woodrats. *Ixodes pacificus* apparently has a broad enough host range to shift to something else. A strategy that might work is to take advantage of the woodrat's packrat habits. Dusky-footed woodrats might take home things like cotton soaked in a good tick killer. Not only might we get rid of Lyme disease in areas frequented by woodrats, ticks and humans, but we might make the woodrat's life a little better in the bargain.

IV

Creepy Crawlers

Jerusalem Crickets

Out working in the garden? Under the car changing the oil? Flat on your back, at eye level with the floor, you suddenly notice the slow, scraping motion of an insect with the size and beauty of an infected thumb? Not to worry, it's just a Jerusalem cricket, out for an evening stroll. Jerusalem crickets belong to a subfamily of grasshoppers that are wingless, ground-inhabiting creatures of large size. They are a smooth and shiny amber brown with dark stripes around a fat and pudgy abdomen. Essig, in his *Insects of Western North America*, states that Jerusalem crickets are the objects of fear and superstition because of the large, almost human head. Mexicans call them "niña de la tierra" . . . "child of the earth." Some call them "potato bugs," others "old-bald-headed-men," a lousy common name, in my opinion.

These soil dwellers remain underground during the day and come out at night in search of fun and frolic. Their idea of fun is munching on the roots and tubers of plants, and for dessert, a crunch or two of some dead animal. Frolic occurs mostly in the early spring when members of both sexes get together. In the process the female tears off the male's sperm sac and carries it around for a time. Afterward the female often makes a meal of her mate. Later in the spring, oval white eggs are laid in small holes in the soil.

During summer days adults stay under boards, logs or rocks and move about at night into the early morning hours. According to Essig, they make a queer track on dusty roads or trails that resemble a smooth trail like a snake's. When disturbed, they stridulate by rubbing the inner surface of their hind legs against abdominal spines. The sound is similar to that produced by rubbing two pieces of sandpaper together.

Raspy noise might frighten off some predators, but,

unfortunately for Jerusalem cricket, not roundworms of the genus *Mermis.* Roundworms or nematodes are an important and extremely common, though seldom seen, animal group. It has been said that if all land forms were removed and nematodes remained, we could still make out the major physiographic features of our planet as a fuzzy, wiggly haze.

Nematodes are the cause of trichinosis if infected meat is not well cooked before eating. The easiest way to get trichinosis nowadays is to eat partially-cooked bear meat or perhaps, if you are really hungry, possum sausage. Pork is another possible source of the trichina worm. Cook it well and don't eat raw pork liver when you drink your beer, as has been done in some countries. But I digress. Let's get back to cricket miseries instead of human ones.

Mermis and its relatives are well-studied roundworms, because pestiferous insects are common hosts. Jerusalem crickets may eat *Mermis* eggs or be infected by young larvae during a molt when cricket exoskeletons are soft. In any event, the parasite reaches extraordinary length in the body cavity eating cricket viscera and body fat. The worm then leaves the emaciated Jerusalem cricket, enters the soil and begins the cycle over. It is almost enough to make one sorry for old, bald-headed men!

Oh, and thanks to MW for mentioning the old bald-headed man she found beneath her dresser.

Cluster Flies

When I got back to my office after Christmas break, I hoped they'd be gone, but they weren't. They used to amuse me. After years of shooting them off the windows with rubber bands and swatting them with whatever was handy (student papers, rolled up quizzes, or missives from the dean), I realized it just wasn't sport. It was about as much fun and sport as I had ground-sluicing flightless game farm pheasants on the breaks of the Rogue at White City. Kind of like the lunker pellethead hatchery trout that fly fisherpersons try to catch in the so-called Holy Waters below Lost Creek Reservoir. Hate to tell you this, but those waters were only holy when there wasn't any dam. The fish were native, and you weren't sure what you were going to catch.

My office sport involved the murder of a few hundred of the thousands of flies that gather together to pass the winter under the tile facade on the science building on the Southern Oregon University campus. The smaller fly on the window is a larger native version of *Drosophila melanogaster,* the famous fruit fly of genetic research. We infer much of what we know about the transmission of genetic traits from generation to generation in a variety of animals, including humans, from studies of these small, honey-colored flies. They are good research subjects because we can control who mates with whom, there are large number of traits to study, enormous numbers can be grown in small spaces and their huge salivary gland chromosomes are easy to study.

The other fly is much larger. At first I thought they might be house flies. But no, they are larger, slower, hairy, darker, and not much sport to kill. Our entomologist, Dr. Coffey, told me they were cluster flies that accumulate in human habitations in enormous numbers to overwinter.

Cluster flies have some pretty creepy relatives. Bluebottle, screwworm, blow flies, and the Congo floor maggot are members of the same family. These products of creation infest flesh, carrion or living. The Congo floor maggot prefers human blood.

Cluster flies are a little more benign, unless you are an earthworm. They spend their adult lives visiting flowers and sunning themselves, mating and laying their eggs, not in sheep's nostrils or dead mice, but in the soil, a few at a time. Starting in April the larvae hatch and wait for a passing earthworm. The larva penetrates the unlucky earthworm through or near its male genital opening. Then the maggot grows, consuming the helpless, hapless worm in the process. In about two weeks the larva exits the still living, but depleted, worm to pupate in the soil. After a month and a half or so, the pupae hatch and a next generation of adult flies appears.

As many as four generations can appear in a season. The last generation is the one that appears in the science building to hibernate. Other than unsightliness, my cluster flies cause no major problems, They don't spread disease or root around in living flesh. If I were an earthworm though, I'd keep it zippered, and if I ever go to the Congo I am certainly staying off the floor.

Earwigs

Many creatures in the living world give humans the creeps, often because that is what the creatures do, creep. The earwig is such an organism. Where we worry about them creeping, is, of course, into our ears, late at night, unknown to us.

We also worry about them creeping into the cabbage patch to munch on our fruits and vegetables or appear unannounced and certainly uninvited as added protein in some vegetarian dish. Like many of our fellow creatures on planet Earth, they are not always bad and often live out interesting, useful lives.

We are most familiar with the common European earwig, *Forficula auricularia* first introduced to the United States in the early 1900s. Our common earwig has an elongated shiny brown body with legs of even length and antennae at one end and a pair of horrific pinchers at the other. The males have larger curved forceps. The females' pinchers are mostly straight. On their backs are two pairs of wings. One pair serves as a scale-like cover over the second large pair that are elegantly folded, origami like, beneath. In spite of their wings, common earwigs are not great fliers. They are, however, rapid runners.

Earwigs are nocturnal, spending their days in humid hideaways under leaves, stones or bark. They prefer tight places, folds in old rags, between the pages of old damp newspapers, where back and stomach touch. After a night of foraging they gather in groups sometimes numbering in the thousands.

Earwigs are greedy, eager eaters. Not only do they use their chewing mouthparts on tender plant parts, but they also eat all kinds of smaller insects including plant lice, fruit caterpillars, even fleas.

The strange forceps serve in defense, to grasp prey, to help unfold hind wings, and in mating. Their social life is especially interesting. They mate indiscriminately in summer but often live monogamously in winter when mates share a burrow. In early spring the female lays 40 to 50 shiny eggs. Her behavior changes. She runs off any intruder, including her mate. She pays close attention to the eggs, continually cleaning them by licking to remove fungal spores and other harmful microorganisms. If the nest is too wet or dry, she makes a new one and moves the eggs one by one. Once they hatch mamma earwig looks after her young. If they stray too far, she brings them back. She washes them by licking. When larger, the young forage for food but return to the nest. A lot of mother love it seems for such a lowly creature. Eventually mommy, weakened by her maternal exertions, dies and her progeny eat her!

If earwigs in your garden trouble you, you could resort to chemicals. Better yet take advantage of their enthusiasm for close places. Set out rags or damp newspapers around your garden and hope that large numbers of them will use them for daytime hiding places. Put on your dancing clogs and dance away. Another option? Put up with them and hope that they eat more harmful bugs than they do damage to your crops. Worried about sleeping tonight? Try ear plugs.

Earthworms

Dog and I ventured forth one morning several weeks ago to discover an earthworm disaster; worms all over the street. It is a kind of gruesome sign of spring.

What happened? Our first relatively warm soaking rains of spring filled available pore space in the soil with oxygen-deficient water. Because of a week or so of relatively warm weather, the earthworms moved up out of their deep winter burrows to the surface to eat and breed. Earthworms normally obtain oxygen for cellular metabolism by direct absorption through their moist skin into surface capillaries and hemoglobin-rich blood. Under most circumstances there is enough oxygen in the soil atmosphere to supply the worms, but there is not enough in the rain water to do the job. So out pop earthworms by the thousands, out of the grass and onto the street, where most of them perish by being crushed or from dehydration as the street dries out. I have never noticed earthworm predators taking advantage of such a bounty. I always expect to see robins and starlings out gorging themselves, but am always disappointed. Perhaps they don't care for petroleum flavored worms. Earthworms can accumulate certain pesticides in their tissues at concentrations many times that found in the soil. Small mammals and birds that eat these earthworms accumulate the pesticides in even higher concentrations, sometimes fatal concentrations, in a phenomenon known as biological magnification.

Our local raccoons are fond of earthworms. Often in summer, after watering the lawn, I have gone to bed only to be awakened in the middle of the night by the "chirring" sound of raccoons talking in the yard. The next morning my lawn is pockmarked with shallow holes where the raccoons have been going after night crawlers.

I have gone stealthily creeping about lawns late at night myself, flashlight in hand, lidded bucket at my side, searching for the mighty nightcrawler. My purpose was not to eat them, but to use them for fish bait. Our large earthworms extend some distance from their burrows at night to forage and to mate.

Sex among earthworms is a curious business. They are hermaphrodites, that is, both boy and girl. Their internal sex organs and their external openings are arranged in such away that self-fertilization is not a possibility. Partners meet head to head in opposite directions, external openings of one meeting that of another... you don't want to hear the rest of this! Children have been known to hear this program unaccompanied by an adult. Earthworm love involves the formation of a mucus sheath and an organ known as the clitellum, for heaven's sake.

Worms' rear-ends often remain in their burrows and they can retract with lightening speed at the slightest vibration or beam of light. You must grab the earthworm quickly, then pull gently, least you pull poor worm in two. This may not be as bad as it sounds for many species can regenerate a head or end and carry on. It is not nearly as bad as being empaled on a fish hook, however. Occasionally, if caught in the act, so to speak, you get two for one. I must confess I always hesitate. Nightcrawling takes great skill and stealth, enough for me to make it almost as much fun as fishing, considering my fishing skills.

Earthworms are extremely important soil organisms. They enhance the soil environment with their burrows by increasing soil aeration and drainage. They speed up the release of nutrients tied up in plant debris by munching up and partially digesting leaves. The partially digested leaves are mixed with soil particles, ground up in the worm's gizzard and excreted as castings. Plant materials in the castings are broken down by soil microorganisms to a form that can be absorbed and reused by plants. Earthworms also mix the soil by bringing up soil from below the surface, as much as 40 tons per acre by some estimates. Earthworms are valuable contributors to the health and welfare of many terrestrial ecosystems.

Demodex

We have suggested the restless movement of water bears in the moss forests of your shake roof as a rather fanciful cause of insomnia (page 221). If you don't have a shake roof, perhaps the nocturnal sexual cavortings of your very own population of hair follicle mites is the cause of your insomnia.

Hair follicle mites? On me? No way. I bathe regularly. Besides, Mamma taught me proper hygiene. I couldn't have tiny eight-legged arthropods in my hair follicles.

Maybe not, but close examination might disclose otherwise. It seems the mites are very common in humans, most numerous in males and more common and easier to obtain in older hosts. Most humans have mites inhabiting hair follicles and oil or sebaceous glands around the nose, cheeks, forehead, and, sometimes, eyelashes and follicles around the nipple of the breast. They were first found in ear wax in 1842 by some inquisitive microscopist.

Our mites are in the genus *Demodex*, the same genus that gives dogs mange and in the same suborder as that scourge of our midwest and south, the chigger. Fortunately for humans, our *Demodex* partners usually cause no major problems, although they sometimes cause small, non-acne-like pimples and have been implicated in hair loss by a cosmetics firm and in inflammation of human eyelids, in at least one case. Mites most often inhabit healthy skin where they consume the cells lining the follicle or cells of the oil gland. They are harmless, low-grade parasites.

Humans host not one, but two species of *Demodex* mites. Both occupy separate niches and lead separate lives. *Demodex folliculorum* lives out its life in the follicle of simple hairs above the level of the oil gland, where three or more mites may be found, head down, feet against the lining of the follicle. The other, shorter, mite, *D. brevis,* lives primarily in the oil glands. It doesn't seem to be as social as its cousin. Usually only one or, at most, two specimens are found together, thought to be a female and her offspring.

The creatures are unisexual, with a ratio of four females or so per male. Each sex has all the suitable accouterments for mating and surely at some time and place they do get together to cavort. In all honesty, their activities in this regard probably don't cause insomnia in their hosts.

The mites might spread from host to host when they leave the safety of their usual habitat to wander out onto the surface of the skin. Here they may move by direct contact when hosts kiss face to face or share towels. Studies on other mammals suggest another mode of contact. Young nursing mammals soon become infested (isn't that an ugly word?) at an early age, while hand-raised babies don't pick up the mites until later. Our first contact as host for these benign little parasites probably began while suckling at our mother's breast. I'll bet Mamma never told you that!

Bedbugs

"Nighty, night, sleep tight, don't let the bedbugs bite." Don't know why Mamma used to tell me that at bed time. No bedbugs at our house. Don't know the source of the saying, although I have looked and looked. Don't know what reminded me of bedbugs, unless it was recent talk of stinky daddy-long-legs (page 148).

Bedbugs, like many of their fellow Hemipterans or true bugs, stink, as in stink bugs. One sure sign of a heavy bedbug infestation is a characteristic odor. Stink bugs suck the vital juices out of plants. Bedbugs suck the vital juices out of humans, early in the morning, just before dawn. Bedbug's relative, the assassin bug, also enjoys animal juices. One, *Triatoma megista,* takes a human blood meal and expresses its thanks by defecating on the bite, which swells and itches. The bitten scratches and in the process rubs the feces containing the parasite that cause Chagas's disease into the wound. Not much fun.

What surprises me is that bedbugs are not vectors, that is, carriers of human disease. However, bedbugs, like other exclusive blood feeders, have symbiotic vitamin B producing bacteria that provide them with that important vitamin missing from blood. The mother bedbug includes the bacteria with each egg laid, ensuring offspring of an essential companion.

The bedbug's *modus operandi* is to lurk about during the day, flattened in various narrow crevices in houses of all sorts. They are fond of baseboards, light switches, moldings, tight spots in furniture, under wallpaper. They hide in places that are difficult to reach for eradication by insecticides or biocides like cyanide gas. If the temperature is above 55°F, the bedbug strikes just before dawn. The warmer it is the better they like it. They draw a blood meal, sometimes taking five minutes or longer. Then they quickly hustle off to digest their meal undisturbed. The bedbugs seem to nibble about, test drilling until they hit a gusher. Each puncture swells and itches, long after the bedbug is safe, "Snug as a bug in a rug," perhaps, or at least in a light switch.

Bedbugs have been with humans for a long time, some think since we were cave dwellers. They are inquilines, species of one sort that inhabit the abode of another. Human examples include, dust mites, silver fish, house spiders, carpet beetles, in-laws, and the like.

Sex among the bedbugs is, well, different. When mating, the male does not insert his member in the usual place, but in a slit in the female's side that enters a special organ. This organ not only serves for mating, but also as a place where amoeboid cells digest many of the sperm. Some sperm manage to slip through the female's body wall into the body cavity where they eventually reach the ovaries to fertilize the eggs. When the act occurs, the partners are catty wampus — the male with his head to the left. Could this be the origin of the expression "crazy as a bedbug?"

Bedbugs do not seem as common today as in the past, but then I may run in different circles. I have no doubt that modern insecticides and sanitation play a role in keeping bedbug populations in check. So, sleep tight, and be thankful the bedbugs don't bite you.

Yellowjackets

Yellowjackets are first-order social insects, not because they like picnics so much, but because they live together in large colonies. The colonies consist of many sterile female workers and a fertile, egg-laying queen. The workers play an active role in making elegant paper nests and looking after larvae. At first, workers are produced. Late in the season queens and males form. In cold and temperate climes, all members of the colony die except new queens who form new colonies in the spring.

Yellowjacket and baldfaced hornet nests are architectural marvels. Workers collect small pellets of wood pulp from plants and carry them to the nest. There the workers mix the pulp with salivary secretions, to form hexagonal cells or the thin papery sheets of the nest's outer layers. The thin paper layers are light and strong with spaces in between that act as insulation.

Yellowjackets are around all summer mostly doing good by killing many insects that we consider pests. Later in the season these prey become less abundant and yellowjackets move on to other food sources, like picnic chicken.

Most humans learn at an early age that black and yellow flying insects generally are equipped with a modified ovipositor that acts as a stinger to deliver a powerful, painful mixture of enzymes and proteins. We learn they can hurt.

Essig's statement describing baldface hornets in his *Insects of Western North America* reminds me of a childhood activity of mine. Essig writes "The workers are very pugnacious, but perhaps no more so than the hundreds of country boys who destroy their nests." God, thinking about it still gives me an adrenaline rush. My friends and I spot the nest, large, ominous and gray, the size of a basketball. We collect rocks. Then the assault begins, first from a distance, then closer and closer. Scared to death we will hit the nest, but driven to continue by some ancient primal urge that some of us outgrow. The barrage continues until bang, someone strikes the target. Out pours the angry band to drive away their tormentors, which they do with little effort. Then, forgive us, we return and continue until someone gets stung.

I have often thought that I stayed out of trouble as an adolescent by throwing rocks at yellowjackets and hornets. Others got their thrills and into trouble by stealing hubcaps and the rings from Buick hood ornaments.

Some advice from an expert. When uninvited yellowjacket guests show up at your next picnic or outdoor meal, don't scream and shout, throw your arms and run about. Stay calm, even if the yellowjacket is on the fork about to go into your mouth or just slipped between your big toe and your sandal. A slow gentle brush or wiggle is more likely to save you from pain and agony than a swat or stomp. As a friend and former colleague used to say, "gentle ways are best."

More Yellowjackets

Yellowjackets, bald-faced hornets and the like don't seem to be particularly bothersome this summer. At least they haven't bothered me much. Our outdoor meals have been mostly devoid of uninvited guests and I haven't had any unpleasant encounters in the field this year. Last year a small paper nest above the front door was done in, forgive me, with a burst of chemicals after dark. They never knew what hit them.

I feel slightly guilty about doing in wasps because they live such interesting lives as social insects, build such complicated and exotic homes and eat many critters we humans consider pests. What drives me to destruction is their modified ovipositor that acts as a syringe to deliver a powerful and painful mixture of enzymes and proteins.

Much of their lives these stinging insects go about minding their own business, eating aphids and other pests. As the summer progresses, easily available natural food slowly disappears and yellowjackets shift to other fare, like picnic ham. They can become a real annoyance, especially to human picnickers who go berserk.

Last summer I had a real lesson in yellowjacket behavior and foreign cultures. My Japanese botanical colleagues were back for another two weeks of gleaning our flora for exotic chemicals. This past summer, at Howard Prairie Lake, Iinuma, the pharmacologist from Gifu Pharmaceutical University did a most amazing thing.

After finishing lunch at the picnic area, most of us wandered off to relax a little before continuing our collecting efforts. As I started back toward our van, I noticed Iinuma at our picnic table, with his elbow on the table, staring at his hand. At first I thought he might be having a cigarette. No smoke. As I got closer I could see that his hand was upright and his thumb and forefingers were together and there was a yellowjacket on his fingertips.

"Iinuma, what on earth is going on?" As I said that, the yellowjacket rose into the air, settled down, then rose into the air again. By this time I was close enough to see that there was a thin thread between the yellowjacket and Iinuma's thumb and forefinger. Suddenly, when the yellowjacket rose again, Iinuma released the string and the insect flew off into the distance with the thread clearly visible. Iinuma had tied one end of a thread to a tiny piece of sandwich ham. He held the opposite end of the thread between thumb and forefinger with the ham balanced on his fingertips, sat still, and waited for Ms. Yellowjacket to arrive. Iinuma explained to me that in the area near Nagano, Japan, where he grew up, yellowjacket larvae, deep-fried and seasoned with sugar and soy sauce, are a much sought-after delicacy. They found yellowjacket nests using the ham bait and silk thread trick. The flying yellowjacket with dangling thread could be easily followed back to its nest. Once in a while a yellowjacket might stop and bite through the thread, presumably to make flying easier. I was amazed, not so much that Iinuma ate yellowjacket larvae, but that the yellowjacket was so docile. The yellowjacket had no intention of stinging the hand that fed it. Another yellowjacket didn't try to sting me, in spite of my record of yellowjacket murder, but flew off, string dangling, for its nest. What is the lesson here?

Ticks and Mites

I spent an hour or so showing off the Biology Department's scanning electron microscope to a group of Ashland mid-high science students. They were at the university to celebrate Science and Technology Week. Dr. Jad D'Allura, of the Geology Department, organized the series of tours, as he has for the past several years.

This year we looked at *Dermacentor*, the dog tick genus, under the SEM, as the scanning electron microscope is called by those of us in the know. We looked at both ends, the back, and the belly for the tick. The head end was the most interesting, though there was some laughter when we examined the other end. I suppose an anus enlarged 4,000 times is enough to cause mirth among middle school scientists. Fortunately I avoided the genital pore. Who knows what might have happened at that sight.

At lower magnifications the hypostome, the mouthpart the tick uses to stay stuck in you while it sucks up its blood meal, appeared to be smooth. Increasing magnification revealed a series of tile-like plates. The tiles all seemed to point toward the back end of the tick. There was absolutely no evidence of left or right threading. The best way to remove a tick stuck in your skin is to have someone pull it gently straight out. Twisting clockwise or counter clockwise will just increase the risk of twisting off the tick's body leaving the head embedded. Don't squeeze its body, you may force tick juice, filled with any manner of pathogens, into your bloodstream. Remember when we used to worry about Rocky Mountain spotted fever, Q fever, tularemia, relapsing fever, Colorado tick fever, Powassan encephalitis, and human babesiosis? Now we worry mostly about Lyme disease, though the others are still with us.

In *Dermacentor* the pair of tiny eyes is located away from what we would call the head. The eyes are more for distinguishing light from dark, rather than forming clear images. The tick's first leg contains a sensory pore with hair-like structures that sense mechanical and chemical stimuli.

When the middle school scientists and I examined the head end of our dog tick, we discovered two pits in what appeared to be the terminal segment of the pair of antenna-like palps on either side of the hypostome. Each pit contained a structure that looked like a cow's udder. I did not know what they were, but thought they might be some special sensory organ. I have since learned the structure is the real terminal segment of the palp and that it might perform a sensory function.

Ticks and mites are a separate order in the same class as spiders. There are a lot of them. Some are so specialized that they are known only in the pitchers of our local insectivorous *Darlingtonia*, others are common inhabitants of house dust. Dust mites can cause major allergies in sensitive humans. The relationship among dust mites, human conjugal relationships, the condom, and runny noses is explained starting on page 135. I'll bet you can't wait.

Dust Mites

Mites are everywhere, in pitcher plants and human hair follicles, on birds, reptiles, mammals and plants, in soil and water, and in household dust. Tiny microscopic dust mites, a third of a millimeter long, look like strange little eight-legged sheep. Dust mites wander about most homes feasting on human skin scales, beard shavings and other organic delectable edibles, found in dust and elsewhere.

Inquilines, animals that inhabit the abode of another, fill our homes. Booklice, silverfish, house centipedes, and spiders are common benign examples. If you are allergic to one of the six or so allergens produced by dust mites, they are hardly benign. People who suffer from asthma are often allergic to dust mites. Asthmatics and some others of us are allergic to the mites and, sorry about this, their tiny, pollen-grain sized, resistant droppings. These particles accumulate in carpets, padded chairs, davenports, beds and bedding.

Dust mites thrive at temperatures between 55 and 75°F and in relative humidities between 60 and 70 percent, conditions common in human bedrooms. Bedrooms are dust-mite heaven. Bedding and mattresses provide ideal dust-mite habitat. Populations can reach spectacular heights in down, feather, and foam bedding: two million dust mites in a double bed. Knowing this, you might think twice about blaming your spouse for moving bedding in the night. Temperature and humidity are just right in human beds. In the beds and bedding of human males and sexually active couples, there often is a much more nutritious food source, semen. Modesty prevents a detailed discussion of semen deposition in bedding, except to say that gravity is strongly implicated. Semen is a complex fluid of sperm, the sugar fructose, enzymes, and hormones. The sperm has little stored food itself and gets its energy from the fructose. Studies show that female mites fed dust without semen laid fewer eggs than females fed dust with semen. More eggs mean more mites.

Getting rid of dust mites can be a major problem that may require removing carpets, covering mattresses, constant cleaning. Apparently various proprietary cleansers, designed to shampoo mites and their feces from household carpets, are available. Ordinary household cleansers are not effective.

In beds where mating couples might spread semen about, condoms might make the bed less hospitable to mites. Cut off the rich supply of nutrients and you might have fewer mites. Fewer mites might lower the population to a tolerable level. Asthma attacks and runny noses might become less severe.

An article entitled "Matrimony, Mattresses and Mites" by Paul Harvey and Robert May in the March 3, 1990 issues of *New Scientist,* a weekly British publication, inspired this commentary.

Slugs

A recent coast field trip reminded me of one of my favorite animals. In the redwoods we saw banana slugs, big, yellow, slimy banana slugs, some with spots, some without, but all with shiny coats that make your last head cold seem like nothing at all. Slugs and I go back a long way. One of my early memories is of Papa wandering around his beloved vegetable garden, salt-shaker in hand, searching for unfortunate, unwary slugs. The yard had strategically placed long, sharpened sticks for the same purpose, slug murder. Victims were mostly European immigrants that do the most damage in gardens. Our slugs met a somewhat painful end, not quick, like the slugs in the backyard of one of my former students. His mamma shot them from her kitchen window with a .22 caliber pistol.

My first major banana slug experience was as a graduate student at the University of British Columbia. I was working on fern cytology and wanted to count the chromosomes in the gametophyte, which have half the number of the root tips. The cell walls kept getting in the way. I read that some European workers used an enzyme from land snails' stomachs to dissolve the cell walls so cells would flatten and chromosomes could be easily observed. I didn't have snails, but I easily collected two gallons of live slithery, slimy banana slugs. I operated and collected 5 cc of stomach contents and pounds of slime. Imagine pouring out an entire jar of rubber cement and running your fingers through the puddle till it dried coating your hands and fingers in a thick, sticky layer. Slug enzyme did not work. Cell walls stayed intact, but not the slugs.

Banana slugs much prefer the damp, moist recesses of their native forest habitat to gardens. They eat most anything. Living plants, decaying plants, fungi, algae, lichens, dung, dead animals are all prized. They play a valuable role in forest ecosystems helping to recycle nutrients tied up in plant and animal bodies.

Banana slugs are shell-less, lunged mollusks. Scientists call them *Ariolimax columbianus.* They are found from southeast Alaska through northern California south to Santa Cruz. They are the second largest land slugs in the world, reaching a maximum length of ten inches. Only the European slug is larger.

Slugs glide along on a trail of slime on their muscular foot. Just behind their four tentacled sensory organs lies the saddle-like mantle that hides the anus and the genital opening. Between is a hole in the mantle that leads to a lung-like cavity that slugs open and close according to need.

Their sex life is enough to make the Marquis squirm. They are hermaphrodites. If you are a sensitive and highly refined sort, may not want to read the rest of this essay. Foreplay consists of a pair of slugs circling into a tight S-shape with much nudging, licking and biting. Then at the height of sluggly passion penetration of each into the other by members of prodigious size occurs. Sperm is exchanged and mutual fertilization follows. No cigarettes are smoked; however, there's more. The prodigious penises get stuck and the only way to disconnect is by apophallation. They bite each others' winkies off! After disentangling themselves, the battered and presumably exhausted slugs crawl off to lay their eggs to assure new slugs for future generations.

For all their strange, and to some, disgusting ways, banana slugs play a valuable ecological role. They are a grand example of a creature uniquely adapted to its way of life.

Thanks to Alice Bryant Harper for her book *The Banana Slug.*

Painted Ladies

News in the *Medford Mail Tribune* that large numbers of painted ladies were headed this way from California certainly caught my attention. I was only sightly disappointed to learn that they were butterflies. I was delighted to learn, however, that these butterflies are in the genus *Veronica*, and that there was a recent attempt to transfer them to the genus *Cynthia*. Wonderful names, it seems to me, for painted ladies.

Painted ladies have the distinction of being the most widely-distributed of all the butterflies. They are found throughout most of the northern hemisphere: Eurasia, Africa, North America and northern South America. Painted ladies of this type are absent from Australia and New Zealand. They don't like cold winters. They can't survive, so are transitory in temperate climes. They emigrate north from warmer southern latitudes, sometimes in prodigious numbers. In Oregon there have been major emigrations in 1958, 1966, 1973, and in 1992. Our entomologist, Marv Coffey, tells of going to a biology symposium on animal migration at Oregon State University in the spring of 1966 accompanied by a great northward emigration of painted ladies. John Dornfeld, author of *Butterflies of Oregon* recounts the same story.

We don't know why painted ladies emigrate or how they navigate. Northward emigrations of millions of painted ladies correlate with optimum growing conditions in the year-round Mediterranean climate of their normal range. They move steadily northward, flitting and swirling within a few meters of the surface. Painted ladies are strong fliers. They have been observed flying 12 miles per hour against a strong headwind; 20 miles per hour with the wind.

Their movement north is not a true migration because they or their progeny generally do not return from whence they came. We refer to their movement as an emigration or pseudomigration. Although a few southward migrations occur, painted ladies seem to move from the safety of warm climates with no intention of ever returning south. Because of their excursions, they may someday survive year-round at northern latitudes if global warming continues.

Navigation is a puzzle. Some think polarized sunlight and/or the position of the sun provides orientation for butterflies. Other possibilities include the use of landmarks or, if flying at night, the moon or stars. They will layover if weather is cold and blustery, but moderate winds do not deter them.

As adults move north they use their stores of reserve fat and arrive at their destination somewhat the worse for wear. There is enough umph left for reproduction. Painted ladies feed on 100 or so different plants, especially thistles, mallows and legumes. They are found on yerba santa, a plant humans use as a stimulating expectorant and to mask quinine's bitter taste.

When you are out enjoying nature, look for medium sized orange-ish butterflies with eyespots aft, and blackish wing tips forward with white bars. They are painted ladies headed north.

Myriapods

Arthropods include insects, spiders, crustaceans and the like. They have external hardened shells that serve as a skeleton and an internal system of muscles. If you have ever eaten cracked crab you know how arthropods are put together. In case you worry about such things, bugs big enough to eat Los Angeles will never happen, science fiction notwithstanding. Even if they had the stomach for such a disgusting task, their structure, physiology, and gravity strictly limit their maximum size.

There are two other groups of arthropods, centipedes and millipedes. Centipedes are fast, have one pair of legs per body segment, and are predatory. Millipedes are slow, have two legs per body segment, and are vegetarians. I first knew these creatures as thousand-legged worms, until study taught me otherwise.

When I was a child wandering through the damp woods of western Washington I would commonly encounter a handsome black millipede with bright yellow spots along its sides. Disturbed, the beast would roll up into a tight spiral, head end in, and begin to stink. Not an ordinary stink, but one, when smelled at a distance, that reminded me of my Auntie Winnie's German Christmas cookies, the faint odor of almonds.

Years later I learned that most millipedes have a series of glands along their bodies. These glands generate various noxious compounds, including hydrocyanic acid and cyanide gas, which has the odor of almonds. The millipede's striking color warns potential predators of an unsavory mouthful.

In 1974 I spent a year-long sabbatical in Texas. Every thing is bigger and better in Texas, including centipedes. I was used to northwest centipedes, a couple of inches long at most, who spend their lives poking around in rotten logs. On a Biological Photography Association field trip I turned over a rock. There was a centipede, *that* was a centipede, six or eight inches long, bright yellow head, sinister black body and almost as fast as I was. There is no photographic record of the encounter. Looked to me like it might eat puppies.

On my second sabbatical in Massachusetts we lived at 10 Swan Street in a house built in 1812 that was rumored to harbour the ghost of a Revolutionary War soldier. One evening out of the corner of my eye I noticed motion along the baseboard. A shifted glance and nothing. A few nights later the same sensation, still nothing. Spooky thoughts on my part. Whatever it was, it was fast. The next night a rolled up newspaper solved the mystery. From what I could reconstruct, it was a long-legged multisegmented creature, that moved fast, real fast. As visiting scholar at Harvard I had the run of the library at the Museum of Comparative Zoology, or the MCZ as insiders say. There I discovered that I had done in a house centipede, a creature that feeds on silverfish, cockroaches, and flies and should be welcomed in any household. The remainder of my time at 10 Swan Street I attributed unexplained motion to house centipedes and not to ghosts — and left both unmolested, just in case.

Moon Snails

Geoducks (page 227) and Puget Sound remind me of other intertidal curiosities I found as a kid while wandering around the bay at low tide. Two of them, seemingly unrelated, are caused by the same sea creature. I'd pick up clam shells on the beaches of Budd Inlet, near Olympia, Washington at low tide. Often there would be a nice neat counter-sunk hole in the shell of the long-gone clam. A hole so nice and neat it looked like it might have been made by an electric drill. Most holes were the same size and on the same part of the shell. What caused the holes?

In the vicinity, usually where the steeper rocky beach met the flatter sandy bottom and beyond, were the strangest looking things. The things that looked like collars made of sand. Things that you might make if you took a plumber's helper, cut off the top and slit one side. Things that lay in the sand surrounded by green and iridescent red algae. Things that begged an explanation.

Walking among the sand collars I often found rounded tops of shells just showing above the sandy muddy surface. Dig one up and you find a very large snail, with a huge pinkish-beige foot. Large is relative. This large would be a double handful. The shell, two-fisted in size, has a large operculum or door that never appears to close. The foot seems to be too large to fit all the way inside the shell. But fit it does, after the loss of large amounts of water. Turns out the snail can't stay inside its shell for long, because there is no room to breathe. I get the same feeling when I sit down, bend over and try to tie my shoes.

Moon snails as they are known, make sand collars and kill clams and other bivalve mollusks for a living. They kill in several ways. A moon snail usually surrounds the bivalve of choice with its muscular foot, drills through the shell with its rasp-like radula, then sucks up its victim through the hole. Other times the snail may suffocate its prey within its foot or cover up the bivalve's siphon. They are, by any definition, pure carnivore.

The strange, sandy plumber's helpers scattered on the shore are, in fact, the moon snail's exotic egg cases. According to Calvin and Ricketts account in their book, *Between Pacific Tides,* the eggs are laid in a gelatinous sheet from the snail's mantle cavity. As the eggs are produced they are encased in a sheet of mucus cemented sand, shaped by the contours of the snail's foot. When the egg case falls apart, half a million free-swimming larvae are released. Released, perhaps, to be eaten by filter-feeding bivalve mollusks in the vicinity. Poetic justice claim Calvin and Ricketts. Poetic clam justice, say I.

Not too many years ago I noticed a recipe in the book, *Edible? Incredible.* All I could see were those huge muscular feet by the thousands, so easy to collect, so easy to eat in unlimited supply. I arranged a visit home to Olympia, Washington. I went to the beach at low tide, then home with a dozen or so, big choice moon snails. (I didn't want to appear greedy.) I cleaned the shells, cut off the feet, and began to pound away with a wooden mallet, to tenderize them. I tried them fried . . . inner tube! I tried them ground as fritters . . . crumbled Art Gum eraser. I didn't try them any other way. I gave up. Edible? Incredible, indeed . . .

Klamath Midge

It's early evening, the wind dies, and near the edge of the marsh a few small flying insects rise. Soon joined by others, the swarm increases and increases and increases until the mass of insects forms a long symmetrical top-shaped mass that swirls about emanating a strong, screaming hum audible at a distance of 100 yards. Cows refuse to eat. Automobile radiators clog. People become nauseated and have trouble breathing.

Where could this happen? Belize, the Mosquito Coast? The swamps of the Congo? The banks of the great gray-green, greasy Limpopo River, all set about with fever trees? Give up? It's the Klamath marsh!

What I have described is the mating frenzy of the Klamath midge, *Chironomus utahensis,* taken from a 1941 paper on the biology of the insect. Perhaps the description was a little overdone, or perhaps conditions have improved somewhat since 1941. For many Klamath residents and visitors, however, the midge is still a nuisance.

Although these tiny midges superficially resemble mosquitos, they are quite different. When they alight they raise their forelegs and not their hind legs as mosquitos do. Midges are not interested in a blood meal, although you may inhale several by mistake. The larvae of midges are often bright red, the blood worms sometimes used by aquarists for feeding tropical fish.

The shallow, nutrient-rich waters of the Klamath aquatic ecosystem support enormous numbers of algae: desmids, diatoms, and especially, a planktonic filamentous blue-green algae, *Aphanizomenon*, as many as 20 million filaments per cubic meter.

All these producers (photosynthesizing plants that put energy into food webs) support and sustain the entire ecosystem, especially the midge larvae — millions and millions and millions of midge larvae. Midge larvae that filter out desmids, diatoms and the bacteria that flourish when the blue-green algae decompose. Midge larvae that are eaten in turn by all 18 species of fish in Upper Klamath Lake, especially the Klamath chub and the Klamath roach, which are preyed upon by trout, huge trout, trophy trout, for which Klamath Lake is famous.

Other consumers (animals that eat producers and other consumers), aquatic beetles, dragonfly larvae, and small marsh birds also use midge larvae for food. These consumers are in turn eaten by other animals. Midge adults are eaten by adult dragonflies, songbirds, toads, and spiders — all part of the Klamath Lake food web.

Insects, no matter how important ecologically, can be a bother. Efforts to control their numbers through modern chemistry have frequently been attempted; however, no major efforts have been made to control the Klamath midge in Oregon. The insect carries no known diseases and does not bite. It is just a nuisance. If the midge is an aggravation, try to find some solace in the important role it plays in the biology of Klamath Lake and the production of trophy trout.

Harvestmen

Consider a fall or winter visit to Oregon Caves National Monument east of Cave Junction in southern Oregon. If fall color is at its peak, you will see ash and cottonwoods in dress yellow, oaks with rusty tunics and big leaf maples decked out in incandescent gold. Red dogwoods add color under somber evergreens. Even if the leaves are gone there is still plenty to see. It is a good idea to stop in at the Visitors Center in Cave Junction to check on road conditions and cave hours before you take the drive to the monument.

The cave and tour are interesting: strange limestone formations, stalactites, stalagmites, drip stone, and soda straws, bats, coprophilic fungi, and harvestmen. The harvestmen are my personal favorites. You may know them as daddy-long-legs.

We saw harvestmen on the walls near the exit, where they entered the cave to spend the winter. There they were, by the dozens. The guide told us that in coldest weather they congregate by the thousands. When disturbed by blowing gently on them they shift slightly. The walls, they move.

When I looked closer, they reminded me of some strange long-legged sea creature. Their eight, long, spindly, walking legs carry their egg-shaped bodies over the ground like some strange science-fiction moonwalker. Harvestmen are arachnids related to spiders, as you might have guessed from their eight-leggedness.

They live in soil or above the ground in herbs, shrubs or trees. Wherever they live, they require moderate temperatures and adequate water. The sense organs on harvestmen's legs must be cleaned of dust and dirt and dinner. After eating they pull their legs gently through their jaws to clean off debris. Finished, the harvestmen seek water to wash their jaws and faces. This is done, not without hazard, by placing their front legs on the surface of standing water, held up by surface tension, then they wet their faces. Occasionally a leg breaks through the surface film, they lose their balance and drown. Bummer. It's those bathroom accidents we hear about.

Some harvestmen eat slugs and snails. Others prefer mites, springtails, spiders, and larval stages of insects. They do not inject a poison as spiders do, but eat their prey alive with large and powerful beak-like jaws. Some are omnivores and enjoy almost anything edible from bread and milk to fallen fruit. They often inhabit compost piles.

Centipedes, large spiders, and arthropod eating birds like wrens prey upon harvestmen in turn. Harvestmen have two tricks. If a predator grasps a leg, off it pops and writhes about, distracting the eater while the eatee makes off to seven-legged safety. Unlike spiders and more like us, the harvestman does not regenerate a new appendage. Harvestmen also have glands that discharge a volatile, foul-smelling fluid that may put off a predator.

Growth is by molting with the skin shed whole. During a harvestman's lifetime there might be seven or eight sheddings, ten days or so apart. The old skin splits and the body is withdrawn. Then, each long leg is carefully removed from the old casing, a long and arduous task. Is it any wonder mommy-long-legs don't wear panty hose?

Take a winter visit to Oregon Caves National Monument and ask the guide to show you the harvestmen, another marvel of the living world.

Glowworms

Many different plants and animals luminesce, glow in the dark. The glow is usually the result of complex chemical reactions involving oxygen. Several different enzymes called luciferases, several different substrates called luciferins, and adenosine triphosphate or ATP as an energy source interact, producing light. The name of the substrate and its enzyme is from the Latin *lucifer* meaning light-bearing. The enzymes and the substrates vary, depending on the organism. The light produced is in the visible part of the spectrum and produces very little heat. When you first see the pale ghostly glow of rotting wood at night, your first thought might be of Lucifer with a capital L.

Biologists occasionally get exciting gifts. A hiker, in the woods after dark without a light, found his trail lighted in places by tiny phosphorescent glows. He collected a glow and brought it back in a film container with some soil. When I peeked in the darkened canister, there was a faint blue-green glow, a single point of light. When we examined the container's contents, we discovered what appeared to be a beetle larva, undoubtedly the source of light. A quick trip down the hall to our insect collection and Dr. Coffey, our entomologist, revealed that we had a glowworm. "Glow, little glowworm, glimmer, glimmer." It was that wee beast immortalized in song. Our glowworm trapper told me he had seen several concentrations along his darkened route. Dr. Coffey tells me that glowworms are not often seen or collected in our part of the country. They are close relatives of the beetles we call fireflies.

Our glowworms are members of the beetle family *Phengodidae*. Adult males have distinctive feathery antennae and short protective wings with flying wings exposed. Males don't glow. Females are wingless like the larval stages of both sexes. Larvae and females both glow; larvae for practice, females to attract mates. The predatory larvae feed on soft-bodied insects and other small organisms.

Larvae of one firefly genus glow and flash like females of a different genus. The larvae attract unsuspecting males who become a meal. How disappointing for the males; how clever of the larvae. Is there a lesson here?

Many wood-rotting fungi bioluminesce to create the so-called foxfires of the forest. The fine strands or mycelium of the fungus that penetrate the damp rotting wood, or its fruiting body, the mushroom, or both, glow in the dark. Several of our local mushrooms, the Jack-O-Lantern and the honey mushroom, luminesce when alive and well. If too dry? No luminescence, no matter how dark it gets. At Boy Scout camp we would peer out between the flaps of our tents to see the eerie glow of fungal mycelia in the damp wood of old, downed, rotting conifer logs. A spooky sight for kids of any age.

My first childhood experience with luciferin was on a warm, dark, windless night on Puget Sound. I was sitting in the stern of a boat my father was rowing. The wake was luminescent and glowing whirlpools from oar strokes marked our progress home.

Years later, when I first came to Southern to teach, I needed live kelp specimens for my plant morphology class. It was in the fall and lowest tides were after sunset. I walked out to the kelp beds with lantern, boots and bucket, collecting as I went, with one eye on the kelp, the other on the sea. When I had what I needed, I walked back across the kelp in darkness. For some reason I turned to see from whence I came. I could with ease for every footstep glowed with phosphorescent brightness.

My latest bioluminescent experience was on a cruise ship that flushed with sea water. My nighttime journey to the head became more than just relief. It became an experience as tiny marine organisms were startled into tiny bursts of light.

V

The Birds

Bald Eagles

Consider traveling to the Klamath Basin in the winter months to see our national symbol, the bald eagle, at Lower Klamath and Tule Lake National Wildlife Refuges. You will see the largest concentration of wintering eagles any place in the lower 48 states.

Many of the birds are from Canada, some from as far north as Northwest Territories, who migrate south to enjoy the warmth and comfort of the Klamath Basin in winter. It really is all relative, isn't it?

The migrants start arriving in November and reach a peak of 500 birds in January and February. All but the four dozen nesting pairs that stay to raise families around the Upper Klamath Refuge and along the Williamson and Klamath Rivers are gone by late March or early April.

The eagles congregate here mainly to feast on waterfowl killed or weakened by disease, accidents, hunting or natural causes. Sometimes eagles will take healthy birds, but the abundance of weak and dead birds is much easier and not as energy-intensive as active hunting.

Another feature of the area is the availability of good roosting sites around the basin. The five major roosting sites have four features in common: a close abundant and reliable food supply, freedom from human disturbance, old mature timber with strong branches to support the weight of many eagles with an open pattern to allow for ease of landing and departure, and a location on northeast-facing ridges to protect the roosting eagles from the prevailing chilly west and southwest wind.

Sometimes 300 birds will roost at a particular spot and then, in time, dwindle to just a few. It is important for human visitors not to disturb, in any way, the nighttime roosting spots, so stay away.

Instead, view the eagles on the ice from the self-guided auto tour routes on the Tule and Lower Klamath

Refuges. Viewing is especially good when ice covers most of the water and waterfowl congregate in the open water and eagles, in turn, concentrate around the same areas waiting for an opportunity to eat.

To reach the area from Ashland take Oregon 66 east to Keno, then take the Worden cutoff to US 97, drive south to Stateline Road, turn east through the Lower Klamath Refuge toward Tule Lake. From Medford take Oregon 140 toward Klamath Falls, then turn south on US 97 to the Stateline Road turn-off.

A wording of warning. It is against federal law to possess eagle parts. You have them? You are guilty, unless you have a permit. Leave feathers on the bird or on the ground.

Hawks

There are three common types of hawks: buteos with broad wings and wide, rounded tails; falcons, with sharp, slender wings and long tails; and accipiters with short, round wings and longish tails. Each set-up allows for the lifestyle of each type of hawk.

Buteos tend to soar and wheel in the open sky. Falcons are power flyers. Accipiters flap, then glide, and can terrorize a feeding station. I recall a falcon incident at Tule Lake. Looking out across a field, a ring-necked pheasant suddenly rose from the field's stubble and twice as suddenly the pheasant exploded in a cloud of feathers. The pheasant was prairie falcon prey. The falcon dropped from high above at great speed to smash, talons first, into the pheasant.

Going to be traveling the I-5 corridor during the winter solstice holiday season? The trip is fairly interesting, with varied scenes and landscapes, until Eugene or Albany depending on your destination. Then you reach the Willamette Valley and the longest highway tangent in Oregon. Tangent is engineering talk for straight stretch. Some 34 miles without a bend to left or right and very little up or down. The lovely pastoral scene soon becomes commonplace, and to many, even boring. But not to me.

In late fall and winter the Interstate is lined with hawks. It seems like every other fencepost has a hawk. As near as I can tell they are red-tails, our most common buteo. I hold boredom at bay by counting hawks and wondering what on earth they are doing there. Good hunting? A place to perch? What?

I asked Stewart Janes, Southern Oregon University's ornithologist and hawk expert, if he had any ideas. He did! He and Pete Bloom of the National Audubon Society have actually researched the question of Willamette Valley hawks. Here is what I learned.

They have discovered that immature red-tails differ from adults in flight morphology. Immatures have longer wings of smaller area, a longer tail, lower wing loading, and a higher aspect ratio. Wing loading has to do with the relationship of bird weight to wing area. An aspect ratio is the relationship of wing length to width. All this adds up to flight differences. Immatures are more efficient flyers. They hunt while flying and don't need high perches. Inefficient mature red-tails seldom hunt while flying and just turn lazy circles in the sky to get from one tall perch to another.

The higher the aspect ratio, the lower the perch. Janes and Bloom conclude that all those freeway birds are immature red-tails using median fences as lower perches. This way the immatures occupy a niche mostly out of the way of nearby mature red-tails, who prefer grander, taller perches.

Dr. Janes tells me that most of the immatures in the southern part of the Willamette Valley are migrants from western Canada and eastern Oregon. Willamette Valley immatures move further south. Mature hawks tend to stay as year-round residents.

I had extra hawk excitement on one trip. One bird came within inches of entering my car through the windshield. I also got a glimpse of two, an adult and an immature, squabbling over the remains of a small mammal along the highway shoulder. It looked like the adult was gaining the upper hand.

To stave off I-5 boredom, count hawks, but pay attention to traffic if you are driving, lest you turn into a cloud of feathers, too.

Bushtits

One September day some years ago a friend and I took a trip to Timbered Crater in Modoc County, California to look for the largest known stand of Baker cypress. Although the stand covers some 7,000 acres, my friend and I did not see a single cypress tree. The trip was just an excuse to get out one last time before the school year ended such spontaneity. We planned and executed the trip in less than 24 hours with no time to contact the federal agencies, or anyone who might have been of any help in locating the trees. But the trip was not a total loss. We got in a 20-mile bike ride, got a beautiful view of Mount Shasta from the rim of Timbered Crater, and got a glimpse of a flock of bushtits.

Bushtits always amuse me: first the name, then the birds themselves. What a happy-go-lucky gang they are. At summers end, after the breeding season, these tiny mites of birds flit about in family groups and then larger groups of as many as 70. They stream from bush to bush in a constant search for insects, gleaning bark for food, dangling upside down or sideways. The group of 15 or so we saw was moving through the native plums lisping and whispering to themselves in their light, insistent way.

Bushtits are nondescript, with gray backs, brownish cheeks, pale underparts and longish tails. Eyes of mature females have pale cream-colored irises, which distinguishes them from the dark-eyed males and juveniles.

When winter comes they often associate with kinglets, chickadees, and titmice in jolly flocks that move through conifers looking for a tasty insect morsel or a juicy spider. They eat a lot of bugs. They need to maintain their body temperature in the cold of winter. Groups of bushtits roost and huddle together in tight masses to decrease their surface area to volume ratio and thus save energy by conserving heat loss.

In the spring the flocks break up and mating bushtit pairs begin to build a most fantastic nest; a gourd-shaped hanging nest with an opening at the top. They weave their nest of mosses, lichens, leaves, grass, flowers, cocoons, all held together by spider webs. Bushtits nested in a tree in the yard of my boyhood home in Olympia, Washington. I remember watching the pair constantly move in and out of the nest with beaks full of undigested solid food for their young.

If you find a bushtit nest, do not disturb it. The pair will often desert the nest, change mates, and then spend another 13 to 51 days to build another nest. I can't, at all, remember if the bushtits returned to use the same nest I watched as a child the following year. I was pleased to see the bushtit flock this year and be reminded that fall, my favorite season, is near at hand.

Another bird that amuses me is the wrentit. First the name. It turns out it is neither a wren nor a tit, as chickadees are called in Britain, which isn't what you naughty boys thought. It turns out wrentits belong to an Old World group of birds called babblers. These small brown birds are active, noisy, and seldom seen, being secretive inhabitants of dense brush and chaparral. Get a glimpse and you might see their eyes' white irises. Wrentits don't migrate, in fact they mate for life and stay within their one to 2.5 acre home range. Their song has been described as a bouncing ping-pong ball, and you are far more likely to hear their song (they sing all year, by the way) than you are to see them. One sunny winter day a pair treated me to a lengthy look as they flitted in and around a small group of shrubs adjacent to their normal brush field. It was quite a treat.

Cedar Waxwings

Those masked bandits are back! Not the short, fat, waddley ones, raccoons (they never left) but cedar waxwings, those handsome, black-masked, top-knotted dandies of the air. Although they are permanent Oregon residents, I seldom notice them except in the fall, when they descend in flocks to strip my *Pyracantha* shrubs of fruits in a matter of hours.

Pyracantha, or firethorn, gets its generic and common names from the painful reaction between human flesh and certain substances on the plant's sharp thorns. I put up with my *Pyracantha* because of its colorful display of orange fruits in autumn and the host of birds it attracts. I hate it when I prune it, but I love it in the fall.

The cedar waxwing is distinctive with its velvety black mask, fawn-colored head and crest that fade to olive yellow on the flanks, and yellow on the belly. The dark tail ends in brilliant yellow, and the shorter wing feathers are often tipped with red appendages.

The cedar waxwing's somewhat larger northern cousin, the Bohemian waxwing, rarely appears in southern Oregon. The Bohemian has white spots on its wings, a grey belly, and a chestnut patch at tail's base; otherwise, they are similar to cedar waxwings with crest and mask.

Sometimes birds visiting fruit-laden shrubs and trees get an unusual surprise. As a child, I recall a flock of waxwings descending upon a fruit-laden hawthorn tree in my parents' yard on cold fall day. After gorging themselves on tiny pomes, the hawthorn's small, apple-like fruits, the birds became unstable, acting as if drunk — which of course they were. After frosts, fruits of many members of the rose family — including hawthorne and *Pyracantha* — convert stored starch to sugar. Native yeasts on the fruits then ferment the sugars to alcohol of proof enough to stagger even larger birds like robins, which can fall victim to

the same fate. I remember that the birds sobered up after a considerable period of staggering about. I wonder what might have happened if the neighbor's cat had come across the bacchanal.

Dippers

When I was growing up in western Washington my father took me fishing. A familiar sight, sometimes more familiar than that of fish, was a stocky slate-gray thrush-sized bird flying up and down the stream, occasionally lighting on an emergent rock or boulder. Once alight, the bird bobbed up and down in a most curious fashion. Papa called them teeter-asses, a name I found both descriptive and hilarious. Not till some time later did I learn that, in the polite society of bird watchers, they were called water ouzels or, to be correct today, the American dipper.

Bobbing up and down on rocks was not the only curious thing they did. They would suddenly fly beneath the water, then disappear to emerge downstream with aquatic insect larvae in their bills. They also include small fish and an occasional streamside insect in their diet. Underwater they can fly to depths below 20 feet with powerful wingbeats. This bird looks like a song bird (which it is) and swims, without the benefit of the usual accouterments of waterfowl: no webbed feet, lobed toes or duck-like bill.

That is not to say they don't have adaptions, they do. They have a much larger oil gland than other songbirds, scales that close the nostrils while immersed, a thick, dense plumage that is difficult to wet, and a white third eyelid that flicks across the eye to keep it clean in murky water. They swim by flying through the swift water of their mountain streams or walking along the bottom, gripping with their oversized feet.

A songbird you say? You bet. The dipper's call is a simple, loud "zeet, zeet," single or repeated. Its song is a clear and ringing rendition of trills and flute-like whistles like a mockingbird embellishing upon a wren's song. It sings year round, rain or shine, by day and occasionally at night. Its song will lift your spirits no matter what your mood or no matter what the weather.

Where do teeter . . . ah, dippers nest? They nest on cliff faces among the mosses and ferns, on midstream rocks, or behind water falls. Nestlings are quite precocious and can climb, swim, and dive when they leave the nest.

Most of our mountain streams support populations of American dippers. A good place to look for them is Ashland Creek in the heart of Lithia Park. If you don't see the birds themselves, look for their calling cards, white speckles on rocks emerging from the middle of the stream, their contribution to the nitrogen cycle.

Feeding Stations

Every year in late fall I find myself in a terrible dilemma. Do I get my bird feeder up and running to attract birds for my and the neighborhood cats' entertainment? Or do I let the local wintertime avifauna shift for itself, which, in most winters it can easily do? I hate discovering the piles of feathers that reveal that I am feeding cats when I think I'm feeding birds.

Cat fanciers, don't fool yourselves, domestic cats kill a lot of wildlife. Studies done in England suggest that a third to a half of all sparrow deaths in one small village could be attributed to cats. Extrapolated to all England, all those sweet little tabbies kill an estimated 20 million birds a year. If that is the impact of Britain's five million cats, imagine how many birds die in the United States.

Feeding may help small species and weak birds through the winter. In one experiment, the daily fat deposit of chickadees was raised by about four percent of their body weight when the birds were given sunflower seeds in place of their normal diet of conifer seeds and berries.

But weak birds might be sick birds, and attracting them as well as healthy individuals may promote the spread of disease. Grain and bread may become moldy with *Aspergillus fumigatus,* whose spores can cause a potentially fatal respiratory disease in birds. In fact, that fine mist you see at the penguin house at the zoo is not to keep the penguins cool but to wash *Aspergillus* spores out of the air before the particularly sensitive penguins can inhale them. You might create problems for birds that establish regular foraging patterns, if you don't keep your feeding station regularly stocked. An oversupply of food in some areas might attract undesirable species like starlings and rock doves (a euphemistic name for city pigeons). In the east, there is some evidence that the ranges of some

species have expanded northward and some, such as the mourning dove, no longer migrate.

Although feeding may help small species and weak birds through the winter, feeders mostly entertain the provider. During extremely cold conditions winter residents like juncos and finches may not be able to find enough food during the day to survive the night. Feeders can help. However, there is a downside.

What you feed can cause problems. Beef suet attracts many species, such as woodpeckers, titmice, chickadees, nuthatches, and wrens, to home feeders. In warm weather, softened suet will mat feathers, reduce insulation and waterproofing and cause inflamed or infected follicles and loss of facial feathers. Colored sugar water in feeders designed for nectar-eaters may ferment within a few days while continuing to attract hummingbirds, resulting in enlarged livers and, one could presume, erratic flight, unless hummers don't drink and fly. If you like small seed eaters like pine siskins and lesser gold finches, try thistle sacks. Thistle sacks are small mesh bags that you fill with rather expensive tiny thistle seeds. Hang them high over a tree limb out of reach of those damn cats and birds can feed in relative safety. Birds seemed to be waiting for me to hang the sacks. They were eating within the hour.

So is feeding birds good or bad? Some of both, but to make it more positive than negative do the following: Keep the food fresh, no moldy or fermented nectar; don't overdo it by attracting enormous numbers of birds; keep the feeder supplied over the winter; stop using suet when the weather warms up (please, no bare-faced hairy woodpeckers); and place the feeder where the birds will be safe from cats. I must remember I am feeding birds for their benefit and not my own, or the local cat's. My choices are limited. Don't feed the birds? Bell the cats, which does not work? Move the feeder? I like my feeder where it is. Damn cats!

Jays

There are four different jay species in our area: scrub jays, Steller's jays, gray jays, and pinion jays in eastern Oregon. None of them are true blue jays. You have to go back east or to Toronto to find them. Jays are bright, clever, fearless. They are, except the gray jay, loud, raucous, and brazen. Both scrub jays and Steller's jays nest in my neighborhood.

In southwest Oregon and northern California, scrub jays inhabit lower elevations. Robin-sized, the scrub jay has a blue head, wing, rump, and tail, a whitish throat and eyebrows, and grayish back and belly. They lack the crest of blue of the Steller's jay. They are residents from southwest Washington through the Willamette Valley then east to Wyoming and Colorado and south to southern Mexico. There are also populations in central Texas and southern Florida. The Florida subspecies has a whitish forehead.

Several years ago I was a botanist on an Alaskan cruise ship, the SS *Universe*. We were sailing north in the Gulf of Alaska just offshore from the Fairview Range. There are no words or photographs to describe the beauty . . . lofty peaks, bathed in pinkish mist rising from a cobalt sea. The only things that compare in my experience are the magnificent oil paintings of Sidney Laurence, dean of Alaskan artists. Early evening the next day I sighted Kayak Island, the only North American landfall of Georg Wilhelm Steller. It was here that Steller found the dark-blue jay that bears his name, a jay that was his clue that he was in North America and not Siberia.

The Steller's jay is deep blue with a blackish head and jaunty crest. It prefers slightly higher elevations and coniferous woodlands in our area. Steller's jay is resident from Alaska south through the western United States to Nicaragua. Steller's jay is the one who lets everyone know

when you are sneaking about in the woods, by greeting you with raucous, derisive laughter. One call has fooled me often. Steller's jays can mimic the call of the red-tailed hawk.

When you stop for lunch at higher elevations in our area, you suddenly discover you are not alone. Gray shadows appear and materialize into the jay some call the whiskey jack, others the camp robber. Gray jays are the quiet members of the group and probably the most fearless, or perhaps the most foolish, trusting humans as they seem to do. They will take advantage of you, helping themselves to nearby or even hand-held edibles. They are gentle companions, with which I don't mind sharing.

The pinon jay is blue all over and inhabits the pinyon pine-juniper woodlands of the intermountain west. They are a gregarious lot, found in breeding colonies of up to 150 birds. According to *The Birder's Handbook,* they fly in flocks that move in a wheeling mass with rear birds constantly replacing the ones in front. Everyone, it seems, has a turn.

Jays have a habit of stashing seeds, large numbers of seeds, far more seeds than they can find, to the benefit of those plants whose seeds are lost. The seeds germinate and grow up to the benefit again of both plant and jay.

One summer at my sister's Sierra cabin I learned how Steller Jays stash goodies and how they might remember where they stashed them. On the flat deck rail my sister laid out a pile of cracked wheat. Steller's jays showed up to stuff their gular pouches with as much grain as they could and then flew off to stash. While I was waiting to stuff my gular pouch with lunch, a jay flew down and landed on the duff in front of me. Bird then proceeded to stash its cracked wheat. It regurgitated 15 or 20 pieces, pecked a hole in the duff, then placed the wheat in the hole and covered up the stash. Then to my amazement the jay picked up a distinctive looking piece of bark or twig and placed it directly on the stash. Bird repeated this at least ten times. Placement of the unusual piece must be the way they recognize their stash. Clever I'd say.

Phalarope

Phalarope *n*: any of various small shorebirds that resemble sandpipers but have lobed toes and are good swimmers.

Dr. Ron Nitsos and I visited Chemult, Oregon. We went to examine the carcass of the ancient tree buried almost instantly by Mount Mazama's mighty fit some 7,700 years ago. Homeward-bound we stopped at Mare's Egg Spring nestled next to the highway northwest of Klamath Lake. Unusually large colonies of a common blue-green alga give the spring its name.

What a sad sight greeted us. Instead of the tree and shrub concealed spring I recalled from earlier visits, we encountered openness — larger trees dead or dying, shrubs gone from the edge, and the water level as low as I have ever seen it. From old downed trees that criss-cross the spring's bottom one could surmise that it is all part of a never-ending cycle of growth, death, and replacement. However, low water could be due to drought or to excessive removal, drainage or whatever for agricultural purposes. A cynic would suspect the latter.

There was a bright spot, three in fact. A *menage a trois* of Wilson's phalaropes, a female and two males busy with that activity that gives *menage a trois* its meaning. Phalaropes are interesting birds who conduct their lives in extraordinary ways. They take polyandry to extremes.

As just mentioned, phalaropes are shorebirds that swim. I have seen them spinning round and round like tops as they dabbled for small aquatic arthropods, insects, crustaceans, and the like. They can turn almost 60 times per minute and still get in 60 dabs. Some think the spinning stirs up the water to make small, potentially edible objects more noticeable. Phalaropes are hatched knowing how to spin untutored. Innate behavior, some say.

Their sex and social lives make phalaropes ideal totems for the more ardent feminists among us. Phalaropes practice sex role reversal and, occasionally, sequential polyandry. The female is the larger and more brightly colored of the sexes, a situation atypical of many bird species. Sequential polyandry, disputed by some ornithologists for Wilson's phalarope, occurs when the female mates with one male, lays her eggs in his nest, then leaves incubation and rearing the young to him. The female then moves on, in sequence, to meet and mate a second male with the same result. Even if sequential polyandry is not true, the female clearly plays no role in caring for the young. The female leaves the nesting area long before the eggs hatch and avoids the rigors of raising nestlings.

The real possibility of phalarope polyandry in humans seems remote. Although human females can mate with more than one male, there is but one nest, the womb, and only females can do that job.

Robins

"Sing a Song of Six Pence, Pocket Full of Rye, Four and Twenty Blackbirds, Baked in a Pie."

I took my first visit to Great Britain several years ago to chase the ghosts of David Douglas and John Jeffrey. I was amazed (I am easily amazed, you know) to discover that the blackbirds of that Mother Goose poem are pretty much like our American robin, except the males are a handsome black with a yellow eye ring and bill. They seemed to act the same.

I knew about the European robin, not a thrush at all, nestled in British checklists between nightingales and bushchats. Seeing one of these bold little birds an arm's length away in the bushes at Kew Gardens was a thrill.

Ever notice how our robins hunt for earthworms? They hop across the lawn, stop, cock their heads to one side, as if listening intently to wormy sounds, trying to locate their prey. Silly us, when we cock our heads to listen, our eyes stare straight ahead. Robin's eyes aren't oriented like ours. When they cock their heads, they stare straight down. We humans naturally assume robins are listeners. Wrong again. Experiments show that robins find their earthworm prey by sight, not sound.

Robins are migratory birds. The robins who nest in our area move farther south in winter and are replaced by robins from farther north. We see two subspecies, the darker northwestern robin from Alaska and Canada, and the lighter-breasted western robin. The robins' sexual dimorphism complicates distinguishing the subspecies. Male robins are darker than females of the same subspecies.

Birds my mother called Alaska robins, I now know as varied thrushes. They resemble their close relative, the orange-breasted robin, in size and shape and habits. Varied thrushes are striped, orange above the eye and

black across the breast. These birds are sleeker, shier and prefer coniferous forests to lawns. They sometimes visit feeding stations in winter when they come down from high mountains. At my childhood home I remember them eating apples on the snowy ground under the big apple tree across the driveway from the living room window.

The famous old-time naturalist and author John Burroughs wrote the following verse when he saw the varied thrush for the first time.

O Varied Thrush! O Robin Strange!
Behold my mute surprise.
Thy form and flight I long have known,
But not in this new disguise.

But, back to robins. My same childhood home had two huge mountain ash trees overhanging the street on either side of the walk to our front door. The trees always seemed to bear an enormous load of fruits in the fall. The trees were orange, the same color as a robin's breast. The same color any automobile became whose unwary driver was foolish enough to park under the tree when robins descended to feast on mountain ash berries. I swear the combination of acid berries and digestive juices caused the automobile's paint to pit.

That reminds me of more poetry, this time Mother Goose. Mother Goose wasn't always the sanitized pablum of today. If you are easily offended, I suggest you stop reading now.

Little Robin red breast,
Sitting on a pole,
Niddle, Noddle,
Went his head,
And poop went his hole.

Sorry folks, but that's the way it is in the real world!

Songbirds

When I taught a Conservation of Natural Resources course, I asked my students if they could connect the disappearance of North American songbirds with North American fast food establishments. We would conclude that converting South American tropical rain forests to pastures for cattle destined to become hamburgers sold in our fast-food emporiums was the connection. Loss of tropical rain forests meant loss of winter habitat that adversely impacts migratory songbird populations. It was so convenient. They, the South American ranchers, were sooo bad, and we were somewhat less guilty by eating tons of hamburger.

Guess what? It isn't that simple. We North Americans may be just as guilty, or more so, than the South American rancher. The decline in songbird numbers is well documented in North America. The United States Fish and Wildlife Service sponsors the annual North American Breeding Bird Survey on every June 18. Since 1966, birders have noted bird species and numbers along designated routes. In the past 25 years many species dropped in numbers. An example is the olive-sided flycatcher, a big fellow, widely distributed in coniferous forests and bogs in the western United States and Canada. It migrates from northern South America. I like this bird. From the top of tall trees and snags he waits for insect prey, calling loudly, "Hey, good cheer" or "Hey, free beer," depending on your mood and inclination. Its numbers have declined some 48% in the last 25 years, 22% since 1980. Many other species are in trouble as well.

The problem at this end seems to be due to a number of factors relating to habitat fragmentation, increase in numbers of cowbirds, and increased access to remaining habitat by various predators. Millions of acres of former habitat have been broken up by logging, farming, and development. Smaller patches of habitat create many more miles of edge around them than one would find in a large, continuous patch. Edges mean intermediate complex habitat that give predators access to songbirds and their nests.

Cowbirds, worse than some people's relatives by marriage, are nest parasites. They lay their eggs in other birdies' nests. Some species toss out the deviant egg, or build another nest atop, *ad infinitum.* Other species feed the cowbird chick at the expense of their own nestlings. As cowbird numbers rise, neotropical songbird numbers plummet. Other predators, from snakes and raccoons to the neighbor's %*$#@^! cat, make further inroads. It's not a pretty sight.

Neither are the once vast temperate coniferous rain forests of the Pacific northwest. When flying north to Vancouver, British Columbia, and back again not long ago, I was once again stricken by the sight of the patchwork quilt below. Clear-cut after clear-cut passed by mile after mile. Some had young trees, more seemed to have the reddish brown aspect of exposed bare soil below the shrubs. I know that those forests provided jobs for many and wood fiber for my home. For that I am grateful. But I also know that those vast forests will never ever be the same and that I may never hear the all excited flycatcher's welcome call again. For that I am sad.

The fragmented forest may no longer be home for flying squirrels, red-backed voles, olive-sided flycatchers and the like, but the haunts of less desirable species like boobs, ninnies, yahoos, and addlebrained nincompoops who think only of themselves, and think that environmentalists are worse than communists. We are not the richer for that.

Spotted Owl

The spotted owl is a resident of dense coniferous and mixed evergreen forests of the western United States and northern Mexico. Ornithologists recognize three subspecies; the northern spotted owl, the California spotted owl, and the Mexican spotted owl. They have different ranges, different habits, different lives.

The spotted owl is darkish, raven-sized, dark-eyed, and without the ear- or horn-like feathers of many other owls. Other large, dark-eyed owls include its close cousin the barred owl of the east — which, by the way, is rapidly expanding its range in the northwest — and the barn owl, with its white, heart-shaped face.

Our spotted owl is the northern spotted owl. We have learned a lot about it since we realized that the owl has a definite liking for old-growth coniferous forests. Much of what we know is based on birds whose movements have been tracked by radiotelemetry. The owls are easily captured and miniature radio transmitters attached. When released, their movements can be monitored by radio receivers.

They are monogamous, mostly nocturnal, long lived and mate for life. Their home range varies from 1,800 to 9,000 acres and contains from 1,200 to 2,500 acres of old-growth. They feed, nest and roost in old-growth or old-growth trees associated with younger forests. They feed mostly on flying squirrels, woodrats, and red tree voles, nocturnal, tree-dwelling mammals whose optimum habitat is old growth.

At the present time infant mortality among northern spotted owls is worse than infant mortality among humans in the United States. When the owls nest, an event that has been decreasing recently, not many of the owlets and subadults survive beyond their second year. They succumb to starvation and the great horned owl. Reports of spotted owls in second growth are cause for cheer *only* when reproduction and survival to adulthood can be demonstrated.

They don't use open areas like clearcuts and reservoirs. There is little evidence that they can change their ways to utilize younger manmade forests. The northern spotted owl is as much a part of the old growth ecosystem as the trees themselves. When the old growth trees are gone, in all probability so will be the northern spotted owl. And it will be too bad, too bad for the owls, too bad for all of us. We must find a way for the northern spotted owl and, as former US Representative Bob Smith put it, the freckle-faced logger, to live in peace and harmony. It won't be easy. Such unhappy circumstances remind me of a quote by the biologist Victor Scheffer from his book *The Year of the Whale:*

> If you believe that human life has meaning or purpose or direction or destiny, you will know in your heart that our life is bound all around and together and forever with the lives of the animals who were present at our creation. If we survive, we will care for the whales and other wild creatures, and if we perish through our own cleverness the end of the wild things will have been an early warning of our folly.

Of what value is the spotted owl? Its presence is a clear indication of a healthy functioning, old-growth coniferous forest ecosystem.

Stilts

A few years ago, I took a group of outstanding middle school science teachers on a field trip to the Lower Klamath and Tule Lake Wildlife Refuges in northern California. The teachers were attending a three week workshop at Southern Oregon University devoted to excellence in middle school science.

As always we saw great sights. A pronghorn antelope with prongs as thick as your wrist, bald eagles on the ground, pelicans with bills that hold more than their bellies can, white egrets, ducks of all sorts with many moms followed by flotillas of fuzzy ducklings churning along behind, and two of my favorites, avocets and black-necked stilts.

Avocets and black-necked stilts are distinctive. Some shorebird species, like sandpipers, are difficult to tell apart, but not avocets and black-necked stilts.

Both species are crow-sized and both have long necks and long, spindly legs. Adult avocets have broad white stripes on black back and wings, buff or rufus head and neck, long, powder-blue legs at one end and a long, slender, recurved beak at the other. Black-necked stilts have solid blackish back, wings and head with white eyebrows, cheeks, and belly. Legs are pink-red and the beak straight.

Both species seem to occupy the same shallow alkaline pond habitat along Stateline Road on the Lower Klamath Refuge. They do not, however, occupy the same niche. The habitat is the birds' address. Its niche is its job. My habitat is Southern Oregon University, my niche is teaching. What determines avocet and black-necked stilt niches is what and how they eat.

Avocets get aquatic crustaceans, insects, seeds and vegetation by sweeping their long, curved bills back and forth beneath the water. They frequently are followed by Wilson's phalaropes eating left-overs from avocets' sloppy

feeding habits. Phalaropes are swimming shorebirds and are discussed in more detail on page 167.

Black-necked stilts move stealthily along picking off their prey, aquatic arthropods, worms, mollusks, and fishes, from water's surface or to six inches deep or more. In this way stilts and avocets divide up food resources occupying similar habitats but different niches.

Some stilts we saw had chicks and raised a terrible ruckus when we stopped to stand beside our vehicles along the road. They use all kinds of ruses to distract predators. They fly and flap around. They try false incubation. They feign injury with pathetic dragging of leg and wing, always just out of harm's way and always away from the chick.

The stilts were not incubating eggs. In hot climates stilts cool off eggs, chicks and themselves by "belly-soaking." They soak up water in their belly feathers, sometimes making over 100 trips a day to keep things cool and humid.

June is the nesting season at Lower Klamath and Tulelake Refuges. Drive south of Klamath Falls on US 97, then turn east on Stateline Road. When you stop, pull off the road and get out with care, least you become mashed by a potato truck. They are big and they are fast. Be careful.

Turkey

The Americas provided the world its largest domesticated gallinaceous bird, a bird that we eat and eat and eat during winter solstice celebrations. Gallinaceous birds belong to an order that includes quail, grouse, sagehens, pheasants, guinea hens, peafowl, as in peacocks, chickens, and the bird that we first eat roasted and then consume as endless sandwiches, soups, and hashes, the domestic turkey.

Our domesticated birds came to us in a round-about way. Europeans first encountered turkeys in Central America and Mexico in the 1500s as large tasty birds kept by local natives. Columbus might have seen the birds on one of his later voyages west. Old dried carcasses found in the southwestern United States had crops full of maize and beans, evidence that local people kept the birds. Turkeys, taken back to Spain, bred readily in captivity. They went hence to France and thence to England, and then, full circle, back to North America with human emigrants from Europe. Domestication has turned the turkey into the true bimbos of the bird world — big breasted and not too bright.

This is not true of their wild relatives. Alert to the point of supernatural, the wily wild turkey seems to detect the slightest motion and then slip silently, invisibly away. The modern wild birds defy domestication. Peterson describes our wild turkeys as a streamlined version of the barnyard turkey.

One striking phenomenon is the turkey's ability to change the colors of its naked head and neck from blue and red to purple, violet and beyond. Depending on the turkey's state of mind, the passage of blood through a subepidermal network of arteries causes the color change.

In the male, that state of mind usually has to do with reproduction. The toms puff up and gobble and strut about with tail feathers erect and fan-like, quills a-rattling, head ornaments tumescent, sights and sounds that hens find irresistible. The turkey is sociable, with flocks of ten to 40 birds feeding together. Turkeys eat mast, that is acorns that have accumulated on the forest floor, in abundance. Their powerful gizzards, that can reduce glass beads to powder in a moment, make quick work of acorns.

Wild turkeys originally ranged from New England south through Florida and Central America west to parts of Arizona and New Mexico, north to South Dakota. Only recently have turkeys been introduced to new areas in the west and elsewhere as a game bird, including parts of southwest Oregon.

Contrary to popular belief, our custom of consuming turkeys at Thanksgiving was not common until the beginning of the 19th century. The noble, resourceful wild turkey lost by one congressional vote of being selected as our national symbol. To call another person turkey is not a compliment, unless, of course, you have the wild and not the domesticated bird in mind.

Turkey Vulture Arrival

Ashland is a place like no other. I was standing in the grocery line wondering what I would do for the next batch of *Nature Notes* when I overheard a conversation that saved the day. A woman in line in front of me told her companion that she had seen a turkey vulture that day, February 21, on the way back from the coast. She was delighted and explained how it was time to celebrate the coming of spring and the arrival of our turkey vultures with a party, featuring at the very least, buzzard's brew and squash pie. What a concept.

We will soon be treated to one of the area's great ornithological events. The most common birds of prey in the state, the turkey vultures, will be returning from their winter vacations in southern California and Mexico. They arrive in numbers, over Siskiyou Summit, down Bear Creek and past Ashland on their way north. Dozens of them, in small flocks or as individuals, soar past. Many will stay in the area to breed and nest, others will continue on.

We distinguish vultures from other raptors (a fancy name for birds of prey derived from the Latin word for plunderer) by the nature of their soaring flight. They hold their wings in a shallow V and teeter slightly like they are trying to keep their balance on a tightrope. As they wheel and turn on rising warm air thermals, they seldom beat their wings and occasionally you can see flashes of the lighter undersurface of their wings.

They nest in what can best be described as dark recesses, caves, old stumps, and hollow logs. Eggs are laid from May to July or later, depending on latitude or local circumstances.

These birds have interesting adaptations that fit their ecologically important, but to our mind, ghoulish, occupation. They are carrion eaters, eaters of dead animals which they find by sight and an incredible sense of smell.

For many years there was great debate over sight or smell. One hint was obtained by an ornithologist who struck up a conversation with some natural gas pipeline workers who told him that they located gas leaks by looking for groups of turkey vultures in the air above the pipe-line. Turkey vultures will fly for miles, seeming to appear from nowhere, to feast at the carcass of some dead animal. Often our closest views are of these large black birds flapping clumsily away from road kills as we come around a curve to see the grisly scene. Their featherless red heads and necks allow them to root around in juicy body cavities and entrails searching for choice morsels without having to worry about dealing with gunky feathers. Their bare heads and necks expose bacteria to the killing ultraviolet rays of sunlight.

Bacteria are killed by their digestive tracts and some think their excrement may be antiseptic. They don't squirt clear like eagles, but whitewash their own legs, maybe to sanitize them, but more likely, to keep them cool. There is evidence that vultures thermoregulate; that is, adjust their temperatures when overheated, by the evaporative cooling power of drying whitewash.

Most think the turkey vulture is ugly as sin at its worst, or merely homely at its best, but turning lazy circles in the sky, the vulture is a thing of beauty. You can view turkey vultures at eye level from the summit of Upper or Lower Table Rocks, north of Medford, as the birds cruise along just off the rim.

In addition to listening in on other people's grocery line conversations, I also listen as closely as I can to other people's cell phone conversations. I can be as rude as they are. Unfortunately, I have yet to hear a single thing of interest.

Turkey Vulture Departure

Some time in September turkey vultures migrate south to spend the winter months in sunny California and northern Mexico. The first broadcast of *Nature Notes* in March of 1989 described the return of the turkey vultures to the Rogue Valley. Their flight south is even more spectacular than their return. They seem to leave the area all at once.

One day in September, we will see turkey vultures headed up the Bear Creek Valley from Medford and points north in large numbers. Two or three hundred vultures may pass by in the course of an hour or so. A spectacular sight by any measure. They soar along, then rise up in a tight circle when they catch a thermal of warm air rising from the ground. After gaining elevation, they sweep along again, perhaps with a rare wingbeat or two (they are such terrific gliders that they seldom need to flap) until they reach another thermal and up they go again until they can make it over Siskiyou Pass and slip into California without stopping at the Agricultural Inspection Station. They are carrion eaters, consumers of dead animals, so I don't suppose the inspectors really care.

According to *The Birder's Handbook*, their short, broad wings and low ratio of bird weight to wing area allow high maneuverability at slow speeds. The short, broad wings also create a lot of drag, a problem that vultures partly solve by flying with their primary feathers extended. Each feather acts like a longer, narrower wing that lowers the stalling speed so the birds can stay aloft at lower speeds.

The different rates at which turkey vultures and black vultures sink in flight play a role in their geographical distribution. Soaring turkey vultures drop about two feet per second. They stay aloft by finding hot-air thermals rising at a greater rate. Black vultures, whose sink rate is 2.6 feet per second, are restricted to the hotter south where stronger thermals prevail. Turkey vultures range as far north as southern Canada, as far as thermals will support them.

Turkey vultures can live on a carnivorous diet without drinking water. In one study, a captive bird was kept for a year without water. They have a nasal gland that excretes excessive electrolytes, especially sodium, a drop at a time.

In the evening, turkey vultures roost in groups in tall trees or, in some cases, man-made structures, such as the observation tower at the Malheur Wildlife Refuge near Frenchglen in eastern Oregon. In the morning, they linger at the roost after sunrise warming themselves and waiting for the ground to heat and thermals to develop so they can soar about with ease. In the evening and early morning, how many of you have noticed local turkey vultures congregated in the tall cottonwoods near Bear Creek along Interstate 5 between Ashland and Medford, Oregon? It is a local roost.

Close examination of the roosting trees reveals a coat of whitewash on the leaves and branches. This makes one wonder who gets the upper branches and to what low act a vulture, a consumer of carrion, must stoop to have to take a bottom branch. On the other hand, the fight might be over who gets the bottom and not the top. Evidence indicates that vulture whitewash has antiseptic qualities. A nightly shower might offer some advantage to one who sticks his or her head in dark, offal-filled cavities on a regular basis.

Try not to think of this in next few weeks as you search the skies for kettles of departing turkey vultures. Their departure is a sight worth waiting for.

Whoopers

One Saturday I visited the Lower Klamath/Tule Lake Wildlife Refuges. It's always a treat. The weather forecast for the day was ominous. I was prepared. Warm clothes, raingear, all were quickly abandoned in the spring-like weather we encountered. Bright sunshine and gentle breezes were the order of the day.

We drove from Ashland to the town of Keno, then past the notorious bio-medical waste incinerator to Worden. We traveled the Township Road just north of the Oregon/California border. There were lots of raptors — birds of prey — everywhere. Both color phases of the rough-legged hawk, red-tailed hawks, kestrels (known to some of you as sparrow hawks), harriers or marsh hawks, and prairie falcons rested on telephone poles, sat in fields, or swooped along, looking for a meal.

Later, at the Tule Lake Wildlife Refuge, we saw an incredibly fearless bald eagle. The bird sat on a telephone pole while we got out of our vehicle and walked right up to it. The bird monitored our progress, and barely ruffled its feathers when we were directly underneath. Fortunately, that's all it did.

The owl cliff had its owls, great horned and barn. They watched us with little interest from their cavities and cavelets high up on the whitewashed cliff face. Later, in the spring and summer, when the shore-side willows are in leaf, great horned owls roost, concealed in the branches, during day time.

This Saturday, we were in for a special birding treat. There was, to use Anne Tyler's words, an accidental tourist at the Lower Klamath Refuge. A whooper swan, a single bird, had appeared a week or so earlier, all the way from Asia. Whooper swans breed across northern Europe and Asia from Iceland to northeastern Siberia and winter in the coastal lowlands of Europe and eastern Asia.

Vagrant birds have been reported in Alaska, where they might have nested, and in New England and California. We saw our whooper at brackish White Lake in the company of several smaller tundra swans.

I have to say I was pleased to be with Mike Uhtoff, owner of the Northwest Nature Shop in Ashland, and Dr. Stewart Janes, both excellent birders. My view, though thrilling, really thrilling, was not very convincing. The small image, in the middle of the spotting scope's wavering, heat-waved field of view, was larger than the nearby tundra swans and the yellow patch on the bill was clearly visible. Enough, Mike and Stu told me, to make it a whooper and not some other swan. Besides, Mike had a much closer, clearer, view the previous Thursday. Birders are a close-knit community with an active rare-bird hotline. Birders from all over have descended on the refuge to add yet another bird to their life list of birds seen.

What about our accidental tourist? We don't know its sex, and spring is just around the corner. I think it will fly north with its distant cousins, the tundra swans. Perhaps it will drop out along the way to become involved with its close relative the trumpeter swan. Perhaps it will find its way back to Asia, from where it undoubtedly came. I wish it well.

I was saddened to learn that Keno's Mia and Pia's Pizza Parlor was no longer in business. We had to find something else to keep us alert on the way home other than the constant reminder of a pizza feeding frenzy.

Hairy Woodpeckers

The other day at breakfast I heard, "peek," "peek," "peek-peek", outside in the birch trees. With that encouragement I peeked as well, out the window. Much to my pleasure, there was a hairy woodpecker very carefully inspecting my neighborhood cat feeder. The feeder was intended for birds and it worked. It worked so well that all the $%^&#@ cats in the neighborhood showed up. After finding piles of junco and jay feathers I decided that birds would be much better off without my seed supplement and cats would have to put up with canned fare.

The hairy woodpecker was a male, black and white with a red patch on the nape of his neck. He peeked, peeked, peeked around, until he noticed me peeking at him, when he flew across the street to the neighbors, the ones with a ferret, not cats. The ferret, we were told, fluffed up like a bottle-brush just before the rock and roll of the 1993 Klamath Falls earthquake, also felt in Ashland.

The sight of the hairy woodpecker got me thinking about the marvelous adaptations for their way of life. Hairy woodpeckers eat woodboring insects. They get this part of their diet by pounding holes through bark and wood with their beaks. Just how they locate their insect prey is not completely understood. They start out with light tapping which might cause grubs to move, which woodpeckers then hear. Hollow, insect-bored wood might sound different from solid wood, similar to carpenters tapping walls for studs. They may smell the insects. All senses may be used.

Once located, then it is bang, bang, bang. Next, the woodpecker's incredibly long tongue comes into play. The tongue's base is near the nostrils and curves up and around the forehead, above the eyes, around behind, then into the mouth. A complicated system of long, slender tongue bones and muscles causes the barb-tipped, sticky tongue to extend out into the hole and impale the unfortunate grub.

You would think, with all that pounding, woodpeckers would suffer from detached retinas, ringing ears, and headaches. But no, their beak attachment and thickened skull protect the eyes, ears and brain from impact.

In wintertime they eat acorns and hazelnuts, and there is some evidence they may cache insects. From 75 to 90 percent of their diet is insects, augmented with sap from sapsucker holes.

Adults pair up in winter. The pair pounds away in unison — duet drumming it is called. The female taps at nest sites and courts the male with what must be a very sexy quivering, fluttering flight. The male selects the nest site, often in live trees. Both work to excavate a nest lavishly lined with wood chips, a task that averages 20 days. Both incubate the eggs, female during daytime, male at night. Parents continue to look after young for several weeks beyond fledging.

Like many of our birds, hairy woodpecker numbers are declining, perhaps because nest sites are often usurped by English sparrows and starlings, two non-native European imports.

Let's hope "peek, peek, peek" doesn't become a thing of the past.

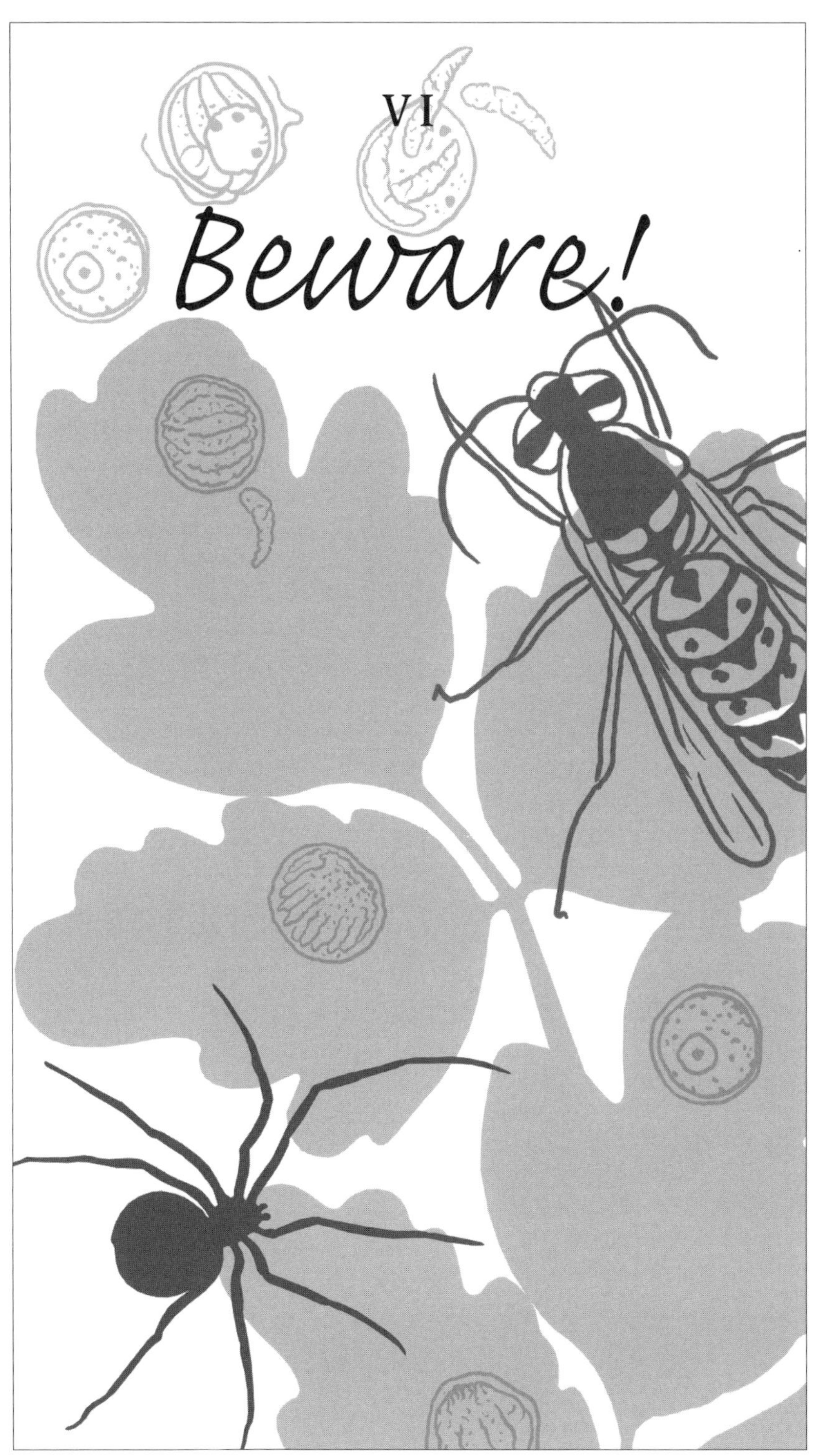

VI

Beware!

Cryptosporidiosis

As if Giardia were not enough, there is a new water-borne disease to watch out for, Cryptosporidiosis. It was first recognized as a cause of diarrhea in humans in 1976, although it has been recognized in animals much longer. It is thought by some to be the most overlooked cause of severe gastroenteritis in humans. We can get it from untreated surface water (watch out hikers and swimmers), in day care centers, (watch out diapered tots and handlers), and, maybe, from pets less than six months old (puppy's or kitty's revenge).

Symptoms include diarrhea, flatulence, abdominal pain, nausea, and in fewer cases, fever, vomiting, and bloating. In one study, symptoms lasted from five to 60 days with a median of 21 days. There is no effective therapy known; it is no fun at all. People whose immune systems have been ravaged by AIDS or leukemia are at serious risk from life-threatening dehydration. Children and babies can also become very ill.

The microorganism lives in the lower intestinal tract of mammals, especially calves and lambs, and a number of other animals including mice, snakes, rabbits, deer and young humans. It is passed from host to host by direct contact with bodily waste or contaminated water supplies. After ingestion, *Cryptosporidium* spores, called oocysts, become attached to the wall of the small intestine where they reproduce, causing the diarrhea. Excreted oocysts can remain viable for up to 18 months.

Because it is carried by domestic stock, there is a risk that Cryptosporidiosis could become yet another contaminate of wildland water supplies where open grazing is allowed. It should be emphasized, however, that only recently has drinking surface water been implicated in the transmission of the disease in humans, and more research is clearly called for.

Sampling surface water is difficult. A sample of at least 1,000 liters must be taken and then the oocysts concentrated by centrifugation. Diagnosis of infected individuals is a relatively simple laboratory procedure.

For those of us who hike and camp, Cryptosporidiosis requires that we use a filtration device or boil our drinking water for 30 minutes. This miserable organism is resistant to most commonly-used disinfectants such as chlorine and iodine. Needless to say, the relatively recent discovery of this parasite in water supplies has been a cause of concern among public health officials.

So if you end up with diarrhea after a trip in the woods and you came in contact with surface water, treated or not, your physician has yet another possibility to consider along with Giardia and all the rest. Cryptosporidiosis. Ugh.

Cryptosporidiosis showed up in Medford water in 1990. Hasn't been seen since. Poor Medford, and poor Ashland, if it gets established in the watershed. Don't worry about it though, it was just Ecological Catastrophe, the fifth Horseman of the Apocalypse's horse pooping in our drinking water. And that tap, tap, tapping? Just one more nail in our ecological coffin.

Domoic Acid

Late fall of 1987 a group of people on Prince Edward Island in eastern Canada became ill after eating seashore mussels. Within 24 hours vomiting, diarrhea, and abdominal cramps appeared. Half complained of devastating headaches. In a quarter of them more serious nervous system problems arose: confusion, disorientation, memory loss and muscular weakness. Nine of them needed tubes inserted in their airways to protect them from drowning in their own copious secretions. Three died. Some survivors developed a chronic memory problem. Five years later several were still without short-term memories.

These unfortunates were victims of ASP, amnesic shellfish poisoning. The cause? High levels of domoic acid, a compound that more than mimics a naturally-occurring neurotransmitter. Domoic acid is 30 to 100 times more potent. Where did the domoic acid come from? The tissues of the mussels they ate. The acid accumulates by a phenomenon known as biological magnification from a marine diatom known as *Nitzchia pungens.* These algae and others like them are the phytoplankton that are the basis of marine food chains. They undergo photosynthesis to provide energy for themselves. When eaten by many of the sea's filter feeders —mussels, barnacles, clams, oysters, and some fish like anchovies and sardines — they provide energy for them as well. Filter-feeders must consume millions of these microscopic creatures. Besides energy, they sometimes accumulate other substances as well, in concentrations far greater than in the individual phytoplankton's cells. Domoic acid doesn't seem to harm the filter feeders. It does seem to harm those that feed on filter feeders.

In the fall of 1991 brown pelicans, feeding on anchovies off the California coast, perished from domoic acid poisoning. November 15, 1991, the Oregon Health

Division closed the Oregon coast to commercial and recreational shellfishing. Why? Razor clams from ocean beaches in Clatsop County and Long Beach, Washington had potentially toxic levels of domoic acid with illness associated with Long Beach clams. A May 1992 CD Summary from the Oregon Health Division: high domoic acid levels still present in northwest razor clams. An October 1992 Summary: domoic acid levels down but paralytic shellfish poisoning up. Bummer. Bad news for clam diggers.

We have known about paralytic shellfish poisoning or PSP for some time. Eating filter-feeding shellfish, clams, mussels, and the like that have concentrated saxitoxin from another phytoplankton known by the grand name of *Alexandrium catenella* causes PSP in humans. Some of you might recognize it by its old name, *Gonyaulax*. Saxitoxin, like domoic acid, affects the nervous system. It upsets the normal transmission of nerve impulses. First symptoms are tingling sensations around the mouth, lips, face, hands and feet. Then nausea, vomiting or diarrhea. Then weakness, lack of muscular coordination, paralysis. Less than ten percent die, usually of respiratory failure, within 12 hours. If you survive, recovery is complete.

Like domoic acid, saxitoxin is not destroyed by cooking. Like domoic acid there is no antidote. Perhaps that is why health departments on the Pacific coast test for shellfish poisoning. Perhaps that is why clam diggers should heed their warnings. Perhaps domoic acid should be renamed demonic acid.

Food Poisoning

With few exceptions, the foods we eat are contaminated with microbes of one kind or another. We keep them under control by eating the food before the microbes do. We refrigerate the food to retard the microbes' growth. We kill'em and can'em in sterilized containers. We put our food in water so salty or acid that nothing can live.

There are two different groups of microbes, those that poison our food and those that spoil it. Food poisoners like temperatures between 60–90°F. Food spoilers do just fine at cooler temperatures. Food spoilers change taste, smell, appearance. If you eat spoiled food, you are either really, really hungry or really, really, unaware. Food poisoners don't change taste, smell or appearance. They just make it toxic. If you eat poisoned food you can get very sick. There has been a lot of food poisoning in the news lately.

Our good and useful friend and constant colon companion, *Escherichia coli,* makes life good for us by converting the nutrients in our digestive tracts that we do not absorb to vitamins we do absorb. We are so familiar with *Escherichia coli* that it has a nickname, *E. coli.* There is, however, a black sheep in our good friend's closet and that is *E. coli* 0157.

0157 inhabits the digestive tracts of cattle and can be found in cow flops. Because of the way cattle are slaughtered, fecal (or flop if fecal is too strong for your delicate ears) contamination of meat is far too common. Contamination is limited to the outside of chunks of meat like steaks or roasts. Grind up contaminated chunks to make hamburger and you mix bacteria throughout. Cooking a rare steak will kill the surface bacteria and you can eat the steak with little risk of food poisoning. Eat a contaminated hamburger patty cooked rare and you have real trouble — hemorrhagic colitis, better known as bloody diarrhea.

There was the recent outbreak in Washington State, Idaho, Nevada and southern California affecting hundreds of people. In 1982 an outbreak occurred in Jackson County, Oregon and in Michigan. Both episodes involved fast-food restaurant burgers. You can also pick up 0157 from raw milk, apple cider and contaminated drinking water. The bacteria can move through child-care centers, nursing homes and other institutions by hand-to-mouth contamination. The incidence of infection in Oregon rises every summer, perhaps correlating with hamburgers slowly warming by the grill, as juicy little incubators for 0157.

The test for *E. coli* is fairly simple and straightforward. It is regularly done to check water supplies for fecal contamination. Special media must be used to test for 0157. Is it worth it to test slaughter houses for 0157? When you consider how much meat is eaten without contamination, the risk doesn't seem that great and every carcass cannot be checked.

You can do something to protect yourself, however. Check your next fast-food patty. If it is pink in the center, send it back. If it is dishwater gray throughout, gag it down. Don't let your hamburger patties warm up at family picnics like tiny incubators. Cook 'em dead.

Lyme Disease

In the western United States west of the Cascade and Sierra Nevada Mountains the tick, *Ixodes pacificus* carries the spirochete that causes Lyme disease. Spirochetes are a nasty group of microscopic organisms that also cause syphilis. A different species of *Ixodes* hosts the spirochete in the east.

The tick's life cycle has three main stages that require a blood meal between hosts. The tick's eggs germinate. The resulting larvae wait in low plants for their first blood meal. Frequently it is from a spirochete infected white-footed deer mouse in the east or a fence lizard, jackrabbit, or dusky-footed woodrat (page 113) in the west. The incidence of Lyme disease infected ticks is 30 to 60 percent in the eastern United States, only 1 to 2 percent in the west. Why? Because lizards are commonly parasitized by up to 40 ticks in the west. Experiments have shown that lizard blood kills the spirochete. This is not so for mammal hosts, however.

After a blood meal the larvae drop off and overwinter, changing to nymphs that wait for larger prey, deer, dogs, or humans. Sometimes people don't realize the tiny comma-sized nymphs bit them. After this blood meal, the nymphs drop off and mature into adults. They need another blood meal before mating and laying more eggs.

Remove a tick by grabbing its head with tweezers and gradually and gently pulling it straight out. Remember the SEM (page 133)? When removing ticks, be careful not to squeeze the tick's abdomen and thus force tick juice (and spirochetes) into your own or someone else's bloodstream. Smearing ticks with Vaseline, daubing them with alcohol, or applying heat won't always work. You may end up with a dead tick still imbedded in the skin. The sooner you remove the tick, the less likely infection will occur. Pull it out yourself; run to the emergency room if problems follow. Be sure to save the tick's carcass for positive identification.

Wait for symptoms to occur before seeking expensive medical help and unnecessary antibiotics. There is plenty of time before a cure is difficult. Lyme disease in humans goes through three stages. In 50 percent of the cases, a distinctive enlarging rash with a central clearing may form. Flu-like symptoms may develop: fever, chills, nausea, fatigue, headache, dizziness, stiff neck. Visit your doctor now!

If diarrhea develops, you are probably suffering from someone's bad cooking and not Lyme disease, although coincidental infection is possible. In the second stage, spirochetes invade many body parts, including the nervous system, causing neurological upsets, like facial paralysis, numbness, or Alzheimer-like symptoms, or may cause abnormal heartbeat. The last stages include arthritis that may start with swollen, painful joints. The disease can be treated with antibiotics, the sooner the better. If a tick bites you, and you develop any of these symptoms, head for the family physician and take your tick with you. Unfortunately, inconclusive blood tests give false positive and negative results.

Lyme disease is no reason to become a recluse. Do take precautions, however. Wear light-colored clothing, tuck long pants into socks, stay out of the bushes, use repellents like DEET, especially in the spring and early summer, and take time out to look for ticks. In the right company, tick checks can be entertaining. Examine children with particular care. Many local cases seem to involve small children and young adults. Not even livestock or the family pet are immune.

Scurvy

Scurvy: a disease marked by spongy gums, loosening of teeth, and a bleeding into the skin and mucous membranes. Symptoms are gradual, starting with general weakness and depression. Muscles ache, gums are tender, eyes recede, complexion turns sallow. Weeks may pass as symptoms worsen, teeth fall out and massive hemorrhages penetrate muscles and other tissues. Night-blindness may occur. Finally total exhaustion, fainting, diarrhea and kidney troubles herald a final, permanent, peace.

Scurvy has been with the human race since diets turned bad. Paleopathologists see signs of scurvy in the skulls of ancients. Scurvy has altered the course of human events. Vasco da Gama lost 100 of his 160-man crew on his return to Portugal from Mozambique in 1499. Jacques Cartier lost 50 of his crew to scurvy locked in the ice of the St. Lawrence River the winter of 1535–36. In 1553, 12,000 soldiers at the siege of Metz died of typhus and scurvy in a single month. In 1564, a Dutchman recommended lime juice as a cure for scurvy. No one paid much attention. In 1593, Sir Richard Hawkins, reported that 10,000 men of the Royal Navy under his command died of scurvy. Hawkins then began a trip around the world. Although he recommended orange and lemon juice as a cure, scurvy continued to decimate sailors and prisoners throughout the 17th century.

By the mid-18th century scurvy was finally controlled based on the experiments of the Scots naval surgeon James Lind. Lind gave 12 scurvy victims aboard the HMS *Salisbury* potions of various sorts from cider to balsam of Peru. Those who received two oranges and a lemon a day recovered in short order. The others malingered. This seems to be the first instance where experiment indicated the efficacy of citrus fruits. The results of his study were published ten years later in 1757.

The Royal Navy finally tested Lind's theory in 1794, the year of his death. A navy squadron sailed on a 23-week voyage to India with hatches filled with lemons. One seaman suffered from scurvy. Cheaper lime juice in their rum became standard fare for British sailors. British sailors were not known as Limeys till 1918, however.

This wasn't the end of scurvy, however. Some 10,000 49ers perished in the California goldfields of the disease. Thousands more avoided scurvy by eating miner's lettuce, an ascorbic acid containing herb, known to botanists as *Claytonia perfoliata.* It is a very common spring wildflower. You might be able to find it in abundance at higher elevations while morel hunting.

The plant is an annual with succulent, spoon-shaped basal leaves and a flower-bearing stalk with a circular leaf just below the inflorescence. Collect young plants at the peak of flowering. The delicate flavor of the younger plants is lost in older, bitter plants. Suffering from scurvy? Eat them anyway.

Rinse and dry the leaves and flowers. Drizzle on a home-made vinaigrette, like James Beard's own. Six tablespoons of olive oil, one of wine vinegar, half a teaspoon of salt, and a quarter teaspoon of ground black pepper. Add some violet flowers for color and aroma and you have a salad fit for royalty.

Watermelon Snow

Skiers have probably noticed lemon snow, but what about watermelon snow? In spring and summer, at higher elevations, receding snow banks often take on a pink or reddish tinge. It happens in the bowl on Mount Ashland, near the summit of Mount Eddy west of Mount Shasta, and on the slopes of Mount McLoughlin, to name a few places. You can find red snow in alpine and polar areas worldwide, even Australia, New Zealand and the glaciers of New Guinea. Once you look for watermelon snow you will discover that it is really quite common on high elevation snow banks where small particles of organic debris accumulate and snow begins to melt.

What causes snow to turn color? To find out, pack small vials of red snow in snow, to keep the samples cold, and bring the samples back to the laboratory for microscopic examination. Make a slide, put on a cover slip, and take a look. What you will see are tiny microscopic algal cells, most likely the resting cells of *Chlamydomonas nivalis,* the snow algae, although it could be one of several other related genera. The single, green, cup-shaped chloroplasts of individual cells are masked by the presence of red pigments. It is the collective presence of these tiny plants that give the snow its color.

These cryophilic, that is, cold-loving algae, carry out their lives and loves in the chilly water-filled spaces among ice crystals in melting snow. It is in these chilly waters that resting cells germinate, producing flagellated cells that swim about, reproducing asexually until motile gametes or asexual resting cells are formed. Gametes unite and zygotic resting cells develop. There is no heat generated by love or sex in these creatures.

Throughout the year, air currents blow the resting cells about, eventually to lodge in soil, trees, and snow. Only in the spring and summer, when melt water is present

for at least 24 hours, does enough extensive vegetative growth of algal cells occur to color snow. Nutrients and minerals are leached from dust, conifer needles, and lichen scraps that litter the surface of the snow this time of year. Algae's own photosynthesis provides for their energy needs and that of other organisms in a snowbound ecosystem. Grazers include snow worms, protozoans, spiders and insects that like it chilly. Nutrients tied up in the bodies of the algae and the grazers are recycled by the action of snow fungi and bacteria.

Next time you are hiking along snow fields in the spring and summer look for watermelon snow. The naturalist Daniel Mathews writes in *Cascade Olympic Natural History* that some say watermelon snow tastes like watermelon. I know from personal experience that it smells like watermelon. He writes that others warn of diarrhea. Except for pure and white, I avoid eating snow of any color.

Herbal Medicines

A week ago I waited in the Grants Pass Fred Meyer store with some visiting Japanese colleagues to purchase duffel bags to ship some 165 species of local plants back to Japan for chemical analysis. For three summers we have searched for plants with anti-viral or anti-tumor medicinal properties. I stopped at Freddie's display of herbal preparations and looked at the boxes. Plenty of information about the contents, only vague reference to why you might want to use a particular preparation.

As a systematic botanist, practitioners of herbal medicine sometimes ask me where such and such a plant grows, or to confirm the identity of a plant they collected. Sometimes I know where the plant grows, sometimes not. Sometimes the plant they want grows in the eastern United States. Often their identifications are correct, sometimes not. Those I talk to are earnest, honest people who want to know the identity of their plants. They also are very knowledgeable about the presumed medicinal properties of the plants they seek.

I once expressed my concern about misidentified species in herbal preparations to a friend. Within a week, an article from the July 15, 1992, issue of *Annals of Internal Medicine* titled "The Myth of Beneficent Nature: The Risks of Herbal Preparations" by Ryan Huxtable, Ph.D. at the University of Arizona College of Medicine, appeared on my desk. Dr. Huxtable studies the toxicology of foods and herbs.

Huxtable's article cites several instances of deaths and poisonings from taking medicinal teas and potions. One example involved the use of the alkaloid rich *Senecio longilobus.* The alkaloids of this butterweed, a member of the sunflower family, appear to cause major liver problems, particularly in young children.

You can't count on labels. Hepatitis has been reported

from the use of germander tea. Apparently, germander has been mislabeled and sold as skullcap, also in the mint family.

A Swiss baby died of a liver aliment at five weeks because mamma persistently used an herbal tea during pregnancy. Coltsfoot was implicated because that was on the label. Analysis showed the presence of an alkaloid not in coltsfoot. Another plant was present in the tea.

Comfrey, rich in liver-crunching alkaloids, is outlawed in Germany, restricted in Canada, and freely available for sale in the United States. Once thought to be the be-all-and-end-all of medicinal herbs, it isn't safe.

Some herbal medicines interact with other medicines such as phenobarbital and heliotrope. Susceptibility to herbal poisoning varies with age, sex, and state of health. Neither Huxtable nor I comment on the effectiveness of herbal preparations. If you think they help, continue to use them. If nothing else, they might represent strong evidence of the amazing curative powers of the human body. However, Huxtable has some guidelines that I also recommend to readers who might take herbal medicines.

- Do not take herbs if pregnant or attempting to become pregnant.
- Do not take herbs if you are nursing.
- Do not give herbs to your baby.
- Do not take a large quantity of any one herbal preparation.
- Do not take any herb on a daily basis.
- Buy only preparations with the ingredients listed on the package. It is no guarantee of safety, but it is better than nothing.
- Do not take anything containing comfrey.

It amazes me that there are no government regulations covering the identity, quantity, or quality of materials used in herbal preparations in the United States. For those of you who think there are too many government regulations, I recommend you turn to herbal medicine to solve your ills. *Caveat emptor,* as the saying goes.

Poison Oak

Compared to other areas of the country, our western outdoors is pretty benign when it comes to things that make us miserable. We do have rattlesnakes (but not copperheads, water moccasins *and* rattlesnakes). We do have deer ticks (but only 1–2% carry Lyme disease). We do have wasps and hornets (but so do they). They have chiggers (we don't). They have fire ants (we don't, at least not yet). They have poison ivy. However we have poison oak, and for about 50 percent of the human population, that's no fun at all.

As most of you know, direct contact with poison oak, any part of the plant, can cause a miserable swelling, blistery, oozing, itching, crusty rash on the skin of a sensitive human. The culprit is a nearly volatile oil, urushiol. Urushiol can cause great excitement in your immune system. The oil penetrates the outer layers of your skin, binds to macrophages there and forms an antigen. The antigen is then presented to T cells from the thymus. In subsequent exposures, lymphocytes and macrophages react intensely attacking and destroying nearby epidermal cells, causing, in varying degrees, the blistery, itchy rash. We are not born with an allergy to poison oak, but must be sensitized, usually as a child. If you were not sensitized as a child, you stand a good chance of avoiding sensitization as an adult. Please note, however, that a good chance is not the same as no chance at all. Only the same kind of fool who handles rattlesnakes and gets bitten also wades right into the poison oak patch bragging about how they don't or won't get it.

The best way to avoid what is the largest cause of workers' compensation claims in California is to learn to recognize the plant. The oil is present in all plant parts all year, except maybe the berries. In the winter look for upright tawny stems with relatively short branches and white

berries. In spring, summer and fall watch out for attractive, shiny, dark-green leaves that change to attractive red in fall. The compound leaves have three leaflets leading to the admonition "leaves of three leave it be." Sometimes you just can't avoid it. Wildfires burning through poison oak volatilize the oil and carry it on smoke particles to whomever might inhale it. Miserable swelling, blistery, oozing, itching, crusty skin is nothing compared to miserable swelling, blistery, oozing, itching, crusty lungs. It is life-threatening.

If you can't avoid poison oak, what should you do? You can try not to touch the plants. Handle your contaminated clothing, especially your shoes, with care. Put your clothes in the washer yourself, lest you bring down the wrath of a sensitive spouse or significant other, around your head. Try using a protective cream like Tecnu Poison-Oak-N-Ivy Armor and washup afterwards with Tecnu Poison-Oak and Ivy Cleanser. Wash in cold water. A strong alkali soap like Fels-Naphtha might work. Ordinary soaps will just spread the urushiol around. Always wash away from exposed areas. Always wash before going to the bathroom or touching your face.

Folk remedies that may or may not work? Drinking goats' milk from goats who eat poison oak; eating small portions of poison oak or taking extract drops to build up an immunity; rubbing on a miner's lettuce poultice.

The rash will not spread from the oozing serum of the rash. You can reinfect yourself from your dirty clothes or shoes. Bowser can give it to you, as can Kitty. One bright note. Once you are above 4000 feet elevation in southern Oregon you are mostly out of poison oak.

Black Widows

Arthropods are the largest group in the Animal Kingdom. Because of their jointed legs, exoskeletons, and circulatory systems, nine-foot ants, or, God forbid, nine-foot spiders are not physically or physiologically possible. There are many different kinds of arthropods that deliver venom to humans. Wasps, bees, ants and scorpions sting. Spiders and centipedes bite. Many other biting arthropods pass disease to humans: lice, ticks, mosquitos and fleas.

Spiders give many humans the creepy-crawly heebie-jeebies. Arachnophobic are you? My mother used to tell me that when you stepped on a spider, it was going to rain tomorrow. Growing up in western Washington, I learned this was almost a certainty.

Nearly all 20,000 spider species produce venom. Fortunately for humans, relatively few have fangs of sufficient strength to penetrate our hides. About 200 species can bite humans and do damage. Often though, spiders are blamed for bites and stings of other arthropods or problems caused by various skin conditions.

Lacrodectus hesperus is the spider that causes most serious spider bites in our area. You know this spider as the black widow. The black widow is typically shiny black with a characteristic red hourglass on the underside of its bulbous abdomen. Color can vary from shiny black to brown and the red mark may be missing. Black widows build their messy webs in various locations. At my house they are in nooks and crannies in the garage, around the wood pile, and in the drip irrigation control box, for very short periods of time after I discover them.

Both sexes are poisonous. Only the female is big enough to bite a human. A female may be 15 mm long, a male 3–5 mm (the little wimps). In the United States, black widows cause most fatal spider bites, about five per year, which is about five percent of all bites. Most deaths

occur in small children and the elderly. Healthy adults are simply in major pain for several days.

It starts as a pinprick or less. Severe pain soon develops that spreads to involve the entire body. Muscles twitch, the abdomen hardens, the body perspires profusely. Dizziness, nausea, and vomiting may follow.

First-aid there isn't. Put an ice cube on the bite if painful and get thee to the nearest hospital, fast. There, professionals will monitor your progress and treat your symptoms accordingly. As in many kinds of venomous bites, the degree of poisoning varies. Trivial signs and symptoms require no specific treatment. Anti-venom is available, but is used only in the most severe cases. Otherwise, treatment might be a warm bath, mild sedation or morphine. Seems to me a certain amount of care not to get bitten is best.

Want to return to the good old days? Here is a fabulous fact for you. The incidence of black widow spider bites in male humans has declined in direct proportion to the disappearance of the outhouse. Ouch!

Spider Bites

I have a new attitude about black-widow spider bites. I learned first hand, actually first arm, about spider bites. I was out in the garage minding my own business. Actually I was not exactly minding my own business. I was killing black widow spiders. Two of the sisterhood fell to my mighty blows. Got them all, I thought.

Several days later, in the afternoon, my elbow became sore. Some kind of tennis elbow, even though I don't play tennis? Something from my early morning exercise class? Bursitis? My forearm started to swell. Maybe it was something else. My wife suggested insect bite. I remembered a little tickle on my elbow sometime earlier that day while I was getting into my truck, I think, or maybe looking through backpacking gear while getting ready to go on an end of the summer pack back to the Ruby Mountains in Nevada. I brushed the tickle off, whatever it was, without giving it a second thought. Didn't notice a thing then, but I certainly noticed something was wrong later. Barfed before bed. Woke up the next morning with a forearm looking like Popeye's but without the tattoo. Headed directly for the doctor. It took painkillers, steroids, several different courses of antibiotics, and time (like weeks) before the swelling dropped and I felt anything like normal.

I was grateful that I didn't have full-blown black-widow spider-bite symptoms: no total incapacitating pain, no rigid abdominal muscles, no hospitalization. I am convinced that I was the victim of a drive-by biting organized by the remaining sisterhood. Because my symptoms were not classic, perhaps the sisters hired someone else, someone new, to do the deed.

The someone new might have been the hobo spider, formerly known as the aggressive house spider. The hobo is a European native, introduced into the Seattle area in the 1920s or early 30s. Hobos, as good hobos should, have

spread their range from Seattle north to the Alaska Panhandle, south through Oregon and east through southern British Columbia, all of Idaho, to western Montana and northern Utah. They are brown and gray and big. Their bodies may be an inch long and have legs that span the hole in a CD-disc. Hobos can move a meter a second. The male is more aggressive and more venomous than the female. Mature spiders are most common in the early fall when males are out searching for mates.

Hobos build funnel-shaped webs in dark, moist places, wood piles, crawl spaces, around the edges of human habitation. Hobos do not like to climb vertical surfaces, so aren't often found above basement or ground level. The Communicable Disease Center recommends personal protection rather than wholesale chemical warfare when dealing with hobo populations. Wear gloves and a long-sleeved shirt when fetching firewood or working in likely hobo habitats. Screen basement and ground-floor windows and use weather stripping under outside doors to keep them out of your house.

If bitten, here is what you can expect. At first, no pain, isn't that good news? Soon red swelling, and blisters developing that then break and may encrust a now cratered wound. Next a scab may form covering an area of dead and dying tissue. The resulting wound will generally heal within 45 days, but longer, like three years, if bitten in a fatty place. The resulting scar may be permanent. There are effects elsewhere in the body, like a severe headache within 30 minutes to ten hours that may last a week. Other symptoms besides nausea and the general blahs, may include aplastic anemia, intractable vomiting, or profuse secretory diarrhea. If things get this bad however, the Grim Reaper may be near and you will not have to worry about a scar. That is the bad news. The good news is that you may not get a full dose of venom. This is frequently the case with bites and stings of venomous animals. Lucky you, lucky me.

Snakebite

In our area, our dangerous poisonous snake is the Pacific rattlesnake, *Crotalus viridus*. Our subspecies, the northern Pacific rattlesnake, is found from south central California to southwest Oregon and east of the Cascades as far north as British Columbia and Idaho, with several isolated populations in the Willamette Valley. Rattlesnakes can be found anywhere in the Rogue Valley, although they seem more common on hotter, drier slopes from the valley floor to the Siskiyou summit. Rocky outcrops, talus, rocky stream courses and ledges are favorite haunts.

Snake venoms are a complex mixture of biologically active proteins designed to make snakebite effective. Some are enzymes that break down proteins and cause tissue death. Others are anticoagulants that hasten bleeding or are substances that speed up the spread of venom. Some are neurotoxic. The venom of our local rattle snake is relatively benign when compared to other species. It takes about 80 times more venom for a northern Pacific rattlesnake to kill a mouse than for a tiger rattlesnake to do the same.

Several facts about snakebite: First, most snake bites occur within a half mile of the victim's home, and, second, often little or no venom is injected when they bite. Most snakebites happen to careless people. About half the snakebites in the United States are sustained by people who either deliberately place themselves at risk by handling snakes or who put their hands or feet where they can't see. Want to avoid snakebite? Watch where you walk, stick you fingers or sit, and don't handle snakes. It is one thing to be bitten by a snake you didn't see. It is inexcusable to be bitten by a snake you can see.

What to do if bitten? The author of a recent article on snakebite feels that the most useful snake bite kit is a set of car keys and a quarter to make a phone call to the

nearest hospital to warn of your arrival. If you are within an hour of medical help, don't do anything, just go. They will know what to do. If there will be a delay in treatment, try a new device that works like a hypodermic syringe in reverse. It forms an atmosphere of negative pressure and sucks out the venom if used quickly. Sawyer Products of Long Beach, California markets the device and it is available at most outdoor stores. It also works on insects bites, or so they advertise. Avoid cold packs and the old hack and suck techniques of yore. More damage to tendons, blood vessels, and nerves can occur than from untreated snakebite. Besides, you may not have received venom. If bitten, don't drink alcohol, take stimulants or medicine. Don't run about or unnecessarily exert yourself. Do get to professional help as soon as possible, but I suppose there is no need to tell you that. Just try to remember, that other than fright, about two-thirds of the time snakebite victims in North America show little or no effect from being bitten.

Occasionally, people confuse our spectacular, but harmless, red, black and yellow banded California mountain kingsnake with the poisonous coral snake. Don't kill our king snakes. We don't have coral snakes. Remember, "Red and yellow kill the fellow (coral snakes), red and black friend of Jack (king snakes)." If you find a king snake here, enjoy its beauty and leave it be. You will not find coral snakes here, but if you do, enjoy its beauty and leave it be as well. However, you should consider giving up excessive alcohol consumption. Look, there is a pink elephant!

VII

From the Rivers to the Sea

Water

"We'll never know the worth of water till the well go dry." This 18th century Scottish proverb has been used and reused, much like water, ever since then. Water is a remarkable substance.

Water is a chemical compound of two hydrogen atoms bound to oxygen; H_2O, as all but the dullest know. It is among the most common and essential substances on planet Earth. Except for the odd meteorite, what we have, is all we have.

Water can be a solid, like ice or snow, a liquid, like a lake or river, or a gas, like steam. Water has near magic properties.

It is a liquid over most of earth's climates. It boils at 212°F and freezes at 32°F. Living organisms — even ice worms — require water as a liquid.

As a liquid, water changes temperatures very slowly. It can store a lot of heat without much change in temperature. Lakes and oceans usually do not change temperature faster than their living organisms can tolerate.

It takes a lot of heat to change liquid water to a gas. As heat is taken up in evaporation of water, the surface cools. Evaporating sweat makes you and your skin feel cooler, or evaporating saliva, if you are a dog.

Liquid water, as a nearly universal solvent, is a mixed blessing. It moves dissolved nutrients and wastes through tissues of the body. The same property allows it to be easily polluted by soluble wastes.

Water molecules' ability to cling together allows a place for water striders to stride. That, and its ability to cling to surfaces, allows tall trees like redwoods to pull life-sustaining water molecules 300 feet or more above the ground.

Water expands on freezing, becomes less dense than water as a liquid. Frozen water floats. Ice floats. Lakes freeze from the top down. If ice didn't float, lakes might freeze from the bottom up, freeze up solid, thus destroying aquatic life.

Somehow humans have the idea that water is in unending supply. It is, but not always when or where we want it. At any given place there might be unexpected drought or deluge. Sometime drought or deluge might be protracted.

We dam, drill, channel and pipe water from all over to support our lives and styles. Are the consequences worth it? Of all the water on planet Earth, three percent is fresh water and only 0.003 percent is readily available. We are using that up as fast as we can. After we use it, we return it polluted with our wastes, diseases, and the chemical discharge of our industries. Our .003 percent is shrinking fast, polluted and made unusable by our activities.

Medford and Milwaukee? Water contaminated by *Cryptosporidium*. Wildland waters contaminated by *Giardia*. Ground water contaminated by leaking gasoline tanks. What is a leading cause of water pollution worldwide? Agriculture. Sediments from soil erosion, pesticides, and excessive nutrients all contribute. Obtaining good, clean drinking water is becoming more and more expensive in energy and money. How much longer till our fancy technological well goes dry? Sooner than we think, perhaps.

Tide Pools

I love tide pools. I like the plants and animals, recognizing the ones I know, trying to identify the ones I don't. I like the colors, shapes and patterns. I like the smell and sound of the sea. I like it all.

Tides are the regular and mostly predictable complex movement of large bodies of water, like oceans, in response to the pull of gravity between the earth, sun and moon, the rotation and tilt of the earth, the influence of weather, and the shape of the offshore bottom and the shoreline. Simply, the water level along our coast rises and falls twice every 24 hours. Tides are 50 minutes later each day and vary in height, depending on the position of the moon.

In the intertidal zone, the space on shore between high and low tides, we find a host of plants and animals specially adapted for life in and out of water. Zones of organisms are present, formed by how long the creatures are exposed to air. At low tide, look at a vertical face like the shore side of the huge rock with the passage through it at Harris Beach State Park at Brookings, Oregon. We see horizontal bands of different organisms in the intertidal zone with rock weeds and other algae that can stand long periods of drying at the top, through a zone of barnacles to mussels and gooseneck barnacles, to lower zones with large brown algae like *Laminaria*.

In depressions are pools of water with a host of different plants and animals: orange and lavender sponges flat against the rocks; pink coralline red algae with calcareous cell walls; starfish, orange and purple; mollusks of all kinds, snails, limpets, and chitons; hermit crabs in castoff snail shells; sea anemones, maybe sea urchins, and who knows what else.

Follow these rules when tide pooling for your safety and the well-being of the critters you came to see. Never turn your back to the sea. Watch out for the sneaker wave that might make you a permanent part of the ecosystem. Never, ever, play on logs in the surf. It's a good way to get squashed. Watch the tide. Check a tide table for the exact time of tides at your location. What went out, will come back in. Don't spend your weekend on a rock. Don't collect anything, just look or photograph. If you turn over rocks to see what's underneath, be sure to turn them back over. The things that live under rocks are there because they need the shelter.

Places to go? There are fine tide pool areas at Cape Arago, if you are in the Coos Bay area. Farther south near Brookings there is North Samuel Boardman State Park, Lone Ranch Beach, and Harris Beach. An additional tidbit about Lone Ranch Beach: until 1800 Native Americans ate and discarded shellfish shells at the site for centuries. It's a kitchen midden, a kind of garbage dump, with more than just old shells. California condor bones were found there in the 1940s. Yum.

Gray Whales

Gray whales are named for their slate-gray color, usually mottled white from patches of barnacles and barnacle scars with splotches of pink or orange caused by cyamid lice. If you were horrified by the thought that you were host to a few benign hair follicle mites (page 125), be pleased you aren't a gray whale. An adult whale is host of up to several hundred pounds of large barnacles embedded in the hide of the head, back and tail. Orange whale lice, up to 2.5 cm long, infest barnacle clusters and folds of skin over much of the whale's body. It makes our human commensal organisms seem minor by comparison.

In southern Oregon we have two chances to see migrating gray whales. One is in late fall and early winter when pregnant females and all the rest head south from chilly waters of the Bering Sea for birthing, fun, and frolic in the shallow waters of Mexico's Baja lagoons.

Newborn calves are a dainty 16 feet long at birth. Calves may gain 60–70 pounds a day on daily diet of about 50 gallons of mother's milk. Mama whale's breasts are whale-sized and can squirt a fountain of yellow, oily-tasting milk that is 35 percent fat six or seven feet straight up. No suckling here. Mama squirts the milk into baby's mouth. By winter's end the calves may weigh two to three tons and may be 18–19 feet long.

Mating in the lagoons of Baja is a clumsy, frenzied, *mènage á trois* affair with many frustrated attempts before success. Two males are frequently involved, one who mates and one who lies across the mating couple to keep them in position.

Our next opportunity to see migrating Gray whales is when they travel north from Baja California to the Bering Sea where they will follow the receding ice until October. Then, well provisioned with six to 12 inches of oily blubber, the whales return south. Northward migration occurs in two phases. The first occurs from February to June, when newly-pregnant females, still interested adult males and juveniles head north retracing their southward route. The second phase, from March to July, consists of new mothers and their calves. Their route is close to shore, along the surf line and kelp beds where they may linger for a day or two. We think that mothers and their calves may be feeding. For calves, this might be their first taste of solid food as mama whale begins to wean them from their usual diet of nutrient-rich milk. Gray whales are bottom feeders that filter out their food by means of fringed baleen plates that hang from their upper jaws like hair combs. They dive to the shallow sea floor, roll to the right (or sometimes left) and suck up the sediments with their mouths. With mouths full, they use their thick, fleshy tongues to force accumulated water and sediments back out through their baleen filters, trapping a swallow of amphipods, bottom-dwelling crustaceans that make up the bulk of their diet. When gray whales were killed for food, oil, and profit, reports of finding ten or more wheelbarrow loads of amphipods in their whale-sized, three-chambered stomachs were common.

Where to go to watch the whales in southern Oregon? Almost any high promontory along the Oregon and California coast will do. From north to south along Highway 101 in southern Oregon try Cape Arago, Cape Blanco, Cape Sebastian, or Cape Ferrelo; in northern California, Point Saint George, Crescent Beach Overlook, or Patrick's Point State Park. Whales are easiest to spot from land in the early morning before wind whips up the whitecaps and when skies are overcast to reduce glare. Call Oregon State University's Marine Science Center in Newport, Oregon to find out where the whales are. It takes good fortune or a lot of patience to have a successful whale watch.

Orcas

Once upon a time, I was a naturalist on a cruise ship to southeast Alaska for four summers. Four, two-week trips in prime Orca or Killer Whale waters and not once did I see an Orca. It wasn't that others didn't see them on the cruise, I just wasn't at the right place at the right time — in my stateroom, at dinner, giving a lecture. Not only that, I had never seen a wild killer whale anywhere. That all changed May 7, 2000.

My first big outing while recovering from Guillian-Barre Syndrome was with wife and friends to a time-share condominium just north of Depoe Bay on the Oregon coast. What a great place: top floor at the north end of the complex with a sweeping view of the ocean. I spent a lot of time looking at the ocean. Got rewarded.

Mid-morning, looking north, some distance away, I noticed a whirling, swirling flock of sea birds, gulls and cormorants, above the sea. Coho salmon fishermen look for this because it indicates salmon feeding on schools of herring, sardines, or candlefish. While I looked, I could see the birds swoop to the surface, then rise up again. I also thought I occasionally glimpsed, not salmon, but the low, triangular fins of harbor porpoises. Then maybe not, no one else who looked could see them.

As the day went on, my attention shifted to land birds along the top of the bluff below. Robins and crows were busy collecting twigs and other debris for nests. Maybe what some say is true. "Hooray, hooray, for the first of May, outdoor sex begins today." Although I didn't see IT going on, I bet it had.

Late afternoon I looked out to the west and noticed another flock of whirling, swirling seabirds. Ah, ha, thought I, I'll find harbor porpoises and show those doubting Thomases. I looked, and much to my amazement, I saw the tall, distinctive isosceles dorsal fins of Orcas. "Wow, look at that!" I said, "Killer whales!" That got everyone's attention, and no arguments. While we watched the pair, a small boat

arrived that crept closer and closer, until the whales couldn't stand it any longer. They spy-hopped, that is, rose vertically out of the water to take a very close look at the boat and its occupants. In spite of the fact there is no clear evidence that killer whales have ever harmed a human, boat and occupants sped quickly away and continued up the coast.

Later, after our attention drifted elsewhere, someone glanced out the window and said, "What is that sticking out of the water? "Oh, it's the buoy," said I, who knows almost everything. "No its not." I looked to discover the six foot tall dorsal fins of two large male killer whales slowly making their way north near shore. And further out were another eight or so smaller juvenile and female orcas having a wild time, breaching, tail slapping, and spy-hopping under a cloud of wheeling, swirling seabirds. My best guess is that they were in a feeding frenzy, banging around to stun the fish. We watched them for quite a while as they headed north toward Boiler Bay and Lincoln City. It was quite a sight.

Bill Hanshumaker, a marine mammalogist at the Hatfield Marine Science Center in Newport, tells me that the orcas we watched were probably part of an off-shore population that likes to dine on seals, porpoises, California sea lions, baby gray whales and the like. These so-called wolves of the sea conduct their lives in what are thought to be matrilineal packs, called pods, of up to 40 or so members. They are top predators in the sea and have no enemies except disease, old-age, themselves, and humans. There are two indirect human impacts today. One is drowning to death in fishnets, the other by poisoning. Hanshumaker arranged to have some blubber from an orca carcass analyzed for pollutants. He was amazed to discover 276 ppm of PCB, and 494 ppm of DED a metabolite of DDT. Way high. Biological magnification at work. These persistent organic pollutants accumulate in fats at each level of the food chain and are known to affect animal hormone, immune and reproductive systems and affect normal development at even low levels. Whale milk is very high in fat. I wonder what is happening to baby orca? I hope you get to see an orca before it is too late.

Water Bears

I like the rustic look of moss and lichen-covered wooden shake and shingle roofs. Mosses and lichens are ecological pioneers, the first plants to invade any bare area: granite outcrop or fresh split shakes. Mosses and lichens put down thin filamentous structures into microscopic cracks and crevices and make them macroscopic. They produce organic acids that soften substrates. They capture wind-blown debris: dust, pollen, fine soil particles and, sometimes, eggs or spores of other organisms. They change the shake or shingle from a place of temperature and moisture extremes to a cooler, damper, place — a place that wood-rotting fungi might find more hospitable.

I tend to ignore the role they play in shortening the life of a wood shingle roof. I like the mosses and lichens on my roof because I know they are the home of bears. Yes, bears. Not the kind of bears that deposited huge piles of manzanita berries along the irrigation ditch above our house before more houses encroached upon the urban wildland interface, but Tardigrades or water bears. These microscopic, multicellular beasts, half a millimeter or less in length, spend their lives wandering about in moss and lichen forests several centimeters high. Their short, stout, cylindrical bodies with down-turned heads have four pairs of clawed, stumpy legs. Their deliberate, pawing locomotion is most bear-like.

Despite their fearsome claws, used for clinging and climbing, they are mostly herbivorous, although they won't pass up a juicy nematode or rotifer. They usually pierce the cell wall of moss leaflets and algal cells with sharp pointed mouthparts and suck out the vital juices.

Tardigrades have an unusually large bilobed brain in proportion to their body size. Do they think? Is left brain, right brain a topic of discussion? Most likely not.

Water bears have an amazing facility for suspended

animation. No expensive cryonics for Tardigrades, whole body or just the head. When summer comes and mosses dry, water bears contract into a dried, inactive state that can last from four to seven years. How long depends on the amount of stored food in their bodies. When moist conditions return, the animals swell with water, and promptly become active after four minutes to several hours. Under laboratory conditions, animals have been dried and revived ten times or more.

So, if you wake suddenly at night, it might be because of the restless wanderings of water bears on your shake roof. If you have asbestos shingles, it just might be the mating frenzy of your own personal herd of hair follicle mites cavorting around your nose and cheeks. But that's a topic for a different *Nature Note* (page 125).

Toads

An Illinois Valley listener wrote me to ask why her ecologically-varied farm pond had lots of singing toads last year, while this year her pond was mostly silent. She wrote, "Is this within the acceptable variation of natural events? Or does it portend something terribly wrong?"

Where had all her toadies gone? Back to Washington, DC to become lobbyists? My initial reaction was to tell her about population cycles, carrying capacities, and the natural rise and fall of populations caused by the interplay of toads and their environment. Disease, predation, and lack of food all can play a role in the rise and fall of populations. Abiotic factors such as temperature and pH are involved as well.

Apparently my listener noticed a widespread phenomenon that recently resulted in a meeting of the nation's herpetologists. Amphibian populations worldwide are in decline and no one knows why. Reports from Mexico, Brazil, Australia, Canada, Norway, Japan, and the western United States, all show major downward changes in the number and species of frogs, toads, and salamanders.

In some areas of southern Oregon, the Cascade frog may be in trouble. Dr. Stephen Cross recently visited his favorite Cascade frog spot — 12 one year, four the next year.

Scientists agree that the declines (though mostly based on anecdotal evidence) are real. But they can't agree on a cause. Many declines might be local phenomena. A rare hard frost at the wrong time, local drought, habitat destruction (golf courses and shopping malls). What is alarming is that many populations from protected places like nature preserves and wildernesses are also affected.

Because of their life cycle and their physiology, amphibians are sensitive to environmental change that might be caused by human activity. Frogs are sensitive to

changes in acidity and ultraviolet radiation. Does that translate to acid rain and holes in the ozone layer? We don't know.

What we do know is that we need more data. Lack of historical information about population size is a major problem. It means we don't know if what we are observing is part of a normal population fluctuation or a major decline.

We frequently designate indicator species, whose health and well-being serve as a measure of the community or ecosystem they represent. Reproducing northern spotted owls generally indicate a healthy, ancient, temperate, coniferous forest ecosystem. Is the loss of frogs and toads and salamanders an indication of the state of our planetary ecosystem? Only time will tell, and I'm not sure how much of that we have. Poor Kermit, poor us.

Sturgeon

What fish is so different looking that it sent a small girl into near hysteria when her father brought it home from a fishing trip years ago? It's a fish that still puts the now-grown woman mightily off.

Let us see if you can guess. The fish is long and slender, flattened more from top to bottom than from side to side. There are five rows of bony, butterfly-shaped plates embedded in its smooth, leathery skin. The crescent-shaped caudal or tail fin is longer on the top than on the bottom. Need more hints?

Its toothless mouth is underneath and back of its prolonged snout. There are four elongated, finger-like projections, barbels, nearer the snout's tip than the mouth. Still more hints?

They are sea run bottom scavengers that can reach prodigious size and age. It is the northwest's largest freshwater fish. Twelve feet long, to 1,387 pounds or more — now that's a monster. A Lochness Monster or an Okanogan Ogopogo? Not long ago, an 11-foot monster weighing nearly a half-ton was found dead in Seattle's Lake Washington. The fish are long-lived 50, 75, a 100 years. One more hint.

After a female is caught, her tiny eggs are removed, separated, salted, drained, dried and packed, then sold as caviar. The fish is? You guessed it. It's a sturgeon.

Locally, white sturgeon are most popular as a sport fish. They are not as abundant as they once were, due to dams and pollution. If you fish for them, the flesh is excellent and virtually boneless. You can keep only those between 40 and 72 inches. Why? They grow slowly, an inch a year when the fish are more than 24 inches. The best, most productive breeders are more than 72 inches long and may live to be one hundred. The object is to protect the kids and best breeders.

Dr. Linn of Southern Oregon University's Biology Department, who helped write this *Nature Note*, has been sturgeon fishing on the Columbia River. He says it isn't difficult fishing. Find a secret sturgeon hole, usually in a deep section of the river, and throw out your specially-rigged smelt-baited hook on 20-pound test line using a heavy-duty rod and reel. Then you wait for the sturgeon to take the bait. You can detect that by a tug on the line. Jerk the line sharply to set the hook, then reel the catch to your boat. Dr. Linn says they don't fight much. It's like reeling in a waterlogged log that rolls some and flips its head occasionally. Some sport. After you get the fish to the boat, measure it. If it is between 40 and 70 inches long, you get to keep it, mostly for its sweet, succulent flesh. Dr. Linn's expedition resulted in three fish all over a yard long, but not long enough. He had to throw them back.

An interesting thing about that now-grown woman. She still refuses to eat the flesh of horrid sturgeons, but seems to manage caviar. Interesting isn't it, the distinctions that we make in life.

Geoducks

Uwajimaya Department Store, Seattle Washington. The basement. One of those grand Japanese supermarkets, just like my wife and I saw in Japan. A supermarket filled with any number of different edibles. Pickled this and pickled that. Fresh this and fresh that. Made me think of *Edible? Incredible!,* a book about seashore foraging.

Born and raised on Puget Sound, I am, through and through, a genuine seafood lover. The seafood counter at Uwajimaya drew me like iron filings to a magnet. What a setup, cooler after cooler of fresh fish of every description. Toward the back, on the right, was a magnificent tile display of cascading seawater that kept the shellfish there alive and healthy. Along the top was a trough filled with dozens of big Dungeness crabs, gray-green and rarin' to go. Then the water poured over hundreds of steamer clams, with shells clamped tight. Next blue mussels, alive, alive-o. And then a sight that warms the cockles of a native Puget Sounders heart, geoducks, pronounced gooey-duck, the biggest damn clams known to man or woman.

These bivalve mollusks can weigh as much as 20 pounds when full grown. Their long, fused neck or siphon can extend to three feet or more. Their living bodies are so large that the mantle and siphon cannot be withdrawn within the shell. If horse clams got their common name the way I think they did, then surely the geoduck should be called the elephant clam — the length of the trunk, you know.

Geoducks live at lower intertidal and subtidal zones from Alaska to Baja California to depths below 60 fathoms. They are most abundant in southern British Columbia and Puget Sound. Adults are buried some distance below the surface in the sandy or muddy bottom they prefer. Their long siphons extend to the surface, where, when the tide is in, they feed by filtering out small planktonic organisms, diatoms and the like.

As a child, summer wasn't summer without at least one geoducking expedition to the bay at minus tide. Sport geoducking (as opposed to commercial taking) must be done with hand tools. After our arrival, we began to search the lowest reaches of the beach for geoduck necks just sticking up above the sand among the seaweed. Then with great care to not disturb the mighty beast, a v-shaped channel was cut above the site of what would become a major excavation in a feeble attempt to divert the water flowing down the beach. At least two hunters were involved, one to grab the neck and one to start to dig. The hole enlarges, the digger and the grabber get lower, first to hands and knees, then laid out flat, front soaked with icy sand and mud, forearm three feet down, head below the surface of the beach, water filling up the hole in spite of v-shaped engineering efforts. The tide starts rising; the walls collapse. Then success! The grabber reaches the enlarged shell and body and begins to fight water pressure and suction and slowly pulls the geoduck from its watery home.

Afterwards, the geoduck was ground up, mixed with egg batter and fried as fritters or pounded to a pulp and fried. There is a big commercial market for live geoducks in Japan. There our mighty geoducks end up as sushi, sliced thin and raw and gobbled up rolled in rice and seaweed. Commercial taking is by SCUBA-diving hunters who wash out the unsuspecting geoducks by hydraulic mining with high-pressure hoses. In 1987, 2,017 metric tons of ducks were taken.

Geoducks don't rapidly repopulate depleted beds. Some populations of the filter-feeding geoduck are saved from exploitation by polluted waters. I discovered one fact when researching this *Nature Note* that makes me not want to eat another one, at least a big one. They are long-lived, the oldest known, 146 years. It seems sacrilegious to eat anything that old.

Fishing

For many Oregonians, spring officially begins the opening day of trout season. The poor souls along the northwest coast of Oregon must wait until the end of May to fish for trout in coastal streams and lakes, to enjoy one of the time-honored rites of spring.

You can enjoy the rites of spring in some Oregon waters any time of year, provided you are willing to fish for spiny-rayed, warm-water pan fish like yellow perch, bluegill, crappie, pumpkinseed and other sunfish, and bullheads, commonly, but incorrectly, called catfish. With some exceptions, there is no season or limit for these species and they may be fished for day or night.

There is good reason for such liberal regulations. Prolific reproducers, spiny-rays frequently increase to such numbers that they compete for a limited food supply. As a result, they become puny, stunted fish; puny, stunted fish that become sexually mature and produce more puny, stunted fish. Regulations are designed to reverse this trend by removing as many fish as possible so remaining fish, without fierce competition, will become larger, fatter fish and make the ole fishin' hole much more attractive.

Waters with cold-water, soft-rayed fish like salmon, steelhead and trout require careful regulation because of their popularity as game fish and resulting fishing pressure. Restrictions have three objectives, designed to control time and rate of fish removal. Enough fish must survive to sustain the population from year to year. Fish must be large enough to reproduce and large enough for fishermen to brag about. Fish must be protected during vulnerable periods and places in their life histories, such as during breeding season or migration.

Attempts to open certain popular trout waters year-round take the edge off the excitement and economy of an official opening day. An official opening day gives anglers

a sense of anticipation that adds to the excitement of the sport.

The fairly complicated fishing regulations cover what waters are open and when, size and limits for different species, and legal fishing gear and methods. So before heading out to your favorite fishing hole, pick up a copy of the latest edition of the Oregon Sport Fishing Regulations at your local sporting goods store. It contains a wealth of information, even for non-fishing folks, on Oregon's fishing resource, including marine shellfish. Oh, by the way. If you are going fishing, don't forget to buy a license when you pick up your copy of the regulations. It might save you considerable embarrassment and money. Besides, most of the cost helps support management of this valuable natural resource.

Bull Trout

We have heard a lot lately about fish species at risk, especially Rogue and Columbia River salmon. Recently, some eastern Oregon endangered suckers were shipped to a New Mexico fish hatchery to be propagated for replanting. These aren't the only fish in trouble. The western brook charr, better known as the bull trout, *Salvelinus confluentus,* is rapidly slipping into oblivion as its Oregon habitat diminishes.

For a long time, we considered bull trout a non-sea running, inland form of the better-known Dolly Varden trout, *S. malma.* In 1978, TM Cavender, after serious study, decided that there were enough anatomical and behavioral differences to consider bull trout a distinct species. One dependable feature is the number of bony rib-like structures that give shape and support to tissues in the throat beneath the head. Bull trout have 25 to 31, while Dolly Varden have 19 to 26. Other differences probably gave rise to its common name. Bull trout have a wide, long head with a big mouth and prominent jaws, and a fleshy knob and notch on the nose. They are voraciously piscivorous, fish-eating. Bulldog-like, I suppose, though I have yet to meet a fish-eating bulldog.

The Dolly Varden was named for a character in Charles Dickens' novel *Burnaby Rudge* because of her pink-spotted dress.

Bull trout are members of the charr genus, characterized by few teeth on the roof of the mouth and light spots on a dark background. Other charrs in Oregon include lake trout and brook trout. Bull trout do not have the deeply-forked tail of lake trout, nor the white-edged pelvic and anal fins of brook trout.

Bull trout were formerly widespread from Alaska south to the McCloud River in northern California. The Columbia Basin is the center of distribution for bull trout.

During the Miocene and Pleistocene, there was a connection among the Columbia, Klamath and Sacramento Rivers that allowed establishment of bull trout in these areas. They were never known in Oregon coastal streams, including the Rogue.

As with many species, the bull trout is becoming extinct over much of its former range. It now exists in isolated pockets, although substantial populations still thrive in the Pend Oreille and Priest Lake basins of northern Idaho and the Flathead River of northern Montana.

In the 1950s, bull trout started disappearing from many of its former haunts — gone also from California and from former habitat in Washington State. What has gone wrong?

Well, big surprise. It's us again, human beings, agents of the largest extinction event since the asteroid did in the dinosaurs. Disappearance may be due to changes in water quality caused by dams, agriculture, logging, livestock. It may be due to competition with imported eastern brook trout or hybridization with it. What hope is there for remaining bull trout populations? Existing populations are preserved in the few remaining undisturbed streams, especially those within public lands managed by government agencies. Remember, bull trout streams are happy streams, clear and clean and healthy, unless of course, you are a fish of another color and food for a hungry bull trout.

Anadromous Fish

Anadromous, from the Greek meaning running upward, describes fishes that run upstream from the sea to spawn. Catadromous fishes live in fresh water and spawn at sea.

Anadromous fish, like salmon, have a major water balance problem. They grow to adulthood in both fresh and salt water, spawn in fresh water streams and then die. A process physiologists call osmoregulation solves this problem. Remember osmosis from high school or college? Fresh water invades fishes' bodies through skin and, especially, gills. Kidneys excrete much of the excess water as large amounts of dilute urine. Special cells in the gills replace salts lost in urination and diffusion by active accumulation. Balance is the name of the game.

Once in the ocean, water constantly diffuses from their gills and skin. Water and salt are gained by swallowing salt water and food. Fish in salt water cope by producing little urine and by pumping excess salts out through the gills using the same mechanism as before, only in reverse.

As coho and chinook salmon mature, they reach a point where they can make the fresh water/salt water conversion with little trouble. There is a period when, as smolts, their internal physiology changes to tolerate salt water. Other salmon, that don't have the long fresh-water immersion of coho and chinook, are salt tolerant soon after the egg sac is absorbed.

Eels are the best known catadromous fishes, startlingly featured in two movies: "The Tin Drum" and "The Crying Game." Eels were a source of mystery to the Greeks and Romans because the fish seemed sterile. They could not figure out how they reproduced. Maybe they arose spontaneously from mud or originated from small worms or horsehair dropped in the water. Maybe young eels were fragments scraped off adults by rocks. Maybe they just didn't know.

It wasn't until the early part of the 20th century that we learned that eels hatch in the southwest part of the Atlantic Ocean in the Sargasso Sea. Small, transparent eel larvae move slowly shoreward and get larger and more pigmented as they swim. Male eels remain in tidewater, while females move upstream eating as they go. They reach adulthood in five to 20 years. Then, mostly at night, females swim downstream to the sea. They and their male friends hang around in tidewater, cease eating, darken to a black color, and disappear.

Until 1977, when adults were photographed in the ocean's depths near the Bahamas, newly-hatched eels in deeper waters of the Sargasso Sea were the only sign of the fate of vanished adults. Adults apparently spawn at sea and die. No large eels swim upstream, just youngsters. There are no eels in the eastern Pacific.

Eels fried, baked, sauteed, jellied, smoked or chowdered can add old-world charm to Christmas. Commercial fishermen ship live eels by the 10,000-pound truckload from Chesapeake Bay and the Saint Lawrence River to Chicago, Boston and New York City, to ensure a happy holiday. Will eels grace your table this holiday season?

Barnacles

This *Nature Note* is going to start out X-rated. Get the kids out of the room, turn down the volume, or, if you are particularly refined or sensitive to the wonders of the natural world, turn off the radio. Is it turned off?

What animal has the longest penis in the world when compared to body size? You will be surprised to learn that it is the barnacle, that lowly sedentary dweller of bays, seas and oceans. Not only that, some think barnacles just might be the single most common ocean animal. One rocky English beach had an estimated 107,000 barnacles per square meter. That's a number just slightly less than I estimated on the Puget Sound beach where I waded and swam as a child. Never could be persuaded to put on wading shoes, always ended up with stinging cuts and bruises.

Scientific talk in 1839 was of Vaughan Thompson's discovery that barnacles weren't mollusks at all, but crustaceans, related to crabs, lobsters and the like. He discovered that barnacles produced two different, free-swimming larval stages, just like crustaceans. There are ignoramuses among us who still think barnacles are mollusks of some kind related to clams and snails because barnacles have similar calcareous protective coverings. Some 950 barnacle species occupy a number of different ecological niches. Many live on rocky shores, pilings and such. Others are pelagic, drifting with ocean currents, attached to floating objects. Some tiny ones live on crab gills. Some are parasites.

The parasites are particularly creepy. Their *modus operandi* is deliciously described in Calvin and Ricketts, *Between Pacific Tides.* One degenerate barnacle is specially fond of kelp crabs.

In the barnacle's free-swimming stage it moves about looking for a suitable host. It attaches to the base of a crab hair with its feelers, then penetrates the soft flexible tissue

of the crab's exoskeleton there. Then it sheds its worldly legs, its covering and some internal organs and, in Ed Rickett's words, it "enters the crab by the nightmarish method of slipping through its own hollow feelers." Talk about aliens, ugh. If you're a kelp crab, aliens are already here. Once inside, the parasite proceeds to fill the crab's body cavity, avoiding vital organs, but reaching to the tips of legs and claws. Needless to say, the crab becomes listless. It sheds its exoskeleton once and the parasitic barnacle takes advantage of the softened crab shell by pushing outside to assume its final shape. The brownish mass it forms contains the barnacle's eggs, which wait for the arrival of male larvae to produce the sperm that will ensure continuation of the parasite's existence.

Ordinary barnacles have some extraordinary features mentioned earlier. Most barnacles are hermaphrodites; that is, have both ovaries and testes. Many do not self fertilize (except in desperation) but cross fertilize. Many marine organisms just let fly with millions of sperm and eggs and hope that chance encounters will result in progeny. Not so, some barnacles. Each barnacle has a penis that precisely places sperm near the ovary of a neighbor, who may eventually return the favor. What makes all this unusual is the knowledge that an 8 mm barnacle has an organ that conveys its sperm as far away as 50 mm. That's more than six times its body size. A six foot human? Thirty seven feet? Oh, Pinocchio!

Bryozoans

Long, hot August days. Maybe it's time to cool off at the coast. A favorite pastime at the coast is beach combing. I walk along the water's edge, moving up and down the beach with the movement of the waves, looking for whatever treasures the tides have brought. On the way back, I follow the wrack line and poke around in the piles of kelp and surf-grass left stranded by high tide.

I often look for small colonial organisms called bryozoans, or moss animals, that grow on the kelps and other larger objects, like stones and shells, that have been beneath the sea. Bryozoans are colonial because they consist of groups of tiny individual organisms joined together. Individual bodies, called zooids, are clearly visible, though tiny. Some colonies are flat encrustations the size of a dime or smaller; others are the height of a fifty-cent piece, delicate and branched. The ones I see are usually dry, dead and pale gray or tan. Like many colonial organisms, some individuals in the colony are modified to perform particular functions.

Avicularia, shaped like a bird's skull, beak and all, are specialized zooids that keep the colony clear of the settling larvae of other organisms looking for a home. In *Bugula*, a common genus, *Avicularia* have been observed snapping onto tiny crustaceans trying to build tubes on the colony. *Avicularia* hold the victim until it decays and its organic debris is swept into adjacent feeding zooids. The colony eats its trespassers.

The action of *Avicularia* is vividly described in Calvin and Ricketts' *Between Pacific Tides*, one of the first and the best books on the Pacific intertidal zone. Ed Ricketts may be better known to some of you as Doc in John Steinbeck's *Cannery Row.*

They write:

"The *Avicularia*e, the "birds beaks" of *Bugula*,

> thought to be defensive in function, are classic objects of interest to the invertebrate zoologist. It is a pity that these, like so many other structural features of marine animals, can be seen only with a microscope. If the moveable beaks of *Avicularia*e were a foot or so long instead of a fraction of a millimeter, newspaper photographers and reporters would flock to see them. The snapping process would be observed excitedly, some enterprising cub would certainly have one of his fingers snipped off, and the *hoi polloi* would amuse themselves by feeding stray puppies into the pincers. *Aviculariae* and similar appendages situated around the stems that support the tentacled zooids probably have a function similar to that of the *Pedicellariae* of urchins and starfish. Whatever else they do they certainly keep bryozoan stems clean, as anyone will grant who has observed their vicious action under the microscope."

Next time you are at the coast, look for bryozoans, and watch your fingers.

Wokas

Upper Klamath Lake's 61,500 or so acres of surface area make it Oregon's largest fresh-water lake and one of the largest in the United States. Although its area is large, it isn't deep — 50 feet at most, with an average of 14. This natural lake's drainage basin is 3,800 mountainous square miles. Klamath Lake is a remnant of ancient Lake Modoc that occupied all the basin during the Pleistocene. Lake Modoc extended from the present lake east through the Langell Valley, south to the Modoc lavalands. As climates and conditions changed, Lake Modoc receded. Except for Upper Klamath Lake, much of what is left has been drained, maimed, sumped and pumped. Farmland reclamation and irrigation have been important European enterprises since the beginning of the 20th century.

The Native Americans, the Klamaths and Modocs, had other enterprises at the lake. They fished in the tributaries, ate duck eggs in season, built mats and abodes from the tules, and collected wokas from the marsh. Wokas, known to us as western yellow pond-lily or *Nuphar polysepalum,* was the Klamath's major source of starch.

What we know of wokas and its preparation we learned from the observations of Frederick Vernon Colville, Honorary Curator of Plants at the US National Herbarium. Colville spent several days in August 1896 and again in 1901 on the Klamath Indian Reservation.

Women of the tribe collected enormous quantities of pond-lily fruits in July and August, then extracted seeds from fruits of different ages. Mature fruits naturally break open and expel seeds in a mucilaginous mess. Less mature fruits were piled to dry. Fruits on the outside dry. Fruits inside the pile rot. The women then extracted seeds from each pile, dried the seeds, ground them to loosen the seed coat, then winnowed the seeds by tossing in a breeze to blow away the chaff. Seeds were parched by heating in thick cast-iron skillets.

Colville thought fresh-parched wokas tasted delicious, like parched corn. I once had a student from Klamath Falls who learned how to make wokas. He brought me some ground meal. Much to my amazement, it was delicious. Better than any breakfast food I've ever tasted. Better, I suspect, than algae from the lake.

Klamath Lake is naturally rich in organic materials and nutrients that have accumulated in the lake for millennia. In addition, run-off from adjacent agricultural lands and pastures each year since the arrival of Europeans adds to the accumulation each year. Shallow, nutrient rich lakes like Klamath support enormous numbers of organisms. You may have already read on page 145 about Klamath's little green bugs, midges, actually, that appear by the bijillions in the summer. And there are the lake's famous algal blooms that turn parts of the lake into a stinking mess. The culprit is the blue-green algae *Amphanizomenon. Amphanizomenon* numbers start out low in the spring, then build to as many as 30,000 filaments per milliliter. Then they die. Their decomposition uses up oxygen in the lake and fills the air with an altogether unpleasant aroma. Some forms of this blue-green also produce an endotoxin similar to the toxin that causes paralytic shellfish poisoning. I wouldn't eat the algae.

Because of the lake's large size and natural inclinations, heroic cleanup efforts probably would be very expensive and not very effective. So, close your eyes, hold your nose, save your money, and don't inhale midges. Do, however, enjoy the lake for what it is — an enormously productive aquatic ecosystem that supports lots of waterfowl, trophy trout and a rare delicious breakfast cereal.

Dicamptodon

Amphibians: frogs, toads, salamanders and newts usually spend part of their lives in water, part of their lives on land. They live double lives. Many amphibians are in decline for reasons that are not totally clear. Lost or altered habitats seem likely culprits. Cool, clear streams turned crock-pot warm by poor land use or increasing ultraviolet radiation are among the possibilities. Maybe it is their parasites.

I like salamanders. Some are big, some are small, some are rough, some are smooth. A personal favorite is Dicamptodon, the Pacific giant salamander. Its range extends from southern British Columbia south along the Puget Trough through southwest Washington, western Oregon and northwest California to Santa Cruz. Like western red cedar, Dicamptodon is also found in Idaho. Its habitat? Cool, moist, coniferous forests near cold, clear streams and mountain lakes. They are big, to 13 inches long, with bulging eyes and vertically flattened tails. The terrestrial adult's smooth moist skin is reddish-brown or chocolate brown with a marbled pattern of tan. The aquatic larval stage, equivalent to tadpoles, is generally drab brown with short bushy gills. Larvae get large as well. Both have prodigious appetites.

Years ago a former colleague brought a large adult Dicamptodon into the lab. We watched as he placed the beast in the sink and then covered the sink with boards and bricks, lest the beast try to escape. Dicamptodon is not a weakling. Next morning I got a call, "Come see Dicamptodon." I did, and much to my amazement I saw two animals in the sink, Dicamptodon and a meadow mouse of size. This was my first realization that Pacific giant salamanders are not only big, but fierce. When agitated they may let out a sharp, low-pitched yelp. A yelp of less volume, I suspect, than that emitted by an unsuspecting human agitator when bitten by a salamander.

Dicamptodon has a powerful bite and can inflict a painful cut. Its name, Dicamptodon, refers to its two curved rows of teeth. Besides small mammals, they eat snakes, other amphibians, insects, snails, slugs and worms. My colleague, Michael Parker, is a Dicamptodon expert. He reports that Dicamptodon may occasionally dine on young steelhead and other salmonid fishes. Human fisher-folk should not be too upset by this. It is part of the environmental sieve that makes for smarter, better, wilier, wild fish. Larval diet mostly consists of aquatic and terrestrial invertebrates.

Most folks who study reptiles and amphibians think the Pacific giant salamander is primitive, most like the original inventions that left water, slime, and ooze for land. It is primitive in many ways but one. Mating Dicamptodons practice internal fertilization, but dear readers, you will, I fear, be disappointed when you learn the details. After a brief in-stream mating ritual, the male Pacific giant salamander deposits gelatinous sperm-capped structures on the stream bed. The female then picks up the sperm packets with her cloacal lips and deposits them within her cloaca, a common opening to her reproductive, digestive, and urinary tracts. There, inside her body, sperm unites with egg, safe from the uncertainty of external fertilization, a common practice where many lower vertebrates squirt sperm over already laid eggs. The female lays her fertilized eggs in water and attaches them to rocks and chunks of wood. She then stands guard until the larvae hatch, presumably to keep them safe from predators.

Large is relative. The giant salamander of China and Japan may measure six feet in length. According to my Harvard pals who have done extensive field work in China, anything that swims, walks, crawls, or flies is fair game for human consumption. During a slide presentation they talked of Wa-wa-u. The photograph was of a really big salamander being readied for the wok. It filled a standard wash basin. Fortunately for pups and babies it mainly subsists on fish and frogs. If you come across Dicamptodon, look, don't touch. And be grateful it isn't six feet long.

Suggested Reading

Books mentioned in the text

Arno SF. 1977. *Northwest Trees*. Seattle: Mountaineers. 222 p.

Baring-Gould WS, Baring-Gould C. 1962. *The Annotated Mother Goose, Nursery Rhymes Old and New*. New York: Potter 350 p.

Becking RW. 1982. *Pocket Flora of the Redwoods*. Covelo (CA): Island Pr. 237 p.

Benjamin DR. 1995. *Mushrooms: Poisons and Panaceas*. New York: Freeman. 422 p.

Brown L, Wolf EC. 1984. *Soil Erosion: Quiet in the World Economy.* Washington (DC): Worldwatch Institute. Worldwatch Paper 60. 49 p.

Buchsbaum R, Buchsbaum M, Pearse J, Pearse V. 1987. *Animals Without Backbones* (3rd Ed). Chicago: Univ Chicago Pr. 572 p.

Clark L. 1976. *Wildflowers of the Pacific Northwest from Alaska to California.* Sydney (BC): Gray's Pub. 604 p.

Correll DS. 1950. *Native Orchids of North America North of Mexico.* Waltham (MA): Chronica Botanica. 399 p.

Ehrlich PR, Dobkin DS, Wheye D. 1988. *The Birders Handbook: A Field Guide to the Natural History of North American Birds*. New York: Simon & Schuster. 785 p.

Eisenbeis G, Wichard W. 1987. *Atlas on the Biology of Soil Arthropods*. Berlin: Springer-Verlag. 437 p.

Essig EO. 1926. *Insects of Western North America*. New York: MacMillan. 1035 p.

Fuller TC, McClintock E. *Poisonous Plants of California*. Berkeley (CA):Univ California Pr. 433 p.

Griffiths AJF, Ganders F. 1983. *Wildflower Genetics: A Field Guide for British Columbia and the Pacific Northwest*. Vancouver (BC): Flight Pr. 215 p.

Harper AB. 1988. *The Banana Slug*. Aptos (CA): Bay Leaves Press 32 p.

Heywood VH. 1985. *Flowering Plants of the World*. Englewood Cliffs (NJ): Prentice Hall. 335 p.

Hickman JC. 1993. *The Jepson Manual: Higher Plants of California*. Berkeley (CA):Univ California Pr. 1400 p.

Leopold A. 1989. *A Sand County Almanac, and Sketches Here and There*. New York: Oxford Univ Pr. 228 p.

Mathews D. 1999. *Cascade-Olympic Natural History* (2nd Ed). Portland OR: Raven Editions. 623 p.

Peattie DC. 1991. *A Natural History of Western Trees*. Boston (MA): Houghton-Mifflin. 751 p.

Peck ME. 1961. *Manual of the Higher Plants of Oregon*. Portland (OR): Binfords and Mort. 936 p.

Pill VP, Furlong M. 1985. *Edible? Incredible!* Shelton (WA): Pill Enterprises. 73 p.

Ricketts EF, Calvin J, Hedgepeth JW. 1985. *Between Pacific Tides*. Stanford (CA): Stanford Univ Pr. 625 p.

Reyes C. 1994. *The Table Rocks of Jackson County: Islands in the Sky*. Ashland (OR): Last Minute Publications. 143 p.

Scheffer V. 1969. *The Year of the Whale*. New York: Scribner. 213 p.

Schneider E. 1986. *Uncommon Fruits and Vegetables: A Common Sense Guide*. New York: Harper Row. 546 p.

Sunset Books, Sunset Editors. 1995. *Sunset Garden Book*. Menlo Park (CA): Sunset Pub. 624 p.

Verts VJ, Carraway LN. 1998. *Land Mammals of Oregon*. Berkeley (CA): Univ California Pr. 668 p.

Index

About the author

Dr. Frank Lang was born and raised in Olympia, Washington. Growing up in the Puget Sound area, his love of biology was fueled by his Boy Scout Merit Badge counselor, the renowned naturalist and author Margaret McKenny. He took his undergraduate degree in botany at Oregon State College (now Oregon State University) his M.S. from the University of Washington and his Ph.D. from the University of British Columbia. Dr. Lang is Professor Emeritus of Biology at Southern Oregon University (SOU) in Ashland, Oregon, where he taught for 30 years. After retiring from SOU, Dr. Lang worked in the Ashland Resource Area, Medford District, of the Bureau of Land Management, on an intensive study of the Cascade/Siskiyou Ecological Emphasis Area. The Emphasis Area was later declared a National Monument by President Bill Clinton. Dr. Lang is the father of two grown children and lives in Ashland, Oregon with his wife of 40 years, Suzanne, and their dog, Inu.